Geo. Garrell   6:00
714

oxygenated blood — darkRed

verns — blue

mou. excreatory   2 | 1 ½
                        1 3 ½
                           8
Pop quiz   —   90   42 ½

1st test   —   83   c

2nd Test   —   92

Pop quiz   —   70   1 | 0
                         42
3th test   —   69   ———
                          68
Condyle   8 | 1
costal   8 | 1

6th sense   68 | 0 | 16

          70   90 3 | 93
                  70   21
      88   50   20
      70 | 9 0   1
      50 | 83
1 3 2 | 0   92
8 | 5   69 | 81
      70   3 | 24 4 | 8
7 0   2 | 8 |
8 |
6 8
   1

INTRODUCTION

to

HUMAN ANATOMY

INTRODUCTION

to

HUMAN ANATOMY

CARL C FRANCIS, A.B., M.D.

Associate Professor of Anatomy, Department of Anatomy
Western Reserve University, Cleveland, Ohio

With 324 text illustrations
and 29 color plates

THIRD EDITION

ST. LOUIS   *1959*   THE C. V. MOSBY COMPANY

To the memory of

T. WINGATE TODD

a pioneer in the teaching of
Living Anatomy

PREFACE TO THIRD EDITION

This is the age of complicated machinery. The human body is infinitely more complex than the most intricate mechanism which has ever been devised. Investigators in many fields are constantly adding to our knowledge of human anatomy. No single person can hope to know or understand all of this immense mass of material. Nevertheless, it is possible for each of us to master enough of the information to appreciate the major activities of the body. It has been my aim to describe the more simple human structures in an understandable fashion. I hope that I have succeeded and that I have stimulated the interest of the readers. I know of no more fascinating study than the anatomy and function of the body.

In this edition many minor alterations have been made. In addition, the chapter on the endocrine system and the section on the autonomic nervous system have been largely rewritten to include modern concepts. Several new illustrations have been added, and review questions have been placed at the end of each chapter.

I wish to express my indebtedness and gratitude to my colleagues, and to the teachers and students who have read the previous editions, for their many valuable and constructive criticisms.

CARL C FRANCIS

PREFACE TO FIRST EDITION

This textbook is an attempt to present in the smallest possible compass the essential facts of human anatomy. Stress has been laid on the function of each part and on the integration of each tissue and organ of the body.

BNA terminology has been used as the official source throughout the text, but synonyms in common use have been indicated.

Miss Helen Williams, artist of the Department of Anatomy, drew almost all the illustrations. Her meticulous work, constructive criticisms and suggestions have been invaluable in compiling the book.

I wish also to acknowledge my indebtedness to my colleagues within the Department of Anatomy, particularly to Dr. Samuel W. Chase and to Mr. M. V. Anders.

CARL C FRANCIS

CONTENTS

9

unit 3   INTEGRATIVE MECHANISMS

unit 4 MAINTENANCE OF THE BODY TISSUES

COLOR PLATES

INTRODUCTION

to

HUMAN ANATOMY

unit 1 THE BODY AND BODY TISSUES

CHAPTER 1

THE BODY AS A WHOLE

The word *anatomy* means literally dissection and therefore implies a knowledge of the structure of the body. An understanding of body structure is essential in order to know how the body functions. This book has been divided into several units and the various parts and systems of the body have been described separately, but it must be kept constantly in mind that these various structures are interrelated and that all work together to maintain the activity of the body as a whole. Each person must eat and assimilate food; he must excrete waste materials; he grows and must constantly repair and replace certain cells and tissues; he produces offspring; he reacts and adjusts himself to his environment. Certain systems of the body have become specialized to carry on these functions and only when all parts are working in harmony is an individual a healthy organism.

The cell is the unit of structure of the body. Each individual begins as a single maternal egg cell which is stimulated to divide after union with the paternal germ cell, the spermatozoon. The first two weeks following fertilization are known as the period of the ovum. During this interval the fertilized ovum divides many times, and a cluster of cells results. This cluster becomes implanted in the wall of the uterus of the mother. The individual cells of the cluster arrange themselves into layers but do not vary greatly in form. The interval between the end of the second week and the end of the eighth week of intrauterine life is known as the period of the embryo. The embryonic cells continue to divide frequently, and certain cells take on specific characteristics of form and activity. A group of similar cells specialized to perform a certain function is a tissue. Several tissues unite in a definite pattern to perform a given function, thus forming organs. A group of organs constitutes a system. By the end of the eighth week the embryo has begun to assume a human appearance and is then called a fetus. The remainder of intrauterine life is therefore called the fetal period. The fetus continues to increase rapidly in size, and there is further differentiation of cells, tissues, organs, and systems.

After birth the baby continues to develop and grow. A child is not a miniature adult. Some of the changes occurring during childhood are discussed in the chapters on the skeletal and nervous systems.

In this book the types of cells which the body uses as building material will be described first. Then the various systems will be discussed, one by one. The skeleton, muscles, and joints must be studied in order to know how we move from place to place. A knowledge of the nervous system will help us to understand how the various parts are integrated and how we secure information about our environment. The endocrine glands are needed to correlate and adjust all of the functions into one harmonious whole. The circulatory, digestive, and respiratory systems are essential for the digestion of food and the maintenance of life. The urinary system excretes waste material. The skin is an organ of excretion and protects the surface of the body. Finally, the reproductive organs are necessary to carry on the race.

In the description of anatomical structures many terms are necessary and the student should refer constantly to the glossary. Some general terms will be used very frequently and should be thoroughly understood at the beginning.

DIRECTIONAL TERMS

1. *Superior or cephalic:* toward the head or the upper part of a structure; the superior extremity includes the arm, forearm, and hand.

2. *Inferior or caudal:* away from the head or toward the lower end of a structure; the inferior extremity includes the thigh, leg, and foot.

3. *Anterior:* ventral or front; the sternum or breast bone forms part of the anterior chest wall.

4. *Posterior:* dorsal or back; the posterior portion of the skull is the back or occipital portion. In human anatomy the terms

anterior and posterior are used in preference to ventral and dorsal because man walks erect.

5. *Medial:* toward the midline of the body; the medial side of the arm is the side nearest the chest wall.

6. *Lateral:* away from the midline of the body; the eyes are lateral to the nose.

7. *Median:* in the middle of a structure; the median nerve is situated in the central part of the upper extremity. Median is not the same as medial.

8. *Intermediate:* between two other structures; the intermediate cutaneous nerve is between the medial and lateral nerves.

9. *Proximal:* toward the trunk or the beginning of a structure; the wrist is proximal to the hand.

10. *Distal:* away from the trunk or the source of the structure; the foot is distal to the ankle.

11. *Central:* toward the center; the brain belongs to the central nervous system.

12. *Peripheral:* away from the center; the nerves of the hand are part of the peripheral nervous system.

13. *Deep:* away from the surface; the humerus is in the depth of the arm.

14. *Superficial:* near the surface; superficial fascia lies just under the skin.

The body or a structure is frequently cut along certain planes.

1. *Sagittal or longitudinal:* a plane vertical to the ground which divides the structure into right and left halves.

2. *Frontal or coronal:* a plane vertical to the ground which divides the structure into anterior and posterior portions.

3. *Transverse, horizontal or cross:* a plane parallel to the ground which divides the structure into upper and lower parts.

Man belongs to the class of animals known as mammals, but he has certain features which clearly distinguish him from all other mammals. Some of the distinctive human characteristics are:

1. The brain and brain case are much larger relatively than in any other mammal and are actually larger than in many mammals of far greater bulk. The average size of an adult human brain is about 1,500 cc.; that of an adult chimpanzee is about 400 cc.

2. The face is smaller than the cranium. Man has the same number of teeth as a gorilla, but they are smaller and closer together. The nasal bones and bridge of the nose are more prom-

inent in man. Human nostrils are pointed downward; in apes they are pointed forward. Man alone has a chin.

3. The spinal column in an adult human being is S-shaped, with curves convex forward in the cervical and lumbar regions and concave forward in the thoracic and sacral regions. In man the head is well balanced on the spinal column; therefore the neck muscles are less developed and the neck is long and slender.

4. Man has an opposable thumb, and the entire hand is extremely mobile and capable of very delicate finger movements.

5. The thorax in man is flattened from front to back and is therefore relatively broad and flat.

6. The pelvic girdle is broad, and the muscles which attach the lower extremity to the trunk are very well developed in order to maintain an erect posture. The muscles of the calf of the leg are likewise large.

7. The great toe is not opposable in man but is in the apes. The foot bones are arranged in arches which assist in absorbing the shock of walking.

Review Questions

1. What is the basic unit of structure of the human body?
2. Distinguish between a fertilized ovum, an embryo, and a fetus.
3. Distinguish between a sagittal plane, a coronal plane, and a horizontal plane.
4. Give five distinctive human characteristics.
5. Distinguish between a cell, a tissue, an organ, and a system.
6. Name five organ systems and give one function of each.
7. Define briefly each of the following directional terms: superior, inferior, anterior, posterior, medial, and lateral.

CHAPTER 2

SURFACE ANATOMY

It is the purpose of this chapter to discuss the more prominent surface features of the regions of the body and to emphasize the large number of structures which may be identified by palpation through the skin.

HEAD

Just in front of the auricle, the pulsation of the superficial temporal artery is felt. The anesthetist frequently uses this vessel in taking the pulse. The frontal branch of the temporal artery often stands out as a tortuous ridge which, in elderly people, runs over the temple. There is considerable anastomosis between the various arteries supplying the scalp; therefore scalp wounds bleed very freely and require pressure on each side of the laceration to control the bleeding. Along the lower border of the mandible, about one-third of the way forward from the angle, the external maxillary (facial) artery may be felt passing over the bone to reach the cheek.

If the teeth are firmly clenched, the temporal muscle may be observed as a bulging in the temple and the masseter as a bulging near the angle of the lower jaw. The mandibular contour is easily felt through the skin. The zygomatic arch, a bridge of bone forming the framework of the cheek, may be palpated along its entire length from a point just in front of the ear to the side of the face below the eye. About one fingerbreadth below this arch and parallel to it, the duct of the parotid gland passes forward on the surface of the masseter muscle and may be rolled under the finger.

Pressure on a nerve trunk produces a peculiar type of sensation which is poorly localized; it is accompanied by tingling and a faint feeling of nausea. This type of pain is caused by pressure on the frontal and supratrochlear branches of the ophthalmic division of the fifth nerve in the middle of the upper margin of the orbit. Pressure on the cheek immediately below the midpoint of the lower orbital margin stimulates the infraorbital branch of the maxillary division; pressure on the mandible below the premolar teeth stimulates the ends of the inferior alveolar branch of the mandibular division.

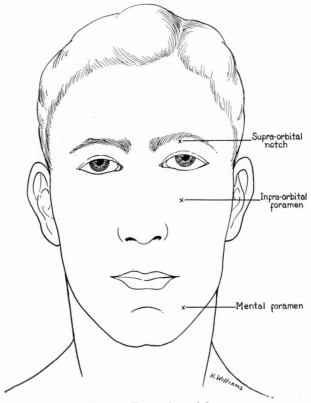

Fig. 1.—Front view of face.

A finger placed just in front of the opening of the external ear will recognize the condyle of the mandible sliding back and forth in movements of the lower jaw.

Behind the ear a lymph node of the posterior auricular group may be identified as it lies on the mastoid process. In infections of the scalp this node becomes enlarged and tender. The submaxillary (submandibular) lymph nodes can be felt along the inferior border of the mandible and are usually enlarged and tender in upper respiratory infections.

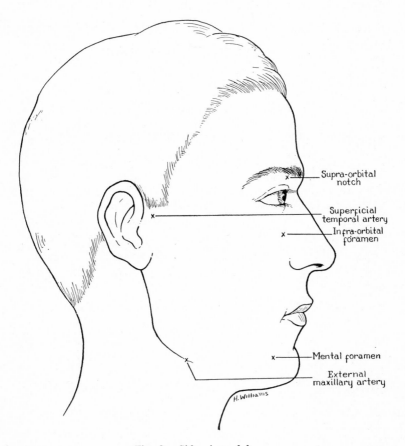

Fig. 2.—Side view of face.

NECK

On each side of the larynx the pulsations of the carotid artery can be both felt and seen. If the collar is too tight or muscular effort is considerable, the veins of the neck, particularly the external jugular, become large and obvious.

Muscular resistance to the pressure of a hand under the chin brings into prominence the entire length of the sternocleidomastoid muscles which can then be palpated from origin to insertion. The suprasternal or jugular notch is the small hollow in the midline just above the sternum and between the medial ends of the clavicles.

The most prominent structure in the midline of the neck is the anterior margin of the thyroid cartilage or the Adam's apple which is larger in men than in women. Above it, the hyoid bone can be traced backward to each end or greater cornu. Below the thyroid cartilage the anterior band of the cricoid cartilage can be felt and below that the upper rings of the trachea. Frequently the isthmus of the thyroid gland can be felt crossing the trachea. If the gland is enlarged, it bulges forward in the lower part of the neck.

Between the muscular columns at the back of the neck the external occipital protuberance of the skull is easily located. In the midline below this and sunk between the columns is the ligamentum muchae passing downward to the spine of the seventh cervical vertebra, the bony prominence at the base of the neck. The prominence below is that of the spine of the first thoracic vertebra. The spines of the lower thoracic and of the lumbar vertebrae are less easily felt.

The muscle mass forming the lateral portion of the back of the neck and extending downward and outward from the skull to the shoulder is due largely to the trapezius muscle. "Stiff neck" is usually an inflammation of this muscle.

SHOULDER

A finger tracing laterally the subcutaneous upper border of the clavicle will encounter the acromioclavicular joint as a slight elevation at the outer end of the clavicle. About one fingerbreadth beyond this is the lateral border of the acromion which forms the tip of the shoulder. Just below the acromion the greater tuberosity of the humerus can be felt moving beneath the overhanging acromion when the arm is rotated medially or laterally. If the finger is placed near the outer end of the clavicle and then brought straight downward for about one inch, the tip of the coracoid process may be felt in the groove between the deltoid and pectoralis major muscles. The entire margin of the acromion and the spine of the scapula are subcutaneous. The vertebral border of the scapula is palpable, but the superior and axillary borders are covered by muscles.

If the arm is slightly abducted, it is possible to feel the head of the humerus by making firm pressure upward in the axilla. This procedure is uncomfortable because the trunks of the brachial plexus are being pressed against the bone.

ARM

The bulging belly of the biceps muscle, a flexor and supinator of the forearm, is evident on the front of the upper arm when the elbow is flexed with the palm upward. On the outer side of the arm the deltoid muscle is readily traced to its insertion on the humerus. When a thin, muscular person contracts a deltoid muscle, the component muscle bundles and the intervening septa of fascia are clearly visible. Just below this it is possible to feel the radial nerve as it passes around the humerus in the radial groove. On the inner side of the arm there is a shallow groove just behind the biceps muscle. Along this groove the brachial artery may be felt as it passes downward toward the cubital fossa. This groove is the place to apply pressure in case of severe arterial hemorrhage in the forearm or hand.

At the elbow three bony prominences should be located: the medial and lateral epicondyles of the humerus and the olecranon of the ulna. When the elbow is extended, these three lie in a horizontal line; when the elbow is flexed, they form the points of a triangle. The ulnar nerve can be felt in the groove behind the medial condyle. It is the so-called "crazy bone" or "funny bone" of the elbow.

When the elbow is extended, pressure in the dimple behind and below the lateral condyle reveals two bony parts. The proximal one is the distal portion of the lateral condyle of the humerus, and the other is the head of the radius. If one presses gently on the head of the radius and then slowly supinates and pronates the forearm, the head of the radius may be felt turning beneath the skin.

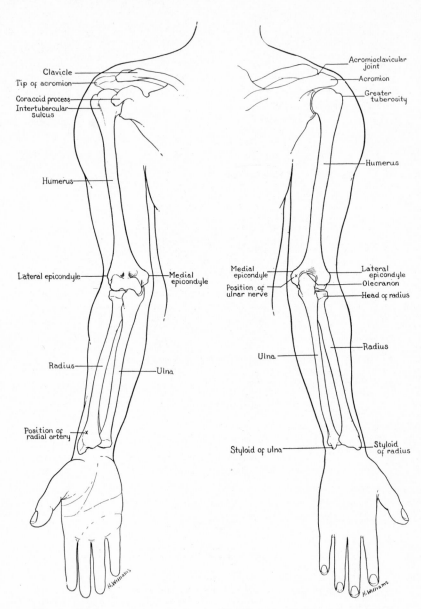

Fig. 3.—Right upper extremity, anterior view, bones outlined.

Fig. 4.—Right upper extremity, posterior view, bones outlined.

On the front of the elbow the median cubital vein can be seen, except in obese persons, and usually the superficial veins of the forearm can be identified. The median cubital vein is the vein of choice in transfusions and intravenous therapy.

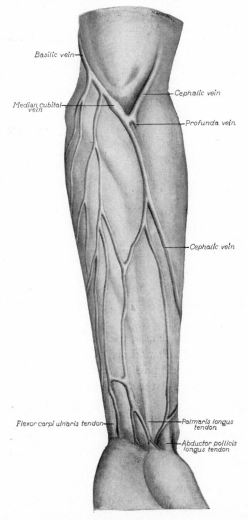

Fig. 5.—Superficial veins of volar aspect of left arm.

WRIST

Numerous muscle tendons are visible at the wrist. Let us study those on the front of the wrist, starting on the thumb or radial side. First, palpate the lower end of the radius. The tendon passing directly over the end (styloid) of the radius out on to the back of the thumb is that of the abductor pollicis longus muscle. Let us now pass a finger across the front of the wrist toward the ulnar or little finger side. First is felt the radial artery as it lies on the surface of the radius. This is the artery usually used in taking the pulse. Next in order may be felt the tendons of the flexor carpi radialis and palmaris longus and, on the ulnar side, the flexor carpi ulnaris. If the tendon of the last mentioned is traced downward, it can be followed to its insertion on the pisiform bone, a small seedlike structure in the heel of the palm. When the palm is strongly cupped, the prominent tendon in the middle of the wrist is that of the palmaris longus. In about one out of ten persons this muscle is absent. The tendons lying deeper than the palmaris longus belong to the flexor digitorum sublimis (superficialis). The median nerve runs parallel to, and immediately on the radial side of, the tendon of the palmaris longus. The ulnar artery and nerve lie just lateral to the tendon of the flexor carpi ulnaris, and it is often possible to feel the pulsation of the vessel in this location.

On the back of the wrist the well-marked tendon of the extensor pollicis longus is seen passing to the distal phalanx of the thumb.

The pit between this tendon and that of the abductor pollicis longus is the "anatomical snuffbox." In the bottom of the pit the radial artery may be felt passing over the navicular bone. The artery then turns around the first metacarpal into the palm to form the deep palmar arch, through which it anastomoses with the deep branch of the ulnar artery.

The other extensor muscles are bound to the wrist by a dense fibrous band, the dorsal carpal ligament, but on the back of the hand the tendons of the extensor digitorum communis can be seen going to the fingers.

THORAX AND ABDOMEN

Just below the inner end of the clavicle the first costal cartilage can be felt as it joins the sternum. The remaining ribs and inter-

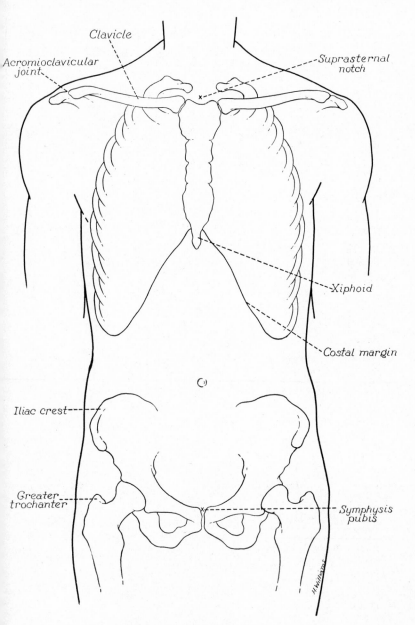

Fig. 6.—Anterior view of torso.

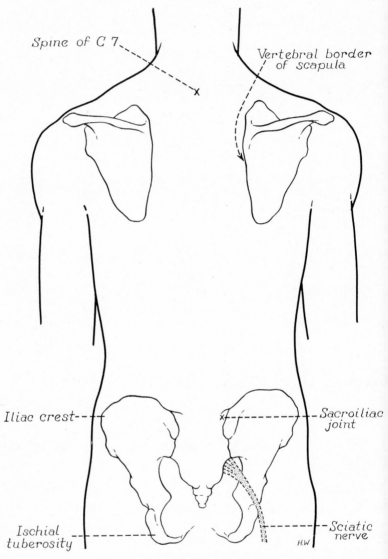

Spine of C 7

Vertebral border of scapula

Iliac crest

Sacroiliac joint

Ischial tuberosity

Sciatic nerve

H.W

Fig. 7.—Posterior view of torso.

costal spaces can be identified except in obese persons. The apex beat of the heart is palpated usually in the fifth interspace about three and a half inches to the left of the midline. Below the apex of the heart, at the costal margin, there is frequently a tympanitic area due to the presence of a bubble of gas in the cardiac portion of the stomach.

In the midline running from the umbilicus to the symphysis is the linea alba. This is the site frequently selected by a surgeon for operations on the urinary bladder and the uterus because there are no large blood vessels or nerves to be injured in this line.

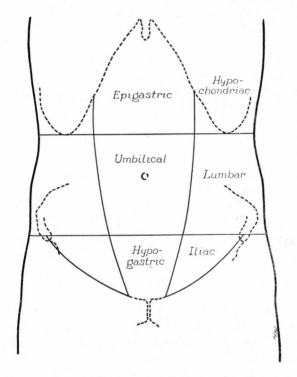

Fig. 8.—Diagram of abdominal regions.

The pit of the stomach is the narrow angle between the two costal margins. The tip of the xiphoid cartilage is palpable just at the lower end of the sternum. Sharp pressure or a blow in the pit of the stomach is very painful because it stimulates the "solar plexus," the collection of visceral nerves about the celiac artery.

For purposes of localization a physician examining a patient may refer to certain vertical lines which are projected directly downward from various points of the shoulder girdle, such as the midclavicular line, the anterior axillary line, the midaxillary line, and the posterior axillary line. By drawing two imaginary lines at right angles to each other through the umbilicus, the surface of the abdomen is divided into four quadrants. A surgeon frequently refers to pain in the right upper quadrant or right lower quadrant.

By another method the abdominal area may be divided into nine areas. An imaginary horizontal line, the subcostal line, is drawn horizontally across the body at the level of the lowest point of the costal margin (usually the lower edge of the tenth costal cartilage). A second line is drawn through the anterior superior iliac spines. A curved line is drawn along the lateral border of the rectus abdominis muscle on each side. The resulting nine areas are named right hypochondriac, epigastric, left hypochondriac, right lumbar, umbilical, left lumbar, right iliac, hypogastric, and left iliac. In the recent revision of the anatomical nomenclature it was proposed to use lateral in place of lumbar, inguinal for iliac, and pubic for hypogastric.

The transpyloric plane is quite useful for localization. This is a horizontal plane passed through the body at a point midway between the upper margin of the sternum and the upper margin of the pubic symphysis. It passes through the pylorus of the stomach and the first lumbar vertebra.

THIGH

Except in the obese persons, the iliac crest can be felt in its entire length from the anterior superior spine to the posterior superior spine. The inguinal ligament lies in the bottom of a furrow extending from the anterior superior iliac spine toward the symphysis. The femoral nerve, artery, and vein pass from the abdomen and into the thigh beneath the midpoint of the inguinal ligament and lie in the order named from lateral to medial. Lateral to femoral nerve the iliopsoas muscle passes beneath the ligament, and medial to the femoral vein is a space containing areolar tissue and lymphatic structures. A femoral hernia protrudes through this space.

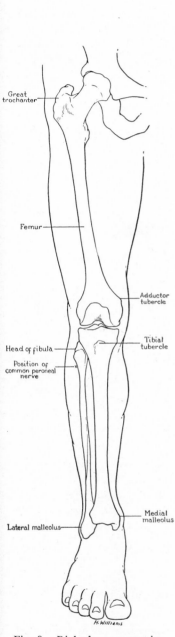

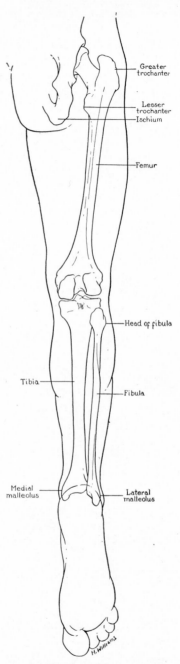

Great trochanter

Femur

Adductor tubercle

Tibial tubercle

Head of fibula

Position of common peroneal nerve

Lateral malleolus

Medial malleolus

Greater trochanter

Lesser trochanter

Ischium

Femur

Head of fibula

Tibia

Fibula

Medial malleolus

Lateral malleolus

H. Williams

H. Williams

Fig. 9.—Right lower extremity, anterior view, bones outlined.

Fig. 10.—Right lower extremity, posterior view, bones outlined.

The femoral artery passes down the thigh directly toward the adductor tubercle of the femur. The pulsations of the femoral artery can be felt only in the upper part of the thigh where it is not heavily overlaid by muscles. If the artery is pressed against the shaft of the femur, it is possible to control an arterial hemorrhage occurring below.

In infants and young children the superficial lymph nodes of the inguinal region are easily palpable. In the adult they are usually too small to be distinguished unless they are diseased.

The greater trochanter can be felt on the outer side of the thigh about eight inches below the highest point of the iliac crest. The ischial tuberosity is the bony prominence in each buttock. In a person who is seated the weight of the body is borne on the ischial tuberosities. Just below the lateral to the ischial tuberosity the sciatic nerve may be palpated.

KNEE

At the knee the medial and lateral condyles of the femur and tibia can be identified, as well as the head of the fibula and the patella. The patella glides over the end of the femur in movements of the knee joint. The distance from the patella to the tubercle of the tibia does not change, and the patella articulates only with the distal end of the femur.

On the outer side of the knee the tendon of the biceps femoris can be followed to its insertion on the head of the fibula. Just below the head, the neck of the fibula can be felt, and the peroneal nerve rolled beneath the finger as it comes around the neck to enter the leg; the nerve is often injured here in fractures of the upper end of the fibula. On the medial side of the knee the tendons of the gracilis and semitendinosus muscles can be felt at their insertion into the tibia. The former is the more superficial. In front of these the tendon of the adductor magnus can be traced to the adductor tubercle.

ANKLE AND FOOT

The medial and lateral malleoli are easily identified. The bones of the medial longitudinal arch of the foot have a definite relation to the medial malleolus; one fingerbreadth below and in front of the distal end of the malleolus, the terminal portion of the sustentaculum tali may be palpated, two fingerbreadths below and in front is the tubercle of the navicular, and three fingerbreadths in front is the base of the first metatarsal. On the front of the ankle the tendons of the tibialis anterior, extensor hallucis longus, and extensor digitorum longus lie in that order from the medial to the lateral margin of the ankle. Just behind the medial malleolus the tendon of the tibialis posterior enters the sole of the foot, and immediately lateral and posterior to it may be palpated the terminal portion of the posterior tibial artery. The dorsalis pedis artery, the termination of the anterior tibial, can usually be palpated on the upper surface of the foot between the first and second metatarsal bones. On the outer side of the foot the tendon of the peroneus brevis muscle passes around the lateral malleolus to be inserted on the base of the fifth metatarsal.

The beginning of the great saphenous vein on the inner side of the ankle is usually visible, and the vein may be traced up to the knee and often to its termination in the femoral vein in the thigh. The beginning of the small saphenous vein on the outer side of the ankle can usually be seen.

Only a few of the more obvious landmarks are mentioned in this chapter to show how much knowledge of living anatomy may be obtained from one's own body. The observing student should be able to pick out and identify many other structures. Good power of observation indeed is essential for the development of a practical knowledge of human anatomy.

Review Questions

1. Where would you palpate for the following arteries: superficial temporal, brachial, radial, femoral, posterior tibial, and dorsalis pedis?
2. Identify by palpation the following structures: lower border of the mandible, zygomatic arch, mastoid process, supraorbital ridge, and external occipital protuberance.
3. When you clench your teeth firmly you are able to feel a bulging beneath the skin over the angle of the lower jaw and in the temple. What muscles produce these bulgings?
4. Name three structures which may be palpated in the anterior midline of the neck.
5. What bony structure forms the tip of the shoulder?
6. Identify by palpation the medial and lateral condyles of the humerus, the shaft of the ulna, and the lower end of the radius.
7. What is the usual place for palpation of the apex beat of the heart?

8. Identify the crest of the ilium, the ischial tuberosity, and the greater trochanter of the femur.
9. Name three bony prominences which may be palpated at the knee.
10. Name three bony prominences which may be palpated at the ankle.
11. Try to palpate your ulnar nerve behind the medial condyle of the humerus and the peroneal nerve just below the head of the fibula.
12. Why is a blow in the pit of the stomach painful?
13. Why do scalp wounds bleed very freely? How would you control bleeding from a wound of the scalp?
14. In the event of severe arterial bleeding from a cut in the hand where would you apply pressure? Why?

CHAPTER 3

CELLS AND TISSUES

CELLS

It is not within the province of this book to give in detail the cellular structure of the body. Nevertheless, since a general knowledge of this subject is essential to a satisfactory understanding of gross anatomy, this chapter gives a brief description of the various types of cells and tissues present in the body.

Cells are the vital units which make up all the tissues of the body, each of which is specialized to perform its particular function. Each organ is composed of several tissues definitely arranged to fulfill their special purposes.

Fig. 11 is a diagram of a conventional cell. It is roughly spherical in shape and is surrounded by a cell membrane. Within the cell membrane there is a fluid called cytoplasm, which contains many substances in solution and certain particulate structures. The appearance of these structures varies greatly with the conditions under which they are observed, that is, whether the cell is alive, in fresh unstained material, or in fixed stained tissue. Special techniques and special microscopes are necessary to demonstrate many of the structures. When stained and observed under the usual microscope, the cytoplasm contains granules and a network of fibrils. The granules are of varied composition; some are protein material, others are carbohydrate in the form of glycogen. In certain tissues there are granules of pigment. Secretory granules are found in granular cells, and there are lipoid or fatty granules. Usually, during the histologic preparation of material, droplets of free fat are dissolved out of the cells, leaving small holes in the cytoplasm.

Within the cytoplasm is a small, denser protoplasmic mass, the nucleus. The granules of the nucleus stain more heavily than those of the cytoplasm. Most of these granular masses are called chromatin granules and are stained by basic dyes; nearly every nucleus contains one or more distinct masses, the nucleoli, which stain with acid dyes.

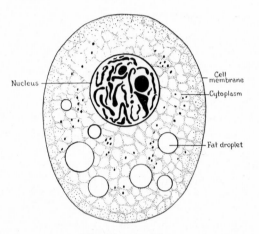

Fig. 11.—A cell.

Composing the body framework and organs are cells of widely differing character. The cells of the common tissues found in an adult will be described.

TISSUES

Tissues are divided into the following groups:

1. Epithelium
2. Supporting structures: fibrous connective tissue, adipose tissue, cartilage, bone, and neuroglia
3. Muscle and tendon
4. Nerve tissue
5. Blood and lymph

Epithelium

Epithelial tissues cover the body surface, line the body cavities, compose the inner coat of blood vessels and lymphatics, and form glands or secreting organs.

Simple epithelium consists of a single layer of cells. The cells may be flat and scalelike, forming simple squamous epithelium, or they may stand side by side, forming simple columnar or cuboidal epithelium. Cuboidal cells are of about equal height and width, whereas columnar cells are tall and thin. Squamous epithelium which lines blood vessels and lymphatics is called endothelium; that lining the body cavities (the peritoneal cavity, pleural cavities, and pericardial cavity) is known as mesothelium. The thyroid gland and the excretory ducts of many glands have simple cuboidal epithelium. The lining of the stomach, intestines, and gallbladder

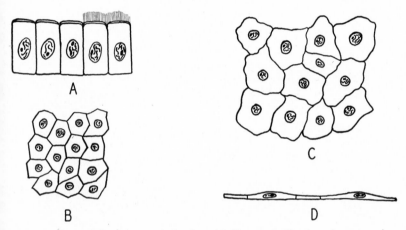

Fig. 12.—Various types of simple epithelium. *A,* Simple columnar epithelium in cross section; *B,* simple columnar epithelium, surface view; *C,* simple squamous epithelium, surface view; *D,* simple squamous epithelium in cross section.

is simple columnar epithelium. Columnar cells may undergo certain modifications. The free surface of each cell in certain air tubes of the lung, the uterine tubes, part of the nasal cavities, and part of the uterus develops cilia which look like fine hairs. Glandular epithelium is composed of cells which have a secretory function.

A gland may consist of a single cell, like the goblet cell found in mucous membranes. Some glandular organs, however, show many cells arranged about a central canal, called the duct of the gland, which carries away the secretion. Glands may be classified according to the form of the duct and may be simple tubular, coiled tubular, branched tubular, compound tubular, saccular or alveolar, branched alveolar, compound alveolar, or combined tubuloalveolar. Other glandular organs possess no ducts but secrete directly into the blood stream. These are called endocrine glands to distinguish them from the exocrine glands which have ducts. Certain glands, such as the liver and pancreas, have both exocrine and endocrine functions.

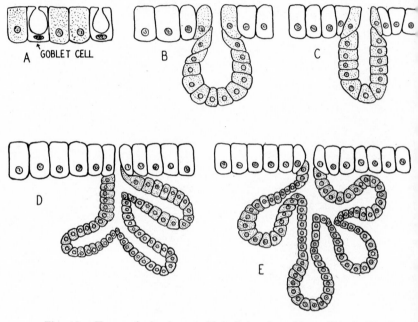

Fig. 13.—Types of glands. *A,* Unicellular (a goblet cell); *B,* simple alveolar (saccular); *C,* simple tubular; *D,* compound tubular; *E,* compound alveolar.

Certain epithelial cells are specialized for the reception of sensory stimuli. Examples are found in the taste buds of the tongue, the olfactory area of the nose, and the rod and cone cells of the retina.

The reproductive cells arise from epithelium in the testis or ovary. The ovum is a large spherical cell with cytoplasm containing granules and fat globules; its nucleus is large, and there are small accessory nuclei. The spermatozoon or male reproductive

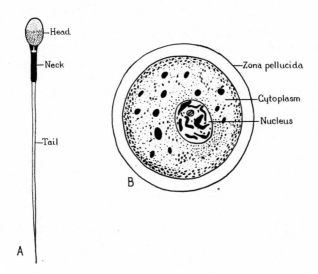

Fig. 14.—Reproductive cells.   *A,* Spermatozoon; *B,* ovum.

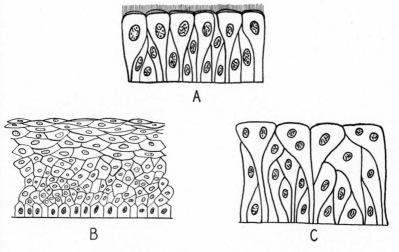

Fig. 15.—Various types of stratified epithelium.   *A,* Pseudostratified, ciliated, columnar epithelium; *B,* stratified squamous epithelium; *C,* transitional epithelium.

cell possesses a globular head containing the nucleus, a narrow neck, and a long slender tail of cytoplasm.

Stratified epithelium has several layers of cells. The outer layer of the skin consists of stratified squamous epithelium. Similar tissue is found on other surfaces also, such as the lips, inside of the mouth, esophagus, pharynx, and anal canal. Stratified squamous epithelium is found on surfaces exposed to friction, abrasion, and the like. For example, the skin of the face is accustomed to extremes of temperature and to wind, and the inside of the mouth is not sensitive to temperatures high enough to cause acute discomfort elsewhere. The outer layers of such epithelia are being constantly thrown off and renewed by the growth of deeper layers.

Pseudostratified columnar epithelium is illustrated in Fig. 15. This type is nearly always ciliated. In cross section it gives a superficial appearance of being stratified, but a close study shows that the base of each cell abuts upon the basement membrane, or structure upon which the epithelium rests. The trachea and bronchi are lined with such cells.

Transitional epithelium resembles stratified squamous epithelium but has fewer layers of cells; the number varies with the amount of tension on the tissue. This type is found in the urinary bladder.

Membranes

A membrane is usually defined as a sheet of tissue which lines a body cavity or covers a body surface and is composed of a layer of epithelium on a layer of connective tissue. Mucous membrane lines cavities and passages open to the exterior, such as the digestive tract. The epithelium of mucous membrane may contain mucous glands which secrete mucus. Serous membranes are covered with mesothelium and line closed body cavities; pleura lines the thoracic cavity, peritoneum lines the abdominal cavity, and pericardium lines the cavity surrounding the heart. Synovial membrane is found within tendon sheaths, bursae, and joint cavities. The lining cells of synovial membrane may simulate simple squamous epithelium. The skin is sometimes referred to as the cutaneous membrane.

The word membrane is also used to describe various definite sheets of connective tissue which separate spaces or connect structures, such as interosseous and thyrohyoid membranes.

Supporting Structures

Fibrous Connective Tissue.—The cells of these connective tissues are enmeshed in an interwoven mass of fibers. Some fibers are composed of an organic compound known as collagen which is white; others are composed of elastin which gives a yellow appearance to the tissue. Connective tissues are classified by the amount of these two types of fibers present in the meshwork. Areolar connective tissue is a loose network of white fibers with a

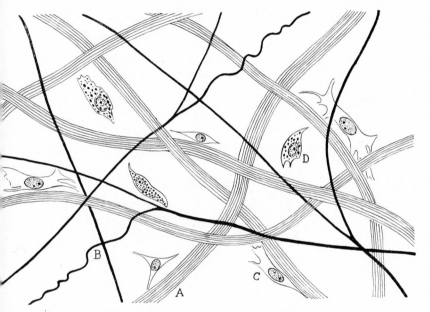

Fig. 16.—Areolar connective tissue. *A*, Collagen fiber; *B*, elastic fiber; *C*, connective tissue cell; *D*, macrophage with ingested granules.

few elastic fibers. This forms the basis of the subcutaneous tissue. If the fibers are numerous and are closely packed together, a dense fibrous tissue results. Examples of this dense form, which is very resistant to a pulling force, are periosteum, aponeuroses, muscle sheaths and tendons, ligaments, organ capsules, and dura mater.

If there are many elastic fibers, yellow elastic tissue results, which has the property of stretching easily and when released of returning to its original form. Certain ligaments of the vertebral column, the ligamenta flava, are composed of this tissue. Fibroelastic connective tissue has both white and yellow fibers. The walls of the large arteries, such as the aorta, have an abundance of elastic tissue.

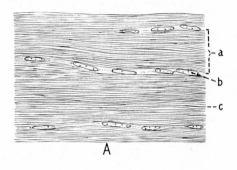

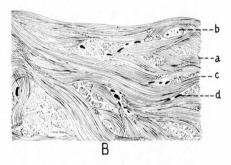

Fig. 17.—Dense connective tissue. *A,* Parallel arrangement as in a tendon; *a,* collagen fiber; *b,* connective tissue cell; *c,* fibril. *B,* Matted arrangement as in the corium of the skin; *a,* collagen fiber; *b,* connective tissue cell; *c,* fibril; *d,* elastic fiber.

Adipose Tissue.—A fat cell looks like a signet ring, the signet being the nucleus pushed to the periphery of the cell, the cytoplasm being the band, and the central portion being a large droplet of fat. In fatty tissue there is always a fine meshwork of areolar connective tissue with fat cells filling in all the interspaces.

Cartilage.—The cells of cartilage appear as islands in a dense noncellular translucent substance called the matrix. The cells are usually spheroidal, occurring singly or in small groups, and each cell lies in a space called a lacuna. In hyaline or glasslike cartilage the matrix appears translucent and of a pale blue color. Articular cartilage, the rings of the trachea, and the cartilage ultimately transformed into bone are all of this variety. Elastic cartilage or yellow fibrocartilage found in the external ear, in the

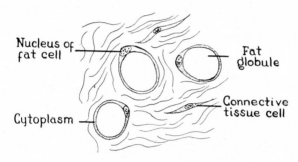

Fig. 18.—Fat cells.

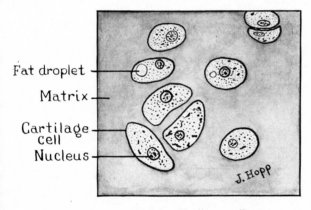

Fig. 19.—Hyaline cartilage.

auditory tube, and in some of the cartilages of the larynx, is composed of a matrix mixed with elastic fibers and has therefore a faint yellow color. In white fibrocartilage, interlacing bundles of white connective tissue run through the matrix. The intervertebral discs are composed of white fibrocartilage. Cartilage has no blood vessels, nerves, or lymphatics.

In most places cartilage is covered by a fibrous membrane called perichondrium, but this membrane is not found on the articular surfaces of hyaline cartilage covering the ends of bony articulations.

Bone.—Most bones are originally composed of hyaline cartilage but some of the bones of the face and skull develop directly from connective tissue membranes. In bone the matrix surrounding the cells is very dense and contains mineral salts, mainly calcium compounds. In bone as in cartilage, each cell lies in a small space

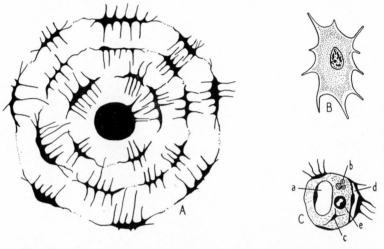

Fig. 20.—Compact bone. *A,* Transverse section of Haversian canal and lamellae; *B,* bone cell in lacuna; *C,* diagram showing detail of a single Haversian canal; *a,* venule; *b,* nerve fibers; *c,* connective tissue cell; *d,* lymphatic; *e,* arteriole. (After Jordan.)

called a lacuna. Bone lacunae differ from cartilage lacunae in that they are connected with each other by very fine channels known as canaliculi. Scattered throughout the matrix are numerous small blood vessels which occupy channels called Haversian canals, and these blood vessels freely anastomose. Lamellae are arranged in concentric circles about the canals. Each canal with its concentric lamellae and lacunae forms an Haversian system.

The outer portion of each bone is composed of a layer of dense, compact bone and in the central portion of most bones there is a space called the medullary or marrow cavity. During life the medullary cavity is filled with yellow marrow which contains fibrous connective tissue, fat, and blood vessels. In the flat bones of the skull there are an inner layer and an outer layer of dense bone, and between these there is a middle layer of spongy bone called the diploë. The ends of certain long bones are filled with small cavities, producing a spongelike appearance, and therefore this sort of bone is known as spongy bone. These small cavities may be filled with red marrow which contains many small blood vessels and immature red cells. In the adult, red marrow is found only in the bodies of the vertebrae, the ribs, the sternum, the middle layer of the bones of the skull, and in the upper end of the humerus and femur.

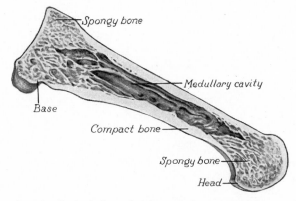

Fig. 21.—Longitudinal section of right second metatarsal bone. (W.R.U. 3590, male, white, aged 72 years.)

Spongy bone is arranged in lamellae or trabeculae to withstand the strain and stress put upon the structure. The arrangement varies, and each bone has its characteristic pattern. The trabeculae in the foot bones, for example, roughly follow an arched pattern. They begin at the back in the calcaneus and pass forward through the other tarsal bones and the metatarsals. This arrangement into definite architectural patterns adds greatly to the strength of the bone without adding to its weight. (See Fig. 155.)

The outer surface of each bone, except for articular surfaces, is covered by a layer of dense fibrous tissue which is closely attached to the bone and is called periosteum. The medullary cavities and the cavities of spongy bone are lined with a delicate fibrous membrane called endosteum.

Neuroglia.—In the brain and spinal cord there are many supporting cells in addition to the nerve cells. This supporting tissue is called neuroglia and its cells are characterized by small oval nuclei and long branching processes which are closely interwoven and give a feltlike appearance to stained tissue.

Muscle and Tendon

Muscle, the contractile tissue of the body, is composed of units which have the power of contraction under stimulation. Muscles under the control of the will, such as those of the limbs, are known as voluntary; the others, such as those of the bowel, are involuntary. Muscles used in walking, writing, and speaking, fall into the former category. These are also called striate or striped muscles because the cytoplasm of the cells has fine transverse bands microscopically visible in longitudinal sections. In striate muscles the individual fibers lie in parallel lines, and the nuclei are usually found on the surface of individual fibers. Each fiber is a long cylinder and usually contains several round or oval nuclei located at the periphery. The fibers are arranged in compact bundles separated by fine connective tissue sheaths. These fine sheaths are septa extending into the muscle from an outer connective tissue sheath which invests the entire muscle.

We have no conscious control over involuntary muscles. The muscles of the stomach, intestines, and blood vessels belong to this group. They are also called nonstriate or smooth muscles because their cytoplasm has no transverse striations. The heart is composed largely of specialized involuntary muscle exhibiting transverse striations. Cardiac muscle fibers anastomose with each other, and the nuclei are found in the central portion of the fibers.

Smooth muscle cells are long and fusiform; the nucleus is located in the central part of the cell. In the walls of hollow viscera smooth muscle bundles may be disposed in longitudinal, circular, or oblique coats, or they may be interwoven. The stomach has three coats: longitudinal, circular, and oblique; the intestine two: longitudinal and circular. In the uterus, the muscle bundles are interwoven.

Tendon.—Most muscles secure an attachment to bone by means of tendons. These are compact parallel bundles of dense white connective tissue. However, certain muscles are attached directly to bone.

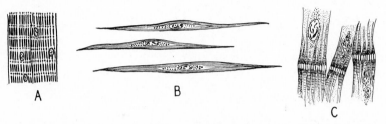

Fig. 22.—Muscle.   *A,* Section of striate fiber; *B,* smooth muscle cells; *C,* section of cardiac muscle, fibrils artificially separated.

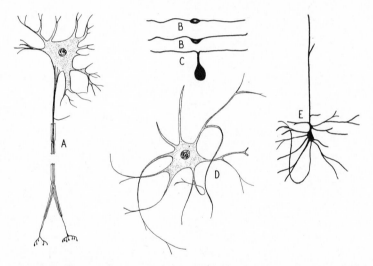

Fig. 23.—Nerve cells.   *A,* Typical neuron; *B,* bipolar cells; *C,* unipolar cell (T-shaped); *D,* multipolar cell; *E,* pyramidal cell from cerebral cortex.

Ligaments are composed of white fibrous connective tissue but the arrangement of the fiber bundles is irregular and the tissue is usually sheetlike in form.

Nerve Tissue

Nerve cells are specialized for the conduction of impulses from one part of the body to another.

A nerve cell consists of a cell body and its processes. The cell body contains a nucleus and a surrounding mass of cytoplasm. The processes which bring impulses to the cell body are called dendrites, and the process that carries impulses from the cell body is called the axon. Bipolar nerve cells have one axon and one dendrite; multipolar cells have several dendrites and one axon. Occasionally a nerve cell is found with but one T-shaped process formed by fusion of dendrite and axon near the cell body, thus forming a unipolar cell. A nerve trunk is composed of bundles of nerve fibers surrounded by a sheath of connective tissue containing blood vessels.

Many axons possess a sheath composed of a fatty substance called myelin. This myelin sheath is constricted at regular intervals, forming the nodes of Ranvier. Outside the myelin sheath there is a second sheath, the neurilemma, which is a thin delicate membrane. The ends of the axon have no sheath. Some axons are entirely devoid of myelin sheaths and are known as naked axons; they are found in nerves going to smooth muscle. Other axons have a neurilemma but no myelin sheath.

Blood and Lymph

Blood.—Blood is a fluid tissue which consists of plasma and cellular elements.

Red blood cells, the carriers of oxygen, are also known as red corpuscles or erythrocytes. The mature red cell has no nucleus and is a biconcave disc. Its cytoplasm contains an organic iron compound called hemoglobin. Under the microscope red corpuscles tend to cling together in columns like a stack of coins. Blood appears bright red in arteries because of the multitude of red cells filled with oxygen-laden hemoglobin, whereas a red cell seen under a microscope is actually not red but a very pale green. When the hemoglobin loses oxygen and the plasma becomes laden with carbon dioxide, the blood is dark red in color. The blue appearance in veins is due to dark blood showing through the skin.

The white cells are called white corpuscles or leukocytes. In inflammation white cells leave the blood stream and gather in large numbers in the infected area where they aid in overcoming the infection. They are much less numerous than the red cells; they have nuclei and are classified into several types by size and

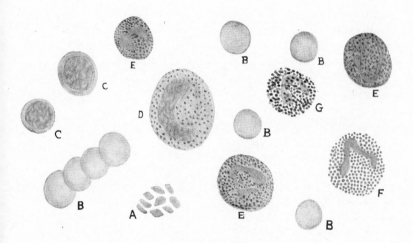

PLATE 1.—Blood cells. *A*, Platelets; *B*, erythrocytes; *C*, lymphocytes; *D*, monocyte; *E*, neutrophils; *F*, eosinophil; *G*, basophil.

shape of the nucleus and by differences in staining reaction. Lymphocytes have a small amount of cytoplasm and a large, dense, round nucleus. There are both large and small lymphocytes. Large mononuclear leukocytes, or monocytes, have a large nucleus which is crescent shaped and cytoplasm which is slightly granular.

Polymorphonuclear leukocytes have a very irregularly-shaped nucleus and the cytoplasm is quite granular. In some cells, if Wright's stain is used, these granules will be lilac, in some blue, and in some red. These are called respectively neutrophils, basophils, and eosinophils. Of these the neutrophils have the smallest granules.

In the plasma there are also many small more or less triangular bodies called blood platelets which are of significance in blood clotting.

One cubic millimeter of blood contains approximately 5,000,000 red blood cells in men, but in women the number is approximately 4,500,000. Both sexes possess 5,000 to 9,000 white blood cells and a number of platelets estimated at between 200,000 and 700,000 per cubic millimeter. The following are the proportions of the different types of white cells:

Lymphocytes	20-25%
Mononuclear leukocytes	3-8%
Neutrophils	65-75%
Eosinophils	2-5%
Basophils	0.5%

Mature blood corpuscles live but a short time, the life span of a single cell being estimated to vary from fifteen to forty or more days. Therefore there must be, throughout life, a continual formation of new cells in order that the number in circulation be kept constant. The process of forming new blood cells is called hemopoiesis, and occurs in hemopoietic organs. Red blood cells, platelets, and granular leukocytes originate in red bone marrow or myeloid tissue; lymphocytes, and probably the monocytes, originate in lymphatic tissue.

In myeloid tissue there is a supporting structure of loose connective tissue containing many small blood vessels. Within the meshes of connective tissue there are a few fat cells and some mature red and white cells, but these are greatly outnumbered by immature blood cells having a great variety of form, size, and staining reaction.

Lymphatic tissue is found in lymph nodes and in the spleen. These organs are described in the chapter on the Lymphatic System. When a lymph nodule is actively producing new cells, it is large and each follicle is packed with a tremendous number of lymphocytes of all sizes. When inactive, a nodule is smaller and the lymphocytes are less numerous, particularly immature forms.

Lymph.—Lymph is similar in composition to blood plasma. It contains a very small number of cells, mainly lymphocytes. It is usually clear, but the lymph contained in the lymphatics from the small intestine appears milky because of fat globules which have been absorbed from the food. These lymphatics are therefore called lacteals and the contained lymph is called chyle.

Macrophages.—There are certain scavenger cells found in the reticular tissue framework of lymph nodes and spleen; in the lining cells of the sinusoids of the liver, adrenal, and hypophysis; and in the outer covering of blood capillaries. These cells have the ability to take up small particles of foreign substances and colloidal dyes. In the lung they ingest particles of dust. In the spleen and liver they pick up worn-out erythrocytes. In lymph nodes they frequently contain any substance which has found its way into the lymph. They tend to increase in areas of local inflammation and are one of the defense mechanisms mobilized by the body to combat infections. In the liver they are called Kupffer cells.

Some of the macrophages arise from cells in areolar connective tissue, others from the monocytes of blood and probably from the lymphocytes, and some from cells of reticular tissue. Reticular tissue is composed of a loose mesh of very fine fibers which are best demonstrated histologically by impregnation with silver. This tissue is always associated with endothelium. All of the macrophages and the reticular tissue are grouped together as the reticuloendothelial system.

Review Questions

1. Name three structures which can be seen in a cell which has been stained.
2. Name six tissues.

3. Give one location in the body for each of the following epithelia: simple squamous epithelium, stratified squamous epithelium, simple columnar eipthelium, pseudostratified columnar epithelium, and transitional epithelium.

4. How are exocrine and endocrine glands distinguished?

5. Where would you find each of the following: mucous membrane, serous membrane, and synovial membrane?

6. Describe briefly dense fibrous connective tissue. Give one location.

7. What is the distinguishing type of cell in adipose tissue?

8. What is the distinctive characteristic of yellow elastic connective tissue? Give one location in the body where it is found.

9. Distinguish between a cartilage and a bone lacuna.

10. Define perichondrium.

11. What is red marrow? Where is it found in an adult?

12. What is yellow marrow?

13. What are the distinguishing features of voluntary, smooth, and cardiac muscle?

14. What is the difference between the axon and a dendrite of a nerve cell?

15. Name five kinds of cells in blood.

16. How many red and white cells are normally present in one cubic millimeter of blood?

17. What cells are formed in myeloid tissue?

unit 2   **POSTURE AND MOVEMENT**

CHAPTER 4

THE SKELETON

The skeleton is the bony framework of the body. Besides protecting the vital organs lying within the body cavities, it serves for the attachments of muscles the contraction of which, by changing the relation of one bone to another, determines bodily position and movement.

There are two main subdivisions of the skeleton: (1) the axial skeleton including the bones of the head, the neck, and the trunk; and (2) the appendicular skeleton including the bones of the extremities.

There are, in addition, seedlike bones, called sesamoids, found near the attachment of certain tendons of hand, foot, and knee. The patella or kneecap, found in the tendon in front of the knee joint, is the largest of these bones. In the sutures, most commonly between the occipital and parietal bones, discrete ossicles of varied size and shape are occasionally found. These are called sutural or Wormian bones.

The axial skeleton is more likely than the appendicular to show variations in the number of its constituent bones. There may be eleven, twelve, or even thirteen thoracic vertebrae, and there may be more or less than twelve pairs of ribs. The last lumbar vertebra and the first sacral may be partially or completely fused. During early childhood the sacrum is composed of five separate vertebrae which fuse to form a single bone in an adult.

Bones may also be classified according to their shape, for example:

1. Long bones: humerus, femur
2. Short bones: carpals, tarsals
3. Flat bones: parietal, sternum
4. Irregular bones: vertebrae, ethmoid

59

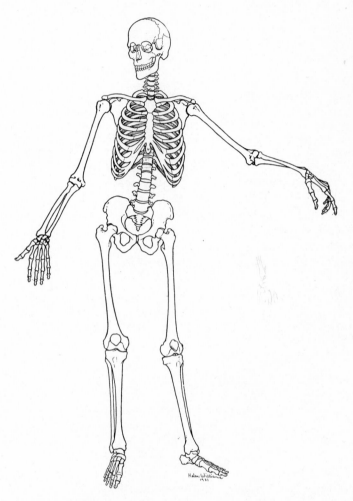

Fig. 24.—Skeleton of a male, anterior view, left hand pronated, right hand supinated.   (Position adapted from Albinus, *Tables of the Skeleton and Muscles of the Human Body;* published by H. Woodfall for John and Paul Knapton, London, 1749.)

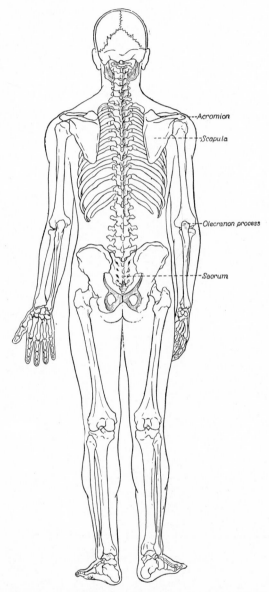

Fig. 25.—Skeleton of male, posterior view, left hand supinated, right hand in a position halfway between supination and pronation. (Illustration courtesy of Dr. N. L. Hoerr.)

Table 1
Table of Bones

NAME OF BONE	SINGLE	PAIRED
Skull		
Frontal ⎫	1	
Parietal ⎪		2
Occipital ⎬ Bones of Brain	1	
Temporal ⎪ Case		2
Sphenoid ⎪	1	
Ethmoid ⎭	1	
Nasal ⎫		2
Lacrimal ⎪		2
Maxilla ⎪		2
Inferior nasal concha ⎬ Bones of Face		2
Zygoma ⎪		2
Palatine ⎪		2
Vomer ⎪	1	
Mandible ⎭	1	
Vertebrae		
Cervical	7	
Thoracic	12	
Lumbar	5	
Sacrum (5 fused)	1	
Coccyx (4 fused)	1	
Thorax		
Ribs		24
Sternum	1	
Upper Extremity		
Clavicle		2
Scapula		2
Humerus		2
Radius		2
Ulna		2
Carpus		16
Metacarpus		10
Phalanges of hand		28
Lower Extremity		
Hip (3 fused)		2
Femur		2
Patella		2
Tibia		2
Fibula		2
Tarsus		14
Metatarsus		10
Phalanges of foot		28
Miscellaneous		
Ossicles of ear (3 pairs)		6
Hyoid	1	
Total		206

BONES OF THE SKULL

The skull is the skeleton of the head and face and consists of twenty-one bones closely joined together and one, the lower jaw or mandible, which is freely movable. To this may be added the three ossicles in each middle ear cavity.

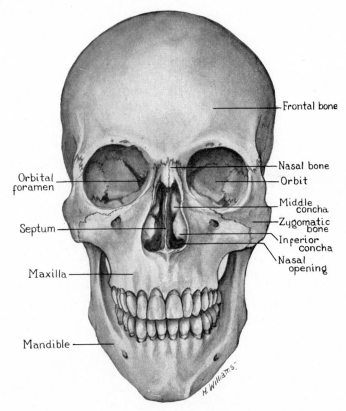

Fig. 26.—Front of skull. (W.R.U. 1091, male, white, aged 25 years.)

The skull has certain very obvious features which are easy to identify and which should be learned before the separate bones are studied. On the front of the skull are the orbits, two large sockets lodging the eyeballs, and above them are the supraorbital ridges. Between and below the orbits is the pear-shaped nasal opening subdivided by the nasal septum into two lateral halves.

The scrolls of bone attached to either side wall of the nasal cavity are the conchae or turbinates. The small, round, external ear opening (external auditory meatus) is in the lower part of the side of the skull. The zygoma is the bridge of bone which springs posteriorly from the side of the skull above and in front of the ear opening, and which is attached anteriorly to the face below the outer edge of the orbit. The temporal fossa is the space above the zygoma and behind the orbit. The mastoid process is the

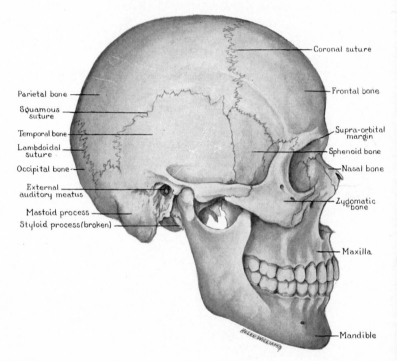

Fig. 27.—Right side of skull.   (W.R.U. 1091, male, white, aged 25 years.)

heavy projection of bone behind and below the external ear opening. On the under surface of the skull is the large opening, the foramen magnum, through which the spinal cord emerges. About two inches in front of that are the two choanae or posterior openings of the nose. The hard palate, or roof of the mouth, forms the floor of the nose. The upper teeth are lodged in a rampart of bone known as the alveolar process, which forms

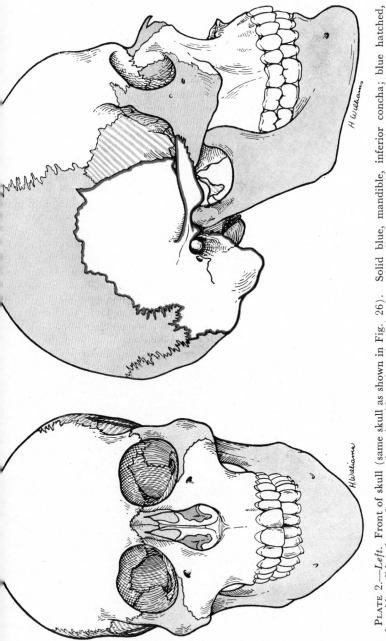

PLATE 2.—*Left.* Front of skull (same skull as shown in Fig. 26). Solid blue, mandible, inferior concha; blue hatched, sphenoid; solid red, nasal, zygomatic, ethmoid, and parietal bones; red outline, temporal; other bones uncolored.

Right. Lateral view of skull (same skull as shown in Fig. 27). Solid blue, mandible, occipital, and lacrimal bones; blue hatched, sphenoid; solid red, nasal, zygomatic, and parietal bones; red outline, temporal; other bones uncolored.

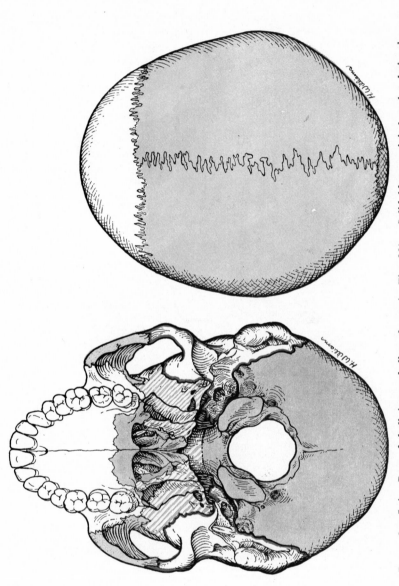

PLATE 3.—*Left.* Base of skull (same skull as shown in Fig. 28). Solid blue, occipital and palatine bones;

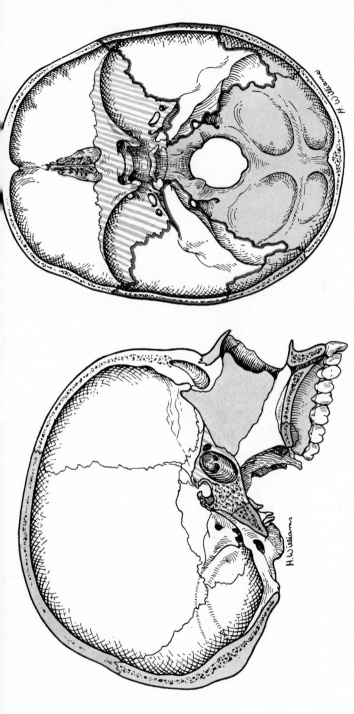

PLATE 4.—*Left.* Sagittal section of left half of skull (same skull as shown in Fig. 31). Solid blue, occipital and palatine bones; solid red, maxilla, parietal, ethmoid, and nasal bones; blue hatched, sphenoid; maxilla colored to distinguish it from vomer. *Right.* Floor of cranial cavity (same skull as shown in Fig. 29). Solid blue, occipital bone; solid red, parietal and ethmoid bones; blue hatched, sphenoid; red outline, temporal; other bones uncolored.

a horseshoelike border for the hard palate. If the top of the skull is removed, the floor of the brain case is seen to consist of three large uneven areas called the anterior, middle, and posterior cranial fossae.

The top or vault of the skull is formed by the frontal, two parietal, and the occipital bones in that order from front to back.

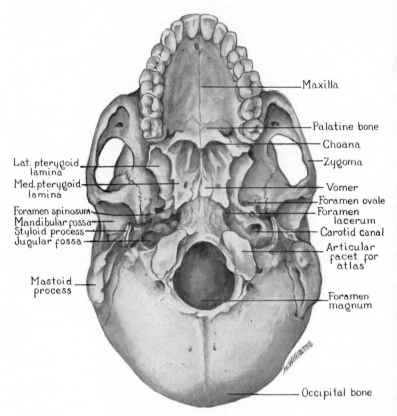

Fig. 28.—Under surface of skull.   (W.R.U. 1091, male, white, aged 25 years.)

Frontal Bone.—The frontal bone is a saucer-shaped bone forming the forehead, the upper part of the orbit, the anterior portion of the anterior cranial fossa, and a part of the septum between the brain case and nasal cavity. The frontal tuberosities, two variable bulgings one on either side of the midline about one and one-half inches above the orbit, form the most prominent part of the forehead. There is a notch (or sometimes a foramen) in the supra-orbital margin, about one third of the way lateral to the medial limit of the orbit, through which passes the supraorbital nerve. In the upper lateral part of the orbit there is a shallow depression for the lacrimal gland.

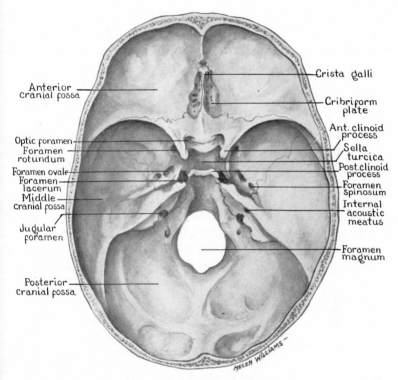

Fig. 29.—Floor of cranial cavity. Petrous (temporal) bones asymmetrical. (W.R.U. 318, male, white, aged 25 years.)

Posteriorly, at the coronal suture, the frontal bone articulates with the two parietal bones; laterally with the great wing of the sphenoid and the frontal process of the zygomatic bone; and below with the ethmoid, lacrimal, maxillary, and nasal bones in that order from behind forward.

In the embryo the frontal bone is formed from two equal parts, with a suture in the midline that sometimes persists into adult life as the metopic suture.

In the substance of the frontal bone above the orbits are two large irregular cavities, the frontal sinuses, which communicate with the nasal cavity. These are further described in the section on air sinuses in the chapter on the Respiratory System.

Parietal Bones.—Each of the parietal bones is shaped rather like a square saucer and forms the upper portion of the side of the skull. The two parietal bones meet in the midline at the sagittal suture. They join the frontal bone in front at the coronal suture, the occipital bone behind at the lambdoidal suture, and the temporal and a little of the great wing of the sphenoid laterally at the squamous suture.

On the inner surface there are well-marked grooves radiating upward from the inferior border of the bone for the middle meningeal blood vessels and there are shallow impressions produced by the gyri of the cerebrum.

Occipital Bone.—The occipital bone constitutes the back and a large part of the base of the skull. The part behind the foramen magnum is the squamous portion which forms most of the posterior cranial fossa. The external occipital protuberance is a well-marked projection in the midline above, halfway up the back of the bone. The superior nuchal line extends laterally to either side of this projection. The inferior nuchal line, roughly parallel to the superior, is about halfway between it and the foramen magnum and in many skulls is poorly defined.

The internal occipital protuberance is the central projection on the inner surface of the squamous portion. Extending upward from this landmark is the sulcus for the superior sagittal blood sinus and extending to either side is a lateral sulcus for a transverse blood sinus. The occipital poles of the cerebral hemispheres lie in the fossae above these lateral sulci and the cerebellar hemispheres in the fossae below.

The lateral parts of the occipital bone lie on either side of the foramen magnum. The smooth, convex area on the lower surface on each side is the occipital condyle for articulation with the first cervical vertebra or atlas. A channel through the boss of bone above this articular surface transmits the twelfth nerve on its way to the tongue and is therefore called the canal for the hypoglossal nerve. The terminal portion of the transverse sinus grooves the deep surface of the lateral part of the occipital bone.

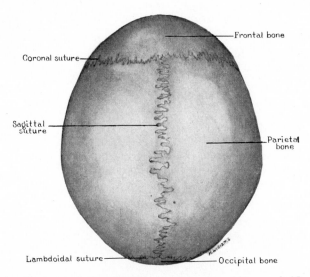

Fig. 30.—Vault of skull.   (W.R.U. 1091, male, white, aged 25 years.)

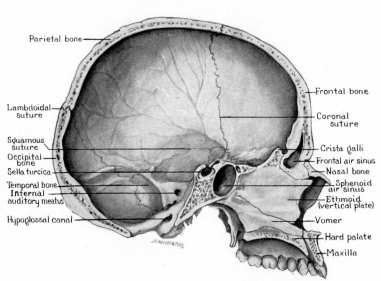

Fig. 31.—Sagittal section of left half of skull.   (W.R.U. 1091, male, white, aged 25 years.)

The basilar part of the occipital bone is the heavy bar extending forward from the foramen magnum to the body of the sphenoid.

The occipital bone articulates above with the parietal bone, laterally with the temporal, and in front fuses with the sphenoid.

Temporal Bones.—The temporal bone forms a part of the lateral wall of the skull as well as of the base. The large, winglike, squamous portion forms the lateral wall of the middle cranial fossa and articulates above with the parietal bone. The mastoid portion forms the prominence which can be felt behind the ear and articulates with the occipital bone. Within the substance of the

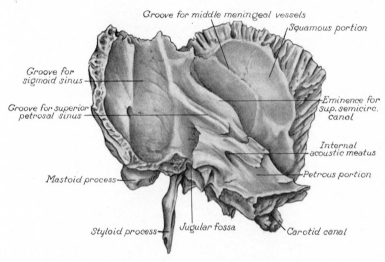

Fig. 32.—Left temporal bone, medial surface.   (W.R.U. museum specimen.)

mastoid are air cells connected with the middle ear cavity. The long, slender, bony spike extending downward and forward, medial to the mastoid process, is the styloid process. (This is frequently broken off in dry skulls.) To the styloid are attached several important muscles and ligaments of the neck. Just in front of the root of the styloid is the round, smooth, mandibular fossa for the lodgment of the head of the mandible.

The zygomatic process of the temporal bone forms the back part of the zygoma and articulates in front with the temporal process of the zygomatic bone.

The inner surface of the mastoid is grooved by the distal or sigmoid portion of the transverse blood sinus. This portion of the blood sinus is separated from the mastoid air cells by a thin plate of bone, and infections occasionally extend from the mastoid to the sinus, causing lateral sinus thrombosis.

The petrous portion of the temporal bone is an uneven, wedge-shaped projection lying mainly in the floor of the middle cranial fossa between the great wing of the sphenoid and the lateral border of the basilar part of the occipital bone. This wedge of bone also forms part of the posterior fossa of the skull, and on this face of the petrous portion of the temporal bone can be seen the internal acoustic meatus which transmits the eighth cranial nerve to the internal ear and the seventh cranial nerve which passes through the petrous portion to emerge at the stylomastoid foramen close behind the root of the styloid process. Within the petrous portion are the cavities of the middle and inner ear. On the under surface there is a depression, the jugular fossa, for the dilated beginning of the internal jugular vein.

In the line of articulation between the petrous portion of the temporal bone and the basal portion of the occiput are two important openings. The anterior and more medial slitlike opening is the foramen lacerum. The jugular foramen is the more posterior and lateral opening through which pass the internal jugular vein and the ninth, tenth, and eleventh cranial nerves. Above, the jugular foramen leads into the posterior cranial fossa. The carotid canal is a channel within the petrous portion which transmits the internal carotid artery. This canal begins just in front of the jugular foramen and takes a curved path through the bone to emerge above at the foramen lacerum where the artery passes upward in the middle cranial fossa. In the fissure between the anterior border of the petrous portion and the posterior edge of the great wing of the sphenoid there is an irregular opening which is the inner end of the bony part of the auditory tube (Eustachian tube).

Sphenoid Bone.—The sphenoid bone is quite irregular in shape and somewhat resembles a butterfly with its two pairs of outspread wings. It forms part of the floor of the anterior cranial fossa above the eyes and nose (small wings of sphenoid) and also that part of the floor and lateral wall of the middle cranial fossa in front of the petrous and squamous parts of the temporal bone (great wings). The body of the sphenoid is shaped more or less like a cube, and its posterior portion extends backward in the midline into the posterior cranial fossa where it unites with the basilar part of the occipital. Within the substance of the central portion of the sphenoid are the sphenoid air sinuses. The pterygoid canal passes through the body of the sphenoid below and lateral to the air sinuses, each canal being about one-half inch from the midline and running horizontally from back to front. The pit in the upper surface of the sphenoid bone above the air sinuses is the sella turcica for the lodgment of the hypophysis. The anterior and posterior margins of the sella terminate laterally as the clinoid processes.

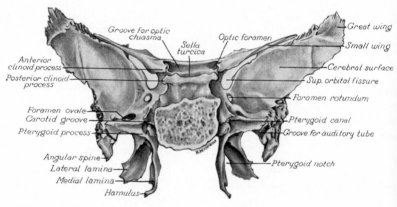

Fig. 33.—Sphenoid, viewed from behind. (W.R.U. museum specimen.)

The pterygoid processes of the sphenoid are downward projections from the body of the sphenoid flanking the posterior opening of the nose. The lower end of each process is subdivided into two thin, flat sheets of bone, the medial and lateral pterygoid plates or laminae. The pyramidal process of the palatine bone fits into the pterygoid notch, a fissure between these two plates. The lower end of the medial pterygoid plate ends in a hooklike process, the hamulus of the pterygoid.

The optic foramen (canal) for the second cranial nerve is the round opening communicating with the orbit at the root of the lesser wing. Lateral to the optic foramen is a long slit communi-

cating with the orbit which is known as the superior orbital fissure and transmits the third, fourth, and sixth cranial nerves and
the ophthalmic division of the fifth cranial nerve. The foramen
rotundum is the opening at the base of the greater wing and transmits the maxillary division of the fifth cranial nerve. The foramen ovale pierces the lower portion of the greater wing and
transmits the mandibular division of the fifth cranial nerve.

The inferior orbital fissure is a cleft between those portions of
the great wing of the sphenoid and the maxilla which form the
back of the orbit. If one looks at the skull from the side, the
lower end of the lateral pterygoid plate is seen to fuse with that
part of the maxilla which forms the posterior wall of the maxillary

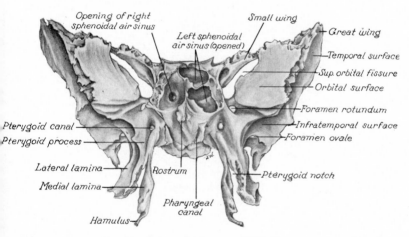

Fig. 34.—Sphenoid, viewed from in front.   (W.R.U. museum specimen.)

sinus. Above the area of fusion is a narrow slot between the edge
of the lateral pterygoid plate and the maxilla called the pterygo-
maxillary fissure, and at the upper end this fissure is continuous
with the inferior orbital fissure.

Ethmoid Bone.—The ethmoid bone is very irregular in shape
and difficult to define in a complete skull. It lies in front of the
sphenoid between the eyes and forms part of the nasal roof where
it is perforated by foramina for branches of the first cranial nerve.
This sievelike plate, the lamina cribrosa, helps to complete the
floor of the anterior cranial fossa. The crista galli is the upward

projection of the median perpendicular plate of the ethmoid between the two cribriform plates, and the upper part of the nasal septum is formed by the lower portion of the median plate. On each side of the median plate of the ethmoid bone is the lateral mass enclosing many small spaces, called the ethmoid air cells or ethmoid labyrinth, and bearing on its inner face the upper and middle nasal conchae or turbinates which are scroll-like leaves of bone projecting into the nose from its lateral wall. The medial wall of each orbit is formed by the outer face of the lateral mass of the ethmoid.

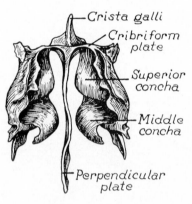

Fig. 35.—Ethmoid, viewed from behind. This is a semidiagrammatic drawing. (W.R.U. museum specimen.)

Nasal Bones.—Two small flat bones form the bridge of the nose. They articulate with each other in the midline and above with the midportion of the frontal bone. Laterally each articulates with the maxilla and on the deep surface with the perpendicular plate of the ethmoid and the cartilaginous septum of the nose.

Lacrimal Bones.—Each lacrimal bone is a thin scalelike bone the size of a fingernail, lying in the medial wall of the orbit upon the ethmoid bone and helping to form the side wall of the nasal cavity where it touches the maxilla and inferior concha.

Maxillary Bones.—The maxillary bones constitute the front of the face and upper jaw, and each forms the floor of the corresponding orbit and lateral wall of the lower part of the nasal cavity. The maxilla may be described as having a large central

mass and four projecting smaller masses.   Within the central
portion or body is a large air sinus, called the maxillary sinus or
antrum of Highmore, which communicates with the nasal cavity.

The orbital surface is marked off from the facial surface by a
ridge of bone which forms the lower and inner half of the orbital
opening.   Just below the outer part of this ridge is the infraorbital
foramen through which the infraorbital branch of the second division of the fifth cranial nerve passes to the skin of the face.

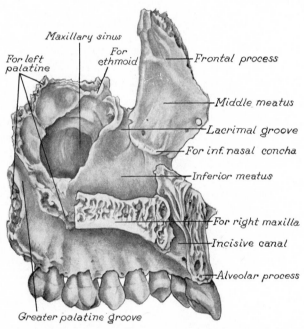

Maxillary sinus

For left palatine   *For ethmoid*   *Frontal process*

Middle meatus

Lacrimal groove

For inf. nasal concha

Inferior meatus

For right maxilla

Incisive canal

Alveolar process

Greater palatine groove

Fig. 36.—Left maxilla, medial surface.   (W.R.U. museum specimen.)

The frontal process is the upward projection which articulates
above with the frontal and nasal bones and medially with the ethmoid and inferior concha.

The zygomatic process is the lateral projection which articulates
with the zygomatic bone and forms the anterior end of the zygomatic arch.

The alveolar process is the dental arch in which are set the
upper teeth.

The palatine process is the horizontal shelf of bone within the dental arch which forms the anterior and lower part of the hard palate. The two palatine processes meet in the midline, forming the intermaxillary suture.

Inferior Nasal Conchae.—Each inferior nasal concha is a shell-like scroll of bone which articulates laterally with the maxillary, ethmoid, lacrimal, and palatine bones. It projects medially as a rolled plate of thin bone into the nasal cavity and is covered with mucous membrane.

Zygomatic Bones.—The zygomatic or malar bone forms the cheek. It articulates medially with the maxilla, above with the frontal bone, laterally with the temporal bone, and behind with the great wing of the sphenoid bone. It forms the midportion of the zygomatic arch, and an upward projection completes the outer wall of the orbit.

Palatine Bones.—The palatine bone forms the posterior portion of the hard palate and part of the lateral wall of the posterior nasal opening or choana. This bone is difficult to identify in an adult skull but has been likened in shape to the letter L. The vertical part forms the side wall of the choana and above a little of the medial portion of the back of the orbit. Just below the orbital surface the sphenopalatine foramen is present in the articulation between palatine and sphenoid bones.

The horizontal portion of the palatine articulates in front with the maxilla and medially with its fellow. At the junction of horizontal and vertical portions is the pyramidal process which fits between the medial and lateral plates of the pterygoid process of the sphenoid.

Vomer.—The vomer forms the posterior part of the nasal septum. Above, it articulates with the sphenoid and perpendicular plate of the ethmoid, and below with the maxillary and palatine bones. In adult skulls it is usually fused with the ethmoid bone and in dried skulls is frequently broken into fragments.

Mandible.—The mandible is the bone of the lower jaw. It consists of a horseshoe-shaped body, the upper or alveolar portion of which lodges the lower teeth, and a strong ramus extending upward and backward from each free end of the horseshoe. Each ramus bears a condyle which articulates with the under surface of the temporal bone. There is a flat tongue of bone in

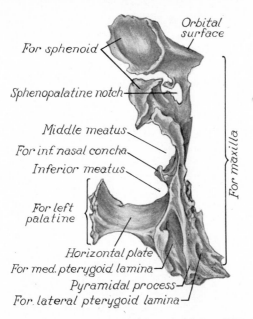

Fig. 37.—Right palatine bone, viewed from behind. (W.R.U. museum specimen.)

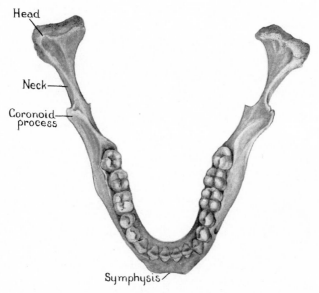

Fig. 38.—Mandible, viewed from above. (W.R.U. 1091, white, aged 25 years.)

front of the condyle, called the coronoid process, to which the temporal muscle is attached.

Above the center of the inner surface of the ramus is the mandibular foramen through which the nerves and arteries for the lower teeth pass into the bone. The mylohyoid groove extends downward and forward from the foramen. The mylohyoid line is the marked horizontal ridge on the inner surface of the mandible below the alveolar portion.

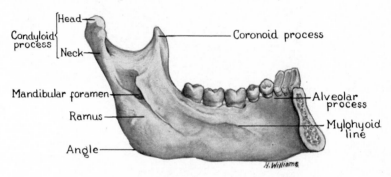

Fig. 39.—Medial surface left half of mandible. (W.R.U. 443, male, white, aged 40 years.)

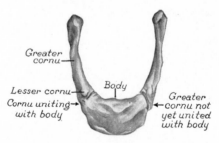

Fig. 40.—Hyoid bone, viewed from above and in front. (W.R.U. 2940, male, Negro, aged 40 years.)

In a baby the mandible is composed of two halves which meet in the midline to form the symphysis of the mandible. During infancy the two halves fuse.

Hyoid.—The hyoid bone, though not a portion of the skull, can best be described here. It is a slender, horseshoe-shaped bone found below the mandible at the upper border of the voice box or larynx. It may be felt just above the Adam's apple of the neck.

The greater horns or cornua of the hyoid are the upward and backward projections of bone from either extremity. The lesser horns are the two small, upward projections from the upper edge of the bone anterior to the greater horns.

Ear Bones.—Within the middle ear cavity of the petrous portion of each temporal bone are three tiny bones called hammer (malleus), anvil (incus), and stirrup (stapes), thus named from their respective shapes.

The arterial or nutrient foramina for the vessels which nourish bones have been omitted as well as many inconstant foramina for emissary veins, and the veins which accompany an artery of the same name. Emissary veins are short communicating vessels between the venous sinuses within the skull and the veins outside the skull.

VERTEBRAL COLUMN

The vertebral column typically has seven cervical (neck) vertebrae, twelve thoracic (chest) vertebrae, five lumbar (small of back) vertebrae, a sacrum composed of five vertebrae fused together in an adult, and a coccyx in which there are four fused vertebrae. The vertebrae, separated from each other by discs of fibrocartilage, are closely bound together by ligaments.

A typical vertebra possesses a central cylinder of bone called the body, with a flattened articular surface above and below. Behind the body is a bony neural arch enclosing the vertebral foramen. In the articulated vertebral column the successive neural arches form the walls of the vertebral canal which lodges the spinal cord. The neural arch consists of laterally placed, backwardly directed processes, the pedicles, united behind by a bridge of bone, the lamina. The pedicles are notched above and below, and in the articulated column these notches form openings, the intervertebral foramina, through which the spinal nerves pass. Projecting backward from the lamina behind the vertebral foramen is the spinous process. There are three other projections of bone extending outward from each side, an upper one called the superior articular process, a lower one the inferior articular process, and between them a thick transverse process.

Table 2
*Skull Bones**

NAME	LOCATION	DISTINGUISHING FEATURES	ARTICULATIONS
Frontal	Front of skull and upper part of each orbit	Frontal part with air sinuses, tuberosities, and zygomatic processes; orbital part	Sphenoid, ethmoid, each parietal, nasal, zygomatic, maxilla, and lacrimal
Parietal	Vault of skull	Grooves on inner surface for middle meningeal vessels	Frontal, temporal, sphenoid, occipital, and other parietal
Occipital	Back of skull and posterior part of base	Squamous part with internal and external occipital protuberances and grooves for blood sinuses; lateral part with articular facets and hypoglossal canals; basal part with foramen magnum and jugular fossae	Sphenoid, atlas, and each temporal and parietal
Temporal	Lateral part of vault and base of skull	Squamous part with zygomatic process and mandibular fossa; tympanic part with external auditory meatus, stylomastoid foramen, and styloid process; mastoid part with air cells and grooves for blood sinuses; petrous part with jugular fossa, carotid canal, and internal acoustic meatus	Parietal, occipital, zygomatic, sphenoid, and mandible
Sphenoid	Anterior part of base of skull and deep part of face	Body with air cells, sella turcica, posterior clinoid processes, optic groove, rostrum and pharyngeal canal; small wings with optic foramen, anterior clinoid processes and superior orbital fissure; great wings with foramen ovale, foramen rotundum, and foramen spinosum; pterygoid processes with pterygoid canal and medial and lateral pterygoid plates	Frontal, vomer, ethmoid, and each parietal, temporal, zygomatic, and palatine
Ethmoid	Anterior part of base of skull, medial part of each orbit and upper part of nose	Perpendicular plate with crista galli; cribriform plates; lateral parts with air cells and superior and middle nasal conchae	Sphenoid, vomer, frontal, and each nasal, maxilla, lacrimal, palatine, and inferior nasal concha

Bone	Location	Parts	Articulates with
Nasal	Bridge of nose		Frontal, ethmoid, maxilla, and other nasal
Lacrimal	Medial wall of orbit		Frontal, ethmoid, maxilla, and inferior nasal concha
Maxilla	Upper jaw, face, and lower part of orbit	Body with air sinus, lacrimal groove, infraorbital foramen and greater palatine groove; frontal process; zygomatic process; alveolar process with upper teeth and incisive canal; palatine process	Frontal, nasal, ethmoid, zygomatic, lacrimal, inferior nasal concha, vomer, palatine, and other maxilla
Inferior nasal concha	Lower lateral wall of nose		Palatine, maxilla, lacrimal, and ethmoid
Zygomatic	Cheek	Temporal process; orbital process; frontosphenoidal process	Temporal, frontal, sphenoid, and maxilla
Palatine	Part of hard palate, nasal cavity, and orbit	Horizontal plate; perpendicular part with pyramidal process and sphenopalatine notch	Sphenoid, maxilla, ethmoid, inferior nasal concha, vomer, and other palatine
Vomer	Back of nasal septum		Ethmoid, sphenoid, each maxilla, and palatine
Mandible	Lower jaw	Body with alveolar process and lower teeth, mylohyoid line and mental foramina; two rami each with coronoid process, condyloid process, head, neck, and mandibular foramen	Each temporal

*From Francis, Carl C., and Farrell, Gordon L.: Integrated Anatomy and Physiology, ed. 3, St. Louis, 1957, The C. V. Mosby Co.

Cervical Vertebrae.—The cervical vertebrae have certain characteristic features. Each presents three foramina, namely, the vertebral foramen and two smaller perforations, one in each transverse process; the vertebral artery runs upward within these lateral perforations to reach the foramen magnum of the skull. The transverse processes of the cervical vertebrae are small and have no areas for articulation with ribs. The spinous process is relatively short and is usually bifid or split at the end.

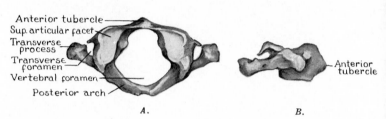

Fig. 41.—Atlas. *A,* Viewed from above; *B,* viewed from right side. (W.R.U. 989, male, white, aged 31 years.)

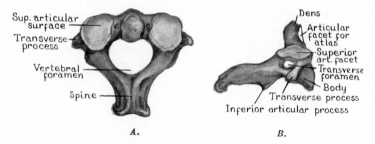

Fig. 42.—Second cervical vertebra. *A,* Viewed from above; *B,* viewed from right side. (W.R.U. 989, male, white, aged 31 years.)

The first cervical vertebra or atlas is a ring of bone with no body and no spinous process but with well-marked transverse processes. On each side of the vertebral foramen there is a bean-shaped smooth surface for articulation with the occipital bone. Nodding movements take place between the skull and the atlas.

The second cervical vertebra, axis or epistropheus, is easily identified by its toothlike process, the dens, which projects upward from the body. Rotating movements of the head occur around the dens.

The spinous process of the seventh cervical vertebra is quite long and blunt. It may be felt at the back of the base of the neck as the uppermost projection in the midline of that region.

Thoracic Vertebrae.—Thoracic vertebrae are characterized by having long spinous processes and articular facets for ribs. The tip of each transverse process bears an articular surface for the tubercle of the rib corresponding to that vertebra. The head of the rib meets the body of the vertebra at its junction with the

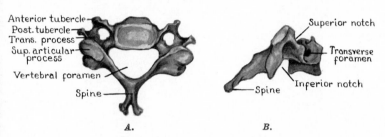

Fig. 43.—Sixth cervical vertebra. *A,* Viewed from above; *B,* viewed from right side. (W.R.U. 989, male, white, aged 31 years.)

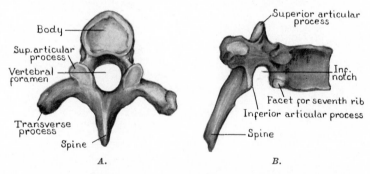

Fig. 44.—Sixth thoracic vertebra. *A,* Viewed from above; *B,* viewed from right side. (W.R.U. 989, male, white, aged 31 years.)

pedicle, so there are two articular areas on each vertebra for the corresponding rib. In the case of the upper ten ribs the head articulates not only with the body of the corresponding rib, but also with the body of the vertebra above.

The superior and inferior processes form joints with the corresponding processes of the vertebrae above and below. Spinous and transverse processes serve for attachment of the muscles and ligaments of the back.

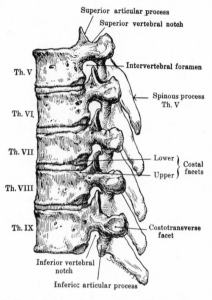

Fig. 45.—Lateral view of thoracic vertebrae five to nine. (From Mettler: Neuroanatomy, St. Louis, 1948, The C. V. Mosby Co.)

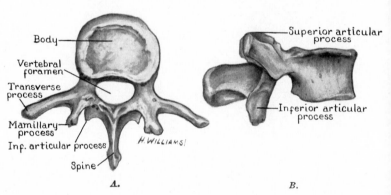

Fig. 46.—Third lumbar vertebra. *A,* Viewed from above; *B,* viewed from right side. (W.R.U. 989, male, white, aged 31 years.)

Lumbar Vertebrae.—The lumbar vertebrae are larger than the thoracic. The superior and inferior articular processes are large. The spinous processes are short, thick, and blunt. The transverse processes are thin and are not perforated. There are no articular surfaces for ribs, but the transverse processes of the first lumbar vertebra are sometimes free and closely resemble short ribs.

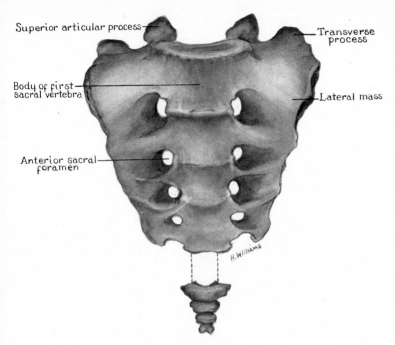

Fig. 47.—Sacrum and coccyx, front view. (W.R.U. 1674, male, white, aged 26 years.)

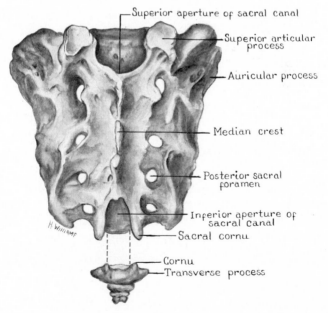

Fig. 48.—Sacrum and coccyx, posterior view. (W.R.U. 1674, male, white, aged 26 years.)

Certain distinguishing features of vertebrae are summarized in Table 3.

Table 3

	CERVICAL	THORACIC	LUMBAR
Size	Small	Larger	Largest
Foramina	3	1	1
Articular facets for ribs	No	Yes	No
Spinous process	Slender and bifid	Long and fairly thick	Short and blunt
Transverse process	Small	Fairly large	Large and blunt

Sacrum.—The sacrum consists of five fused sacral vertebrae. Together with the two hip bones it forms the pelvis. The first sacral vertebra is the largest and each succeeding vertebra dwindles in size. The smooth, concave, anterior surface of the sacrum forms the hollow of the pelvis. The posterior surface is rough and uneven for attachment of the muscles of the back. On each surface there are four pairs of foramina for the four upper sacral nerves. On each side there is a large, sharply defined, ear-shaped area for articulation with the ilium (upper portion of the os coxae or os innominatum).

Coccyx.—The coccyx is a small, rough, triangular bone lying at the end of the spinal column below the sacrum.

BONES OF THE THORAX

The bony thorax surrounds the heart and lungs. Participating in its composition are twelve pairs of ribs attached behind to the twelve thoracic vertebrae. In front the upper ten ribs are attached either directly or indirectly to the sternum or breast bone by means of costal cartilages.

Ribs.—A typical rib is a long, slender, curved bone. Its head articulates with two thoracic vertebrae, namely, the one corresponding to it and the one just above it. The lowest two ribs, however, possess only one articular surface, namely, that for the corresponding vertebra. The first rib may have but one.

Beyond the head of the rib is a narrow portion called the neck, and just beyond this again, except in the lowest two ribs, is a knob called the tubercle which has a smooth area articulating with a transverse process of the corresponding vertebra.

The first rib is short, sharply curved, and relatively broader than any of the others. The great vessels and lowest nerves for the arm pass over this rib, making distinct grooves on its upper surface.

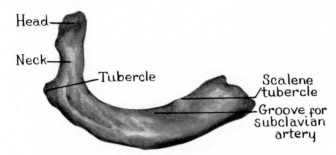

Fig. 49.—First rib, right side, viewed from above.   (W.R.U. 989, male, white, aged 31 years.)

Fig. 50.—Seventh rib, right side, deep aspect. This rib is shown two-fifths life size, whereas ribs in Figs. 49 and 51 are drawn two-thirds life size. (W.R.U. 989, male, white, aged 31 years.)

Fig. 51.—Twelfth rib, right side, viewed from above.   (W.R.U. 989, male, white, aged 31 years.)

The second rib is considerably longer than the first and much more slender. The third to seventh ribs are increasingly longer, whereas the succeeding ones diminish regularly in length. Each of the upper seven ribs is joined to the sternum by a separate costal cartilage. The costal cartilages of the eighth, ninth, and tenth ribs are joined respectively to the costal cartilage of the rib next above and so indirectly to the lower part of the sternum. The costal cartilages of the eleventh and twelfth ribs are not joined to the sternum and are therefore sometimes called "floating ribs." The free tips of their costal cartilages are easily felt low down on the side wall of the thorax.

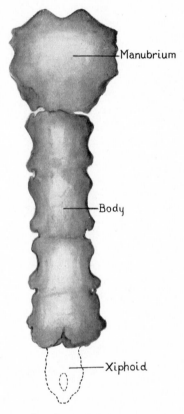

Fig. 52.—Sternum, anterior view. Missing xiphoid is indicated by dotted lines. (W.R.U. 989, male, white, aged 31 years.)

Sternum.—The sternum or breast bone is shaped somewhat like a blunt dagger. It forms the chest wall in the median line in front. Its upper end is broad and articulates on each side with the clavicle or collar bone and with the first rib. The sternum tapers toward the lower end or xiphoid which forms a small projection in the upper portion of the "pit of the stomach" between the costal margins.

The sternum consists of an upper portion (the manubrium), a middle portion (the body), and an inferior portion (the xiphoid). The xiphoid is cartilaginous in early life but later ossifies and fuses with the body of the sternum.

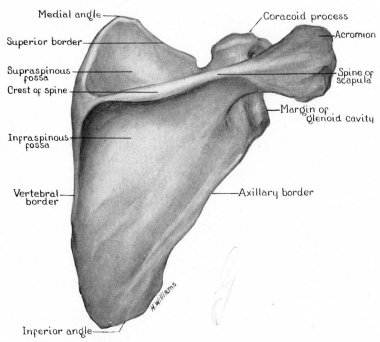

Fig. 53.—Right scapula, posterior view.   (W.R.U. 989, male, white, aged 31 years.)

BONES OF UPPER EXTREMITY

In the upper extremity are included the shoulder, upper arm, forearm, wrist, and hand.

Scapula.—The scapula or shoulder blade is largely covered by muscles. The main portion is a flat, triangular body. The angle nearest the armpit bears a smooth, slightly depressed, oval area, the glenoid surface or the glenoid cavity, for articulation with the head of the humerus. The other two angles delimit the vertebral border which parallels the vertebral column. The deep face of the scapula is concave and is known as the costal surface because it lies next to the ribs. In movements of the shoulder the scapula glides freely over the posterior chest wall. The superficial surface of the scapula presents a backwardly projecting spinous process terminating laterally in an expanded knob, called the acromion,

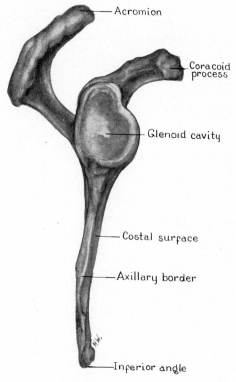

Fig. 54.—Right scapula, lateral view. (W.R.U. 989, male, white, aged 31 years.)

which forms the tip of the shoulder. The acromion articulates in front with the lateral end of the clavicle. The entire length of the spinous process is subcutaneous. On the upper border of the scapula there is a hooklike process, the coracoid, which curls forward beneath the clavicle.

Clavicle.—The clavicle or collar bone is a long, curved, slender bone which lies in the root of the neck between the upper end of the sternum and the acromion.   The medial end is rounded, articulates with the sternum, and is the only joint between the upper extremity and the trunk for all the other attachments are made by means of muscles and tendons.   The outer end is broad and flat and articulates with the acromion.

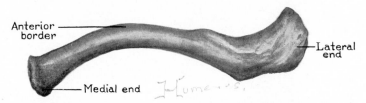

Fig. 55.—Right clavicle, viewed from above.   (W.R.U. 989, male, white, aged 31 years.)

Humerus.—The humerus is the bone of the upper arm.   Its upper end has a thick, rounded knob on the medial side, called the head, which articulates with the glenoid surface of the scapula. There are two rough projections lateral to the head, the greater and lesser tuberosities or tubercles, with an intermediate groove, the intertubercular sulcus, for the tendon of the long head of the biceps muscle.   When the arm hangs freely by the side, the great tuberosity of the humerus projects just below the acromion of the scapula.

On the lateral side of the shaft of the bone, about halfway between the two ends, there is a V-shaped, roughened area for attachment of the deltoid muscle below which is a spiral groove for the radial nerve.

The central portion of the shaft is round, but the bone becomes flattened in the distal portion.   The sharp border thus formed on either side ends in a roughened projection, the medial and the lateral epicondyles.   The lower end of the humerus has an articular surface divided into two parts.   The outer is a smooth, round knob, called the capitulum, which articulates with the upper end of the radius.   The inner is a smooth, pulley-shaped surface, called the trochlea, which articulates with the upper end of the ulna.

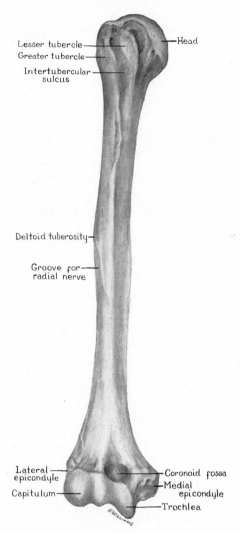

Lesser tubercle

Greater tubercle

Intertubercular
sulcus

Head

Deltoid tuberosity

Groove for
radial nerve

Lateral
epicondyle

Capitulum

Coronoid fossa

Medial
epicondyle

Trochlea

Fig. 56.—Right humerus, front view. (W.R.U. 989, male, white, aged
31 years.)

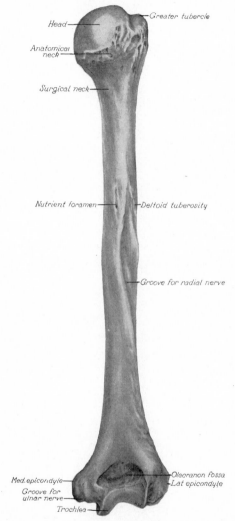

Fig. 57.—Right humerus, posterior view. (W.R.U. 989, male, white, aged 31 years.)

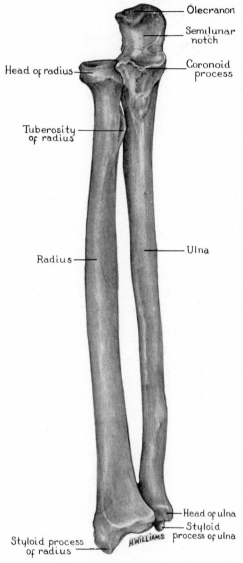

Fig. 58.—Right radius and ulna, volar aspect. (W.R.U. 989, male, white, aged 31 years.)

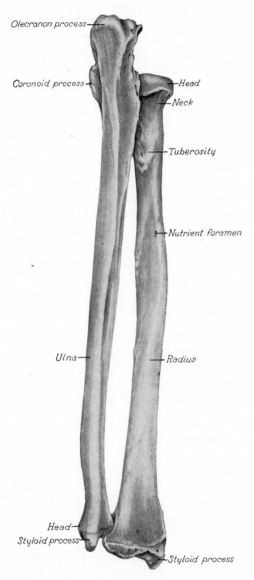

Fig. 59.—Right radius and ulna, posterior or dorsal aspect. (W.R.U. 989, male, white, aged 31 years.)

On the front of the lower end of the shaft of the humerus just above the articular area is the coronoid fossa, so called because it lodges the coronoid process of the ulna when the elbow is flexed. On the back of the lower end of the shaft of the humerus is the olecranon fossa which lodges the olecranon process of the ulna when the elbow is extended.

Ulna.—The ulna is the longer of the two bones in the forearm. It is on the medial side and can easily be felt in its entire length by running the finger from the tip of the elbow down the back of the forearm to the small projection on the back of the wrist on the little finger side.

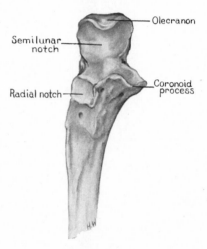

Fig. 60.—Upper end of right ulna. Rotated to show radial notch or articular surface for head of radius. (W.R.U. 989, male, white, aged 31 years.)

The upper end of the ulna has two large, beaklike projections between which the trochlea of the humerus snugly fits. The upwardly projecting process is the olecranon and the forwardly projecting process is the coronoid. The lower end of the ulna, smaller than the upper, has a knobbed portion called the head, beside which is a conical projection known as the styloid process.

Radius.—The shorter of the two bones of the forearm is called the radius. It lies on the outer or thumb side and is for the most part well covered by muscles. At the proximal end is a circular disc, the head, which articulates with the capitulum of the humerus and also with the ulna. A short distance below the upper end there is a low, rough projection on the inner side (toward the ulna) called the tuberosity to which is attached the tendon of the biceps muscle of the arm.

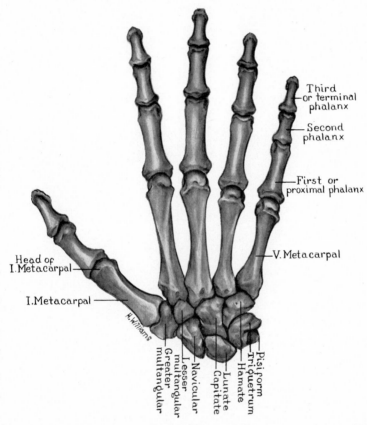

Fig. 61.—Bones of right wrist and hand, dorsal aspect. (W.R.U. 989, male, white, aged 31 years.)

The distal end of the radius is much larger than the upper end and has a final tip on the thumb side called the styloid process. At its lower end the radius articulates with two bones of the wrist, the navicular and lunate. There is also an articulation with the head of the ulna.

Table 4
*Bones of Upper Extremity**

NAME	LOCATION	DISTINGUISHING FEATURES	ARTICULATIONS
Scapula	Back of shoulder	Shoulder blade; head with neck and glenoid cavity; acromion; spine; coracoid process; supraspinous fossa; infraspinous fossa; subscapular fossa	Lateral end of clavicle; head of humerus
Clavicle	Junction of neck and thorax	Collar bone; medial and lateral ends	Medial end with sternum; lateral end with scapula
Humerus	Upper arm	Head; anatomical neck; surgical neck; lesser and greater tubercles; intertubercular sulcus; deltoid tuberosity; medial and lateral epicondyles; capitulum; trochlea; coronoid and olecranon fossae	Head with scapula; capitulum with radius; trochlea with ulna
Radius	Lateral part of forearm	Head; neck; tuberosity; styloid process; ulnar notch	Head with humerus and ulna; lower end with ulna and carpal bones
Ulna	Medial part of forearm	Olecranon; semilunar notch; coronoid process; radial notch; head; styloid process	Upper end with humerus and radius; lower end with radius
Carpus	Wrist	Eight bones arranged in two rows; proximal row navicular, lunate, triquetrum, and pisiform; distal row greater multangular, lesser multangular, capitate, and hamate	Proximal row with lower end of radius; distal row with metacarpals; with each other; the pisiform with triquetrum only
Metacarpus	Hand	Five bones each with head, shaft, and base; numbered from one to five beginning on the thumb side	Bases each with each other and with distal row of carpal bones; heads with corresponding finger bone
Phalanges	Fingers	Fourteen; two for thumb and three for each of the other fingers	Proximal with respective metacarpal; with each other

*From Francis, Carl C, and Farrell, Gordon L.: Integrated Anatomy and Physiology, ed. 3, St. Louis, 1957, The C. V. Mosby Co.

Carpus.—The eight bones in the carpus or wrist are arranged in two rows. In the proximal row are navicular, lunate, triquetrum, and pisiform; in the distal row are greater multangular, lesser multangular, capitate, and hamate. The projection at the front of the wrist on the little finger side is produced by the

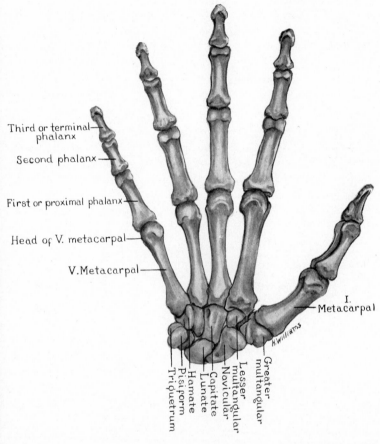

Third or terminal phalanx

Second phalanx

First or proximal phalanx

Head of V. metacarpal

V. Metacarpal

I. Metacarpal

Triquetrum
Pisiform
Hamate
Capitate
Lunate
Navicular
Lesser multangular
Greater multangular

Fig. 62.—Bones of right wrist and hand, volar aspect. (W.R.U. 989, male, white, aged 31 years.)

pisiform bone. The other bones, being firmly held together by ligaments, cannot be separately distinguished through the skin. This group of eight bones permits the characteristic range of movement possible at the wrist.

In the recent revision of the anatomical nomenclature it was suggested that the navicular bone of the hand be called the scaphoid, the greater multangular the trapezium, and the lesser multangular the trapezoid.

Hand Bones.—In the palm there are five metacarpal bones; the four medial ones articulate at their bases with each other and are closely bound together by ligaments; the first metacarpal articulates at its base with the greater multangular and is freely movable. The other metacarpals articulate proximally with other carpal bones and distally the head of each metacarpal articulates with its proper finger bone. The heads of the metacarpals form the knuckles.

In the fingers there are fourteen phalanges, two in the thumb and three in each of the fingers. In the flexor tendons of the thumb are found sesamoid bones near the metacarpophalangeal and interphalangeal joints and there is occasionally a sesamoid bone near the metacarpophalangeal joint of the index and of the little finger.

BONES OF THE LOWER EXTREMITY

The bones of the lower extremity include those of the hip, thigh, leg, ankle, and foot. The term "leg" is sometimes used in a limited sense to designate that part between the knee and ankle joints; the term "thigh" refers to that part between the hip and knee joints.

The two hip bones are firmly held together with the sacrum by strong ligaments to form a rigid ring of bone which supports the weight of the body on the two lower extremities. The two hip bones form the pelvic girdle.

The pelvic cavity contains the urinary bladder, the lower end of the large intestine, the organs of reproduction (in the female) or a portion thereof (in the male), and the large vessels and nerves to the lower extremity.

Os Coxae or Os Innominatum.—Each hip bone has a broad, expanded blade, the ilium; a downwardly projecting portion, the ischium; and a remaining part which completes the ring or obturator foramen, the pubis. On the outer side at the junction of these three is the acetabular cavity. Capping the ilium is the iliac crest, which ends in front and behind in bony bosses known respectively as the anterior superior spine and the posterior superior spine to distinguish these from other projections placed lower on the margins of the blade and designated anterior inferior and posterior inferior spines. The ilium forms the upper portion of the

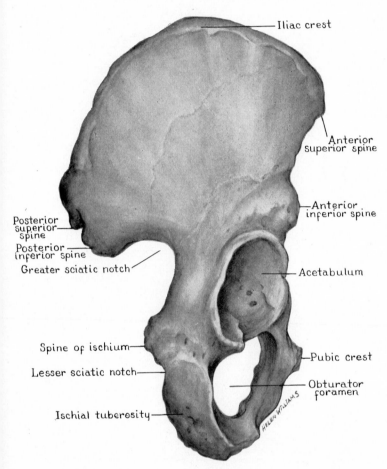

Fig. 63.—Right os coxae, lateral view. (W.R.U. 989, male, white, aged 31 years.)

acetabulum into which fits the head of the femur. The ischium forms the lower and hinder portion of the acetabulum and terminates in a rough knob called the ischial tuberosity. The pubis forms the front lower portion of the acetabulum. The two pubic bones articulate with each other in the midline at the front of the pelvic girdle, and their inferior rami diverge to form the pubic arch.

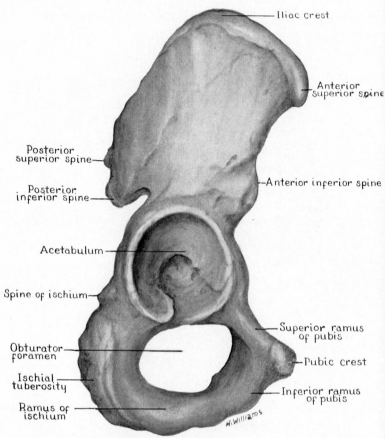

Fig. 64.—Right os coxae. The bone has been turned to give a view directly into the acetabulum. (W.R.U. 989, male, white, aged 31 years.)

The obturator foramen is bounded behind by the ischium, below by the inferior ramus of the pubis united with the ramus of the ischium, and above by the superior ramus of the pubis.

Femur.—The femur is the thigh bone. It is the longest and heaviest bone of the body and, for the most part, is deeply embedded within the large thigh muscles.

At the upper end are the head, the neck, and the greater and lesser trochanters. The smooth and almost spherical head fits into the acetabulum, and the neck is the stout bar of bone which supports the head on the upper end of the shaft. The angle of the neck with the shaft is characteristically greater than a right angle.

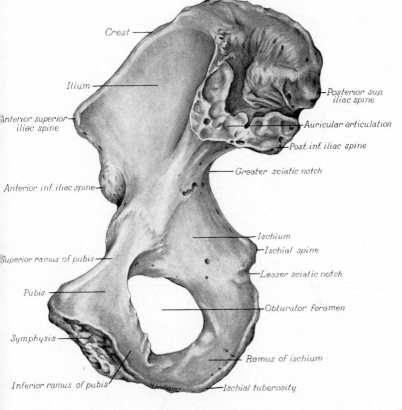

Crest

Ilium

Anterior superior iliac spine

Anterior inf. iliac spine

Superior ramus of pubis

Pubis

Symphysis

Inferior ramus of pubis

Posterior sup. iliac spine

Auricular articulation

Post. inf. iliac spine

Greater sciatic notch

Ischium

Ischial spine

Lesser sciatic notch

Obturator foramen

Ramus of ischium

Ischial tuberosity

Fig. 65.—Right os coxae, medial view. (W.R.U. 989, male, white, aged 31 years.)

The greater trochanter is the massive projection on the lateral side of the shaft at its junction with the neck, and the lesser trochanter is the smaller, rounded boss of bone on the inner side of the shaft just below the neck. The ridge for attachment of muscles in the midline of the back of the shaft is called the linea

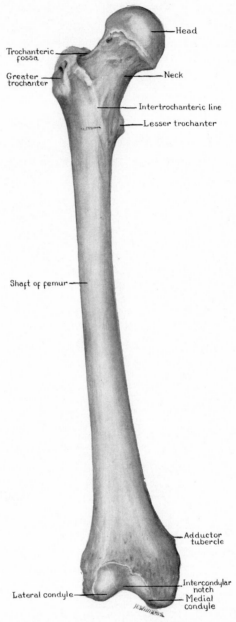

Fig. 66.—Right femur, front view.   (W.R.U. 989, male, white, aged 31 years.)

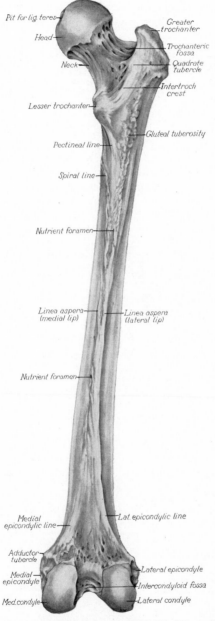

Pit for lig. teres
Head
Neck
Lesser trochanter
Pectineal line
Spiral line
Nutrient foramen
Linea aspera (medial lip)
Nutrient foramen
Medial epicondylic line
Adductor tubercle
Medial epicondyle
Med. condyle

Greater trochanter
Trochanteric fossa
Quadrate tubercle
Intertroch crest
Gluteal tuberosity
Linea aspera (lateral lip)
Lat. epicondylic line
Lateral epicondyle
Intercondyloid fossa
Lateral condyle

Fig. 67.—Right femur, posterior view. (W.R.U. 989, male, white, aged 31 years.)

aspera. The trochanteric fossa is a pit on the inner edge of the greater trochanter. The ridge on the back of the upper end of the shaft joining the two trochanters is the intertrochanteric crest, and the quadrate tubercle is a small mound near the center of the crest. The intertrochanteric line begins on the front of the shaft just below the greater trochanter and runs medially and distally around the bone below the lesser trochanter and blends with the medial side of the linea aspera.

The lower end of the femur is modeled into the medial and lateral condyles between which there is a deep groove, the intercondylar fossa, especially marked behind and below. The condyles bear articular surfaces for the upper end of the tibia and for the patella.

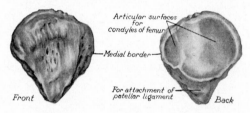

Fig. 68.—Right patella. (W.R.U. 989, male, white, aged 31 years.)

Patella.—The patella or kneecap is a large sesamoid bone embedded in the tendon of the great extensor muscle of the thigh. It is the bony prominence on the front of the knee when the leg is extended, but it sinks into the intercondylar fossa during flexion at the knee joint.

Tibia.—The tibia or shin bone is the larger bone of the leg. The medial surface is entirely subcutaneous. The thickened proximal end supports the medial and lateral condyles with their articular surfaces for the lower end of the femur. Between these two smooth, articular surfaces projects the intercondylar eminence. On the front of the bone, about one inch below the upper end, is the tibial tuberosity into which is inserted the tendon of the great extensor muscle of the thigh. Immediately beneath the outer ridge of its lateral condyle the tibia has an articular facet for the fibula. The popliteal line is seen on the back of the shaft of the tibia, beginning just below the articular facet for the fibula and passing downward and medially to the inner border of

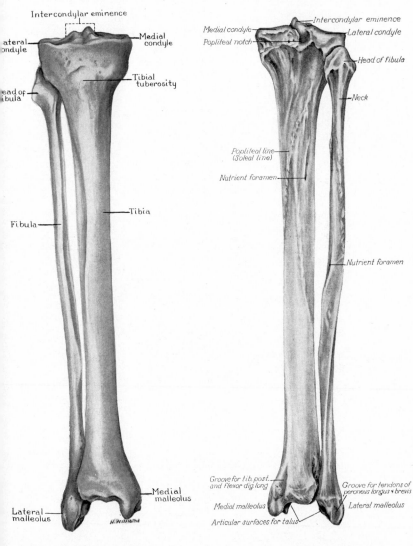

Intercondylar eminence
Medial condyle
Lateral condyle
Head of fibula
Neck

Fig. 69.—Right tibia and fibula, front view. (W.R.U. 989, male, white, aged 31 years.)

Fig. 70.—Right tibia and fibula, posterior view. (W.R.U. 989, male, white, aged 31 years.)

the bone. The distal end of the tibia has a downward projection on its inner side, the medial malleolus, which forms the prominence on the inner side of the ankle. The outer side of the lower end articulates with the fibula and the distal surface with the talus.

Fibula.—The fibula is a slender bone in the outer side of the leg. The knoblike, upper end or head articulates with the outer side of the lateral condyle of the tibia just beneath the lateral ridge. The fibula does not articulate with the femur nor patella and does not help to form the knee joint. The fibula ends below in the lateral malleolus, the prominence of the outer side of the ankle.

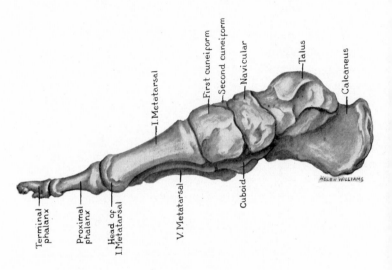

Fig. 71.—Bones of right foot, inner side. (W.R.U. 989, male, white, aged 31 years.)

Tarsus.—The seven tarsal bones form the posterior half of the foot. Of these the talus is the bone which articulates with the tibia and fits between the malleoli of the tibia and fibula. Below the talus is the calcaneus which is the largest of the tarsal bones and forms the heel. In front of these on the outer side is the cuboid, on the inner side the navicular, and in front of the navicular the three cuneiform bones in a row. The calcaneus, navicular, and cuneiforms together with the three medial metatarsals and corresponding phalanges constitute the medial longitudinal arch of the foot.   The calcaneus, cuboid, two lateral metatarsals, and corresponding phalanges form the lateral longitudinal arch.

In recent revision of the anatomical nomenclature it was proposed that the term "navicular" be used solely to indicate the bone of the tarsus, and the term "scaphoid" for the bone which formerly was called the navicular of the hand.   It was proposed

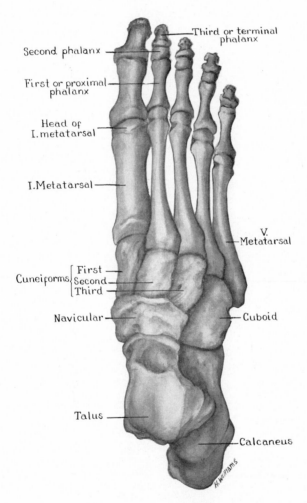

Fig. 72.—Bones of right foot, viewed from above.   (W.R.U. 989, male, white, aged 31 years.)

Table 5
Bones of Lower Extremity*

NAME	LOCATION	DISTINGUISHING FEATURES	ARTICULATIONS
Os coxae (innominate)	Hip	Acetabulum; pubic arch; obturator foramen; greater and lesser sciatic notches; formed by union of ilium, pubis, and ischium *ilium* with crest, anterior superior and inferior spines, posterior superior and inferior spines, auricular articulation *pubis* with crest, tubercle, symphysis, superior and inferior rami *ischium* with ramus and tuberosity	Sacrum, femur, and other pubis
Femur	Thigh	Head; neck; greater and lesser trochanters; trochanteric fossa and crest; intertrochanteric line; shaft with linea aspera; medial and lateral condyles and epicondyles; adductor tubercle; intercondylar fossa	Head with acetabulum; condyles with patella and tibia
Patella	Knee	Kneecap	Femur
Tibia	Medial bone of leg	Shin bone; medial and lateral condyles; intercondylar eminence; tuberosity; medial malleolus	Femur, fibula, and talus
Fibula	Lateral bone of leg	Splint bone; head; neck; lateral malleolus	Tibia and talus
Tarsus	Back of foot	Seven bones; talus, calcaneus; cuboid, navicular, first, second, and third cuneiforms	Talus with lower end of tibia and fibula; cuneiforms and cuboid with metatarsals; with each other
Metatarsus	Front of foot	Five bones each with head, shaft, and base; numbered from one to five beginning on the great toe side	With distal tarsals; with each other; with corresponding toe bone
Phalanges	Toes	Fourteen (some may be fused); two for great toe; three for each of the other toes	Proximal with respective metatarsal; with each other

*From Francis, Carl C., and Farrell, Gordon L.: Integrated Anatomy and Physiology, ed. 3, St. Louis, 1957, The C. V. Mosby Co.

also that the cuneiform bones be called medial, intermediate, and lateral instead of first, second, and third, respectively.

Metatarsus.—Anterior to the tarsus lie the five metatarsal bones. The bases of the inner three articulate with the three cuneiform bones and those of the outer two with the cuboid. The heads of the five metatarsal bones form the ball of the foot. The head of the innermost (first) metatarsal forms the main feature of the front end of the medial longitudinal arch, and the head of the outermost (fifth) metatarsal the main feature of the front end of the lateral longitudinal arch. There is also a transverse arch produced by the manner of interarticulation of the anterior tarsal and of the five metatarsal bones.

Toe Bones.—Theoretically there should be fourteen phalanges in the toes, two for the great toe and three for each of the others. Often the middle phalanx of the fifth toe and sometimes that of the fourth is absent or fused with the corresponding terminal phalanx.

Sesamoid bones are to be found in the tendons passing to the great toe and also in the tendons passing from the leg into the foot on either side of the ankle.

SEX DIFFERENCES IN THE SKELETON

As a general rule the bones of a man are heavier and larger than those of a woman. The articular ends are more massive compared with the shaft, and the various ridges, tuberosities, and lines are proportional to the relative size of the muscles.

Specific sex features in the skeleton are confined to the bony pelvis. The pubic arch in the female is broad; in the male it is narrow. Although the bones of the pelvic girdle are smaller in a woman, the pelvic cavity is relatively capacious, and the greater sciatic notch between ilium and ischium on each side in the articulated pelvis is large.

AGE CHANGES IN THE SKELETON

Throughout the entire life of a person changes are occurring in the skeleton. Due to the ossification of cartilaginous ends of bones these changes are more obvious in childhood. After the adult features of the bones are completed, age changes are confined to the texture and to the margins of articular surfaces. The

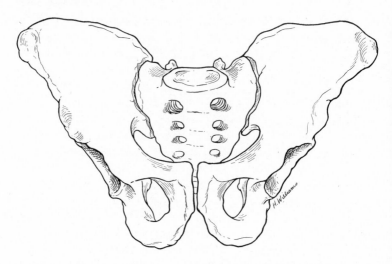

Fig. 73.—Male pelvis, front view. (W.R.U. 1559, male, white, aged 44 years.)

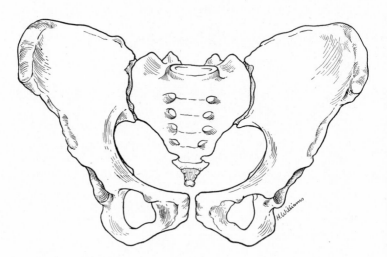

Fig. 74.—Female pelvis, front view. (W.R.U. 781, female, white, aged 23 years.)

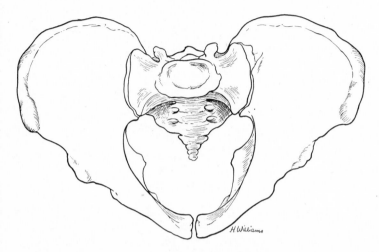

Fig. 75.—Male pelvis, viewed from above.   (W.R.U. 1559, male, white, aged 44 years.)

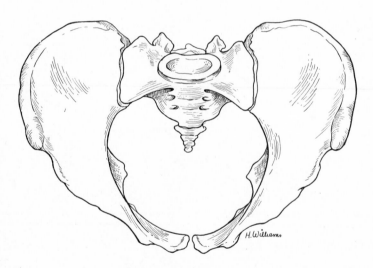

Fig. 76.—Female pelvis, viewed from above.   (W.R.U. 781, female, white, aged 23 years.)

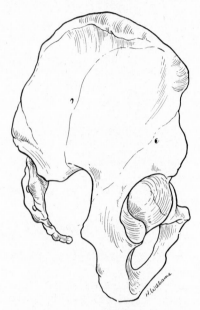

Fig. 77.—Male pelvis, right side. (W.R.U. 1559, male, white, aged 44 years.)

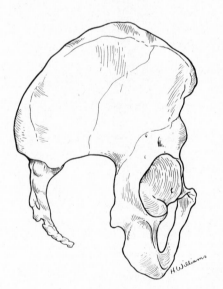

Fig. 78.—Female pelvis, right side. (W.R.U. 781, female, white, aged 23 years.)

approximate age of a person at death can always be estimated from an examination of the skeleton.

Between the sixth and eighth weeks of fetal life the skull bones which form in the cartilage of the base begin to ossify. At birth the base of the skull is well ossified, as are also the bones forming the face. In the vault of the skull there are wide, fibrous strips between the edges of the bones and between the bones several large unossified areas called fontanelles. The largest is in the midline between the two parietal bones and the frontal bone. It

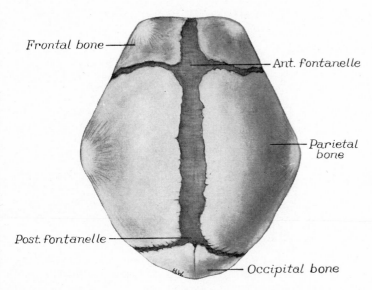

Frontal bone

Ant. fontanelle

Parietal bone

Post. fontanelle

Occipital bone

Fig. 79.—Skull at birth, viewed from above.   (W.R.U. E1985, male, white, term fetus.)

is diamond shaped and is called the anterior or frontal fontanelle. In the midline between the parietal bones and the occipital is a smaller area called the posterior or occipital fontanelle. There are several other small fontanelles, but the frontal and occipital are the ones of chief importance. A physician occasionally secures samples of blood in infancy by passing a hypodermic needle through the anterior fontanelle into a blood sinus (the superior sagittal sinus) which lies just beneath the vault.

During infancy the skull grows rapidly because it houses the rapidly growing brain. The unossified areas are gradually replaced by bone, and by eighteen months the fontanelles are closed.

At birth the brain case has a capacity of about 350 cc.; this has increased to 750 cc. by the age of 1 year and at 2 years of age it is 900 cc. The brain case reaches its approximately adult size of about 1,500 cc. by the age of 6 years and in well-grown children it may be practically adult in size by 4½ years of age. Thereafter the increase in the size of the brain case is very small. The sutures or joints between the several bones of the skull begin to fuse between the ages of 20 and 30 years. By the age of 60 years almost all the sutures have united.

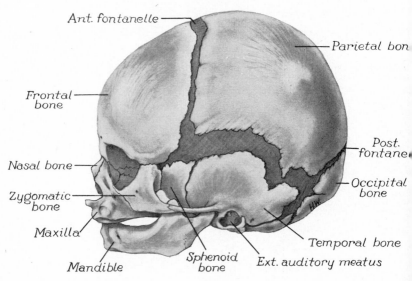

Fig. 80.—Skull at birth, lateral view.   (W.R.U. E1985, male, white, term fetus.)

Since at birth much of the brain case is still membranous, during delivery the skull may be molded into various irregular shapes. These usually disappear during the first few months of life, and the head becomes fairly symmetrical. If an infant is too frequently left lying on its back or on one side, the side next the pillow becomes flattened. This is one reason for altering the baby's position at frequent intervals.

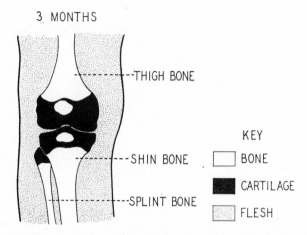

Fig. 81.—Ossification of male knee at three months.   (Traced from x-ray SS 3983.)

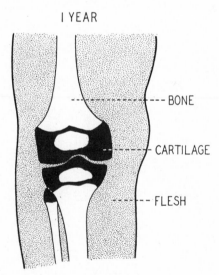

Fig. 82.—Ossification of male knee at one year.   (Traced from x-ray SS 3406 A.)

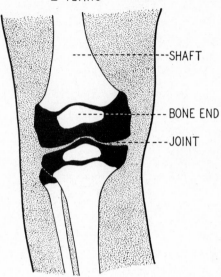

2 YEARS

---SHAFT

---BONE END

---JOINT

Fig. 83.—Ossification of male knee at two years. (Traced from x-ray SS 3097 E.)

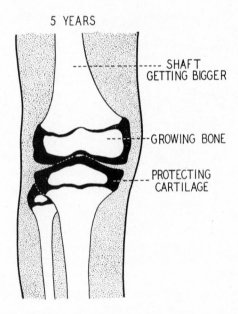

5 YEARS

--- SHAFT GETTING BIGGER

--GROWING BONE

--PROTECTING CARTILAGE

Fig. 84.—Ossification of male knee at five years. (Traced from x-ray SS 3078 B.)

After the fontanelles have ossified, the brain case becomes a closed box, and alterations of intracranial pressure are possible only by way of the circulation. Therefore any disease or injury which increases intracranial pressure soon gives rise to serious symptoms.

IO YEARS

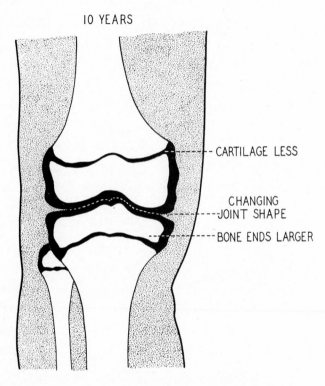

CARTILAGE LESS

CHANGING
JOINT SHAPE

BONE ENDS LARGER

Fig. 85.—Ossification of male knee at ten years. (Traced from x-ray SS 45 B.)

The bones forming the face grow steadily but relatively slowly until the late teens. This contrasts with the practical cessation of growth in the brain case in earlier childhood and is conditioned by the need for increasing the size of the respiratory passages and the jaws which lodge the teeth.

The early growth of the brain case results in its relatively large size as contrasted with the small face. The facial region makes up about one eighth of the skull at birth, about one fourth at 5 years of age, and one half in the adult. Part of the increase in size of the face during childhood is due to the development of air sinuses, rudiments of only the maxillary and mastoid sinuses being present at birth. This explains why small babies rarely have mastoiditis although middle ear infections are common. The sphenoid, eth-

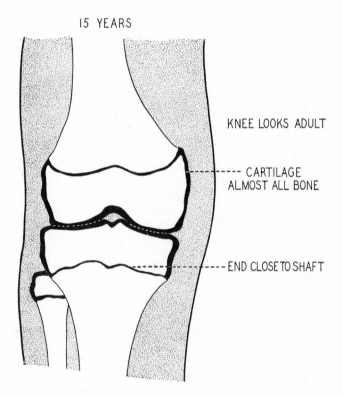

Fig. 86.—Ossification of male knee at fifteen years. (Traced from x-ray SS 1246.)

moid, and frontal sinuses are present as shallow grooves in the nasal mucosa in infancy. The sphenoid sinus and ethmoid air cells usually appear as definite structures at about 6 years of age and the frontal sinus at about 7 years. The sinuses, particularly the frontal, increase rapidly in size at adolescence. These air spaces are extensions of the nasal chambers and permit increase in size without corresponding increase in weight. The mandible and maxilla continue to grow until the last teeth, the third molars or wisdom teeth, have erupted.

In a newborn infant the external auditory canal is short and the tympanic membrane is more obliquely placed than in an adult. When the eardrum of a baby is examined, it is usually necessary to pull the ear down and back, whereas in an adult the ear is pulled up and back.

20 YEARS

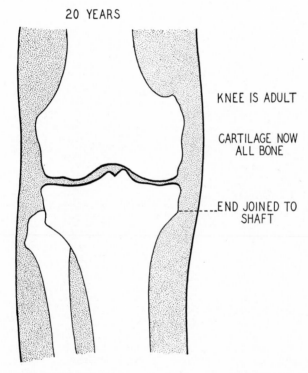

KNEE IS ADULT

CARTILAGE NOW ALL BONE

END JOINED TO SHAFT

Fig. 87.—Ossification of male knee at twenty years. (Traced from x-ray.)

The bones of the rest of the skeleton also begin to form early in fetal life, and the central portion of the shaft of nearly all bones is fully ossified at birth. The clavicle is the first bone to begin ossification, during the fifth fetal week.

All long bones grow more rapidly at the ends than at the periphery of the shaft. Over the growing end is a protective cap of cartilage, called the epiphysis, in which a secondary center of ossification appears and gradually spreads until all the cartilage is transformed into bone except that which remains permanently

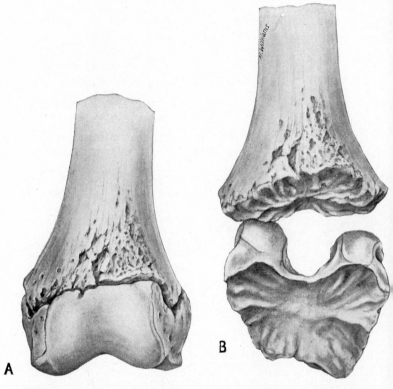

Fig. 88.—Lower end of left femur. *A*, Epiphysis of lower end (condyles) in position on lower end of shaft; *B*, epiphysis lifted off and turned downward to display the deep surface. (W.R.U. 485, female, Negro, aged 16 years.)

as the articular cartilage. After the cessation of growth in length, the epiphysis and shaft unite. Because of the relative density of bone tissue, it is possible to follow the growth changes occurring in the skeleton by means of roentgenograms and thus to measure the rate of change. (Figs. 81-87.)

Definite changes appear in the proportions of the skeleton during childhood. The chest is barrel shaped during infancy, and the downward slope of the ribs is less pronounced than it is in later childhood and in adult life. Duing infancy the pelvis is relatively small, and organs which lie within the abdomen in a child sink into the pelvis as with approaching adolescence the pelvic cavity grows larger.

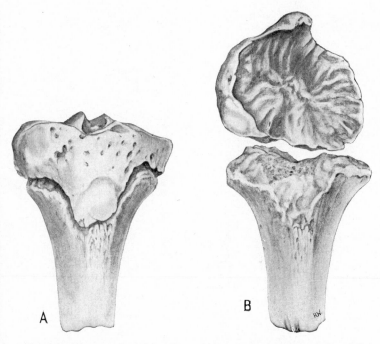

Fig. 89.—Upper end of right tibia. *A,* Epiphysis of upper end (condyles) in position on the upper end of the shaft; *B,* epiphysis lifted off and turned upward to display the deep surface. (W.R.U. 485, female, Negro, aged 16 years.)

The change in gait evident at about the age of 3 years results from a widening of the pelvic girdle and an increase in the relative length of the legs.

The adult vertebral column shows a forward curve in the cervical and lumbar regions and a backward curve in the thoracic and sacral regions, whereas at birth there is a single backward curve from neck to sacrum. The forward, cervical curve appears

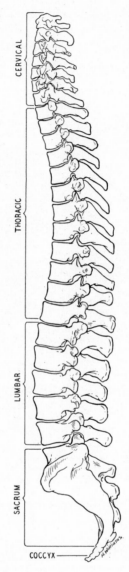

Fig. 90.—Lateral view of articulated adult vertebral column to show curves.

at about 3 or 4 months of age when the baby has learned to hold his head steady. The forward convexity of the lumbar region follows at about 3 years of age. This marked forward curve in the lumber region is characteristic of man alone. (See Fig. 90.)

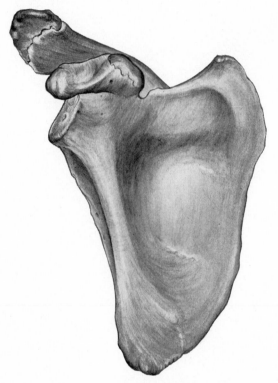

Fig. 91.—Right scapula, costal surface. (W.R.U. 98, male, white, aged 18 years.)

In an infant the head is large, the trunk is long, and the limbs are short. During childhood limb growth is more rapid than increase in trunk length. In the preadolescent years arms and legs appear to be too long for the trunk. During the teen age the legs stop growing before the trunk, and the final adult proportions are attained at about 18 years of age. These changes in bodily proportion are a part of the normal process of growing up.

In old age bones tend to lose mineral salts, thus becoming lighter in weight and more easily broken. The margins, particularly of articular surfaces, become roughened and more pronounced and may interfere with freedom of movement. This piling up of bone about an articulation may be associated with arthritis and may actually produce ankylosis or pathological union of the bones

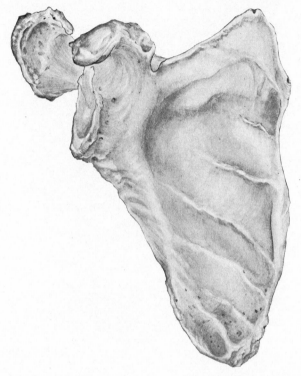

Fig. 92.—Right scapula, costal surface. (W.R.U. 1732, male, white, aged 84 years.)

which form the joint. Figs. 91 and 92 show the scapula of an 18-year-old boy and that of a man 84 years of age. In the youth the articular margins are even and the various markings have a definite order and pattern. In the old man the heaped up bone is without pattern, and the ridges for the attachment of the muscles are more prominent.

Review Questions

1. What are the functions of the skeleton?
2. What are the two main subdivisions of the skeleton?
3. What bones are included in each subdivision?
4. How may bones be classified? Give an example of each class.
5. List the bones of the skull. Which are paired and which unpaired?
6. What bones form the brain case?
7. What bones enter into the formation of the face?
8. Name five foramina in the base of the skull. What structures pass through each?
9. What bones form the orbit?
10. Describe a typical vertebra.
11. List the bones which form the vertebral column.
12. Describe the sacrum.
13. What bones are located in the upper extremity?
14. What bones are located in the lower extremity?
15. Name three ways in which the female pelvis differs from the male.
16. Describe briefly the differences between the skull of a newborn child and that of an adult.
17. How are the bones of an aged person different from those of a young adult?
18. What is the first bone to ossify?
19. Describe briefly the growth of a long bone such as the tibia.

CHAPTER 5

ARTICULATIONS

A joint or articulation is a connection between two separate segments or parts of the skeleton. Joints are variously classified, but a very satisfactory classification, according to degree and variety of movement, follows:

Classification of Joints

I. Synarthrosis

In this type of joint no movement is possible; there is no joint cavity, and there is close contact between the two adjacent bone surfaces.

A. Suture

Sutures are found only in the bones of the skull, and union is effected by fibrous tissue. Sutures unite with increasing age.

B. Synchondrosis

In this type of joint, union is effected by hyaline cartilage. Such joints are found in growing bones, between the shaft of the bone and the epiphysis. The joint disappears with fusion of the epiphysis after the cessation of growth.

C. Syndesmosis

In this type of joint the union is effected by dense connective tissue. The joint between the lower ends of the tibia and fibula is an example.

II. Amphiarthrosis

In this type of joint there is limited movement. Union is effected by fibrocartilage. There are supporting ligaments called capsules; there may also be a joint cavity. Amphiarthroses occur in the midline of the body and include the joints between the bodies of the vertebrae, the symphysis pubis, and between the manubrium and body of the sternum.

III. Diarthrosis

Joints of this type permit variable amounts of movement. There are a series of investing ligaments, a true joint cavity, and hyaline cartilage over the articulating surfaces of the bones forming the joint. Diarthroses are subdivided according to the type of movement.

A. Gliding joints

Examples are the joints between carpal bones and the joints between tarsal bones.

B. Pivot joints

Movement is in the long axis of the bone. Examples are the joints between the radius and ulna and between the dens of the axis and the atlas.

C. Hinge joints

Examples are elbow and knee joints.

D. Biaxial joints

Movement occurs in two planes at right angles to each other. The condyloid joint at the wrist (between the radius and carpal bones) is biaxial; so is the saddle joint at the base of the thumb.

E. Ball and socket joints

Examples are hip and shoulder joints.

The movements possible in diarthroses are:

1. Sliding or gliding
2. Pivoting about a longitudinal axis
3. Flexion or decreasing the angle of the joint
4. Extension or increasing the angle of the joint
5. Abduction or drawing the part away from the midline
6. Adduction or drawing toward the midline
7. Circumduction, describing a cone, the base of which is a circle

Each diarthrodial or synovial joint has a capsular ligament which encloses the joint cavity and binds together the skeletal parts. This ligament is attached in a continuous line around the articular portion of the bone at a short distance from the edge of the articular cartilage. The capsular ligament has an outer layer of fibrous connective tissue and an inner synovial membrane which is a specialized layer of connective tissue that lines the capsular ligament and covers the ends of the bones within the capsule but does not cover the articular cartilage The cells of synovial membrane are simple squamous in form and resemble mesothelium. The synovial membrane forms synovia, a colorless fluid similar in consistency to the white of an egg. This fluid lubricates the joint and nourishes the articular cartilage. The capsular ligament of each joint is well supplied with blood vessels and sensory nerves, branches of neighboring vessels and nerves. The capsular ligament is frequently re-enforced by accessory thickenings of dense connective tissue or by muscle tendons.

Mandibular Joint.—The mandibular joint is the only diarthrodial joint between skull bones. All the others are sutures and are immovable. The mandibular joint occurs between the glenoid cavity or mandibular fossa of the temporal bone and the head of the mandible. Interposed between the articular surfaces is a disc of fibrocartilage which separates the joint cavity into two parts. The capsular ligament has a thickening on the outer side, the temporomandibular ligament, which helps to prevent backward displacement of the mandible. (See Fig. 264.) The stylomandibular ligament, a band of dense fascia running from the tip of the styloid process to the posterior edge of the angle of the mandible, is entirely separate from the joint but does give support to the mandible. The sphenomandibular ligament is another supporting band of fascia which runs from the spine of the sphenoid to the inner surface of the ramus of the mandible.

In the upper compartment of the joint the head of the mandible and the articular disc glide as one structure on the articular surface of the temporal bone, thus producing the movements of protraction and retraction of the lower jaw. In the lower compartment the head of the mandible rotates on the concave lower surface of the disc, thus permitting opening and closing of the mouth. The complicated grinding movements used in chewing food are produced by combinations of the simple movements just described.

Atlanto-Occipital Joints.—The two atlanto-occipital joints are placed one on either side of the foramen magnum and each has a distinct capsular ligament. The anterior and posterior atlanto-occipital membranes are attached to the edge of the foramen magnum above and to the arch of the atlas below and strengthen the joints.   Nodding movements occur at these joints.

Atlanto-Axial Joints.—The atlanto-axial joints are three joints between the first and second cervical vertebrae.   The two lateral articulations occur between the lateral masses of the respective vertebrae, and the single medial articulation occurs between the anterior surface of the dens of the axis and the posterior surface of the anterior arch of the atlas.   Each joint has an articular capsule, and the central one is further strengthened by the cruciate ligament of the atlas.   The horizontal crossbar of the cruci-

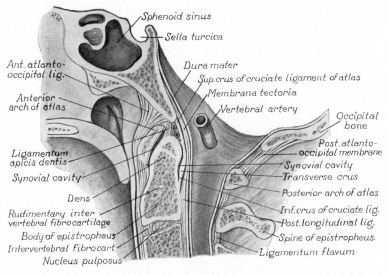

Fig. 93.—Sagittal section of atlanto-axial joint and upper cervical joints. (W.R.U. museum specimen.)

ate ligament passes behind the dens and at either end is attached to the atlas; the vertical bar or crus is attached above to the occipital bone and below to the axis.   There is a well-defined joint cavity between the dens and the crossbar of the cruciate ligament.   The ligament of the apex of the dens extends upward from the tip of the dens to the anterior margin of the foramen magnum.

The alar ligaments are two short strong bands extending one from either side of the dens to the occipital bone.

The anterior and posterior longitudinal ligaments of the vertebral column are continued upward in front of and behind the axis to attach above to the occipital bone. The upper end of the posterior ligament has a special name, the membrana tectoria.

Rotating movements of the head occur at the joints between the first and second cervical vertebrae. Movement is free but the large number of ligaments mentioned above increases the stability of the joint.

Vertebral Joints.—The joints between the vertebral bodies are amphiarthroses, each with an intervertebral fibrocartilage (23 in all). The amount of movement at a single joint is not great, but the range of movement in the entire series is considerable. Movement also occurs in the gliding joints between the articular processes.

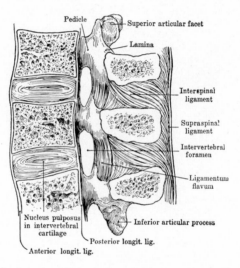

Fig. 94.—Sagittal section through three lumbar vertebrae. (From Mettler: Neuroanatomy, St. Louis, 1948, The C. V. Mosby Co.)

The laminae of adjacent vertebrae are connected by sheets of yellow elastic connective tissue, the ligamenta flava. The tips of the spinous processes are joined by supraspinous ligaments and in the cervical region these ligaments are especially well developed, forming the ligamentum nuchae which contains much elastic tissue. There are also fairly well-defined interspinous and intertransverse ligaments between vertebrae. The anterior and pos-

terior ligaments of the vertebral column pass up the entire length
of the column behind and in front of the bodies of the vertebrae.

Clavicular Joints.—The medial end of the clavicle articulates
with the manubrium of the sternum, forming a gliding joint with
an articular capsule and having within the capsular ligament an
articular disc of fibrocartilage.   This is the only joint between

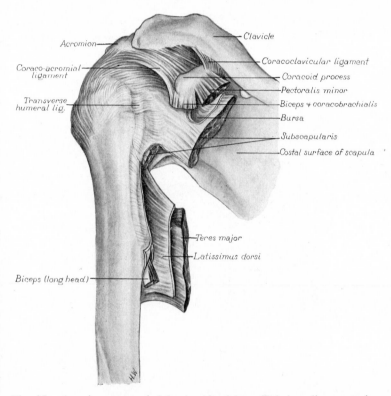

Fig. 95.—Anterior aspect of right shoulder joint. This is a direct anterior
view.   (W.R.U. 3168, male, Negro, aged 53 years.)

the upper extremity and the axial skeleton. The costoclavicular
ligament joining the first costal cartilage and the under surface
of the inner end of the clavicle is an important factor in maintaining the clavicle in its normal position.

The lateral end of the clavicle articulates with the acromion,
forming a gliding joint. The capsular ligament is re-enforced by

the coracoclavicular ligament, a strong fibrous band uniting the lateral end of the clavicle and the coracoid process.

A variable amount of movement occurs in the clavicular joints during movements of the arm and shoulder.

Thoracic Joints.—The joints of the heads of the ribs with the bodies of the vertebrae and of the tubercles of the ribs with the transverse processes of the vertebrae are gliding joints, each one having a distinct capsular ligament.

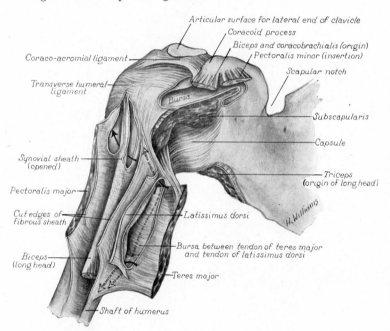

Fig. 96.—Anterior aspect of right shoulder joint, showing the axilla and the relation of the muscle tendons to the joint. The clavicle has been removed and the various bursae have been opened. (W.R.U. 3168, male, Negro, aged 53 years.)

The anterior end of each of the first seven ribs is joined to the sternum by a bar of hyaline cartilage, and usually there is a small synovial cavity where each cartilage joins the sternum. There may also be small synovial cavities in the costal cartilages of the eighth and ninth ribs.

The joint between the manubrium and body of the sternum is an amphiarthrosis, and no joint cavity is present. The connecting plate of fibrocartilage may be replaced by bone in old age.

Shoulder Joint.—The head of the humerus articulates with the glenoid cavity of the scapula. The capsular ligament is strengthened by the tendons of the subscapularis, supraspinatus, teres minor, and infraspinatus muscles which fuse with it and is further re-enforced by the tendon of the long head of the biceps brachii muscle and by the coracohumeral and coracoacromial ligaments.

There is a tubular extension of the synovial membrane of the joint downward around the upper end of the tendon of the long

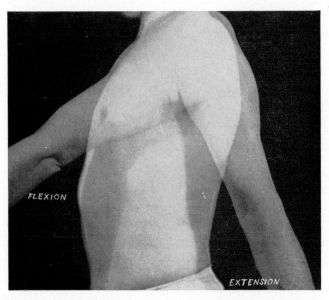

Fig. 97.—Flexion and extension at the shoulder joint. (Photograph by Dr. D. R. L. Duncan.)

head of the biceps, and there is a bursa between the joint capsule and the tendon of the subscapularis muscle which communicates with the joint cavity. Beneath the deltoid muscle there is an extensive synovial sac called the subdeltoid or subacromial bursa; there is usually a bursa beneath the tendon of the infraspinatus muscle, and one between the tendons of insertion of the teres major and latissimus dorsi muscles. The latter bursae do not communicate with the joint cavity.

Elbow Joint and Radioulnar Joints.—The elbow joint is a hinge between the humerus and the two bones of the forearm. The semilunar notch of the ulna articulates with the trochlea of the humerus, the head of the radius with the capitulum. The capsule of the elbow joint also encloses the proximal radioulnar joint.

The joint capsule is thin and loose anteriorly and posteriorly

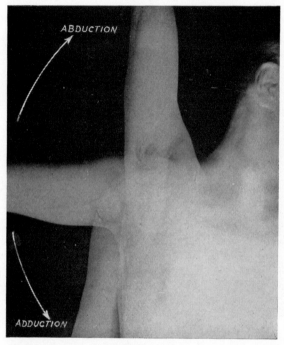

Fig. 98.—Abduction and adduction at the shoulder joint. (Photograph by Dr. D. R. L. Duncan.)

to permit freedom of movement but is quite thick and strong on either side, forming the ulnar and radial collateral ligaments. The interosseous membrane between the radius and ulna is regarded as an accessory ligament of the radioulnar joints. The annular radial ligament is a thickened portion of the capsular ligament attached to the margins of the radial notch of the ulna and closely applied to the head and neck of the radius.

During flexion and extension of the elbow the upper end of the
ulna moves about the trochlea, and at the same time the head of
the radius glides over the capitulum. The movements of supination and pronation of the palm result from movement of the

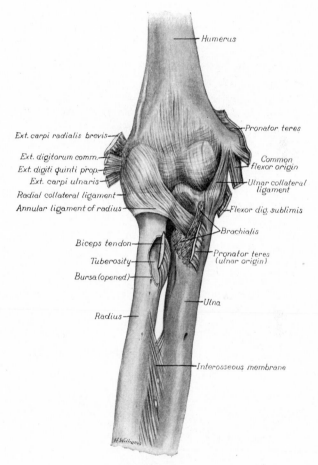

Fig. 99.—Anterior view of right elbow joint. (W.R.U. 3168, male, Negro,
aged 53 years.)

radius upon the ulna. When the palm is turned upward (supination), the upper end of the radius rotates about its own axis and
the lower end moves about the head of the ulna to a position

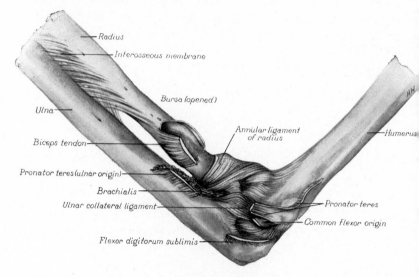

Fig. 100.—Medial view of right elbow joint.   (W.R.U. 3168, male, Negro, aged 53 years.)

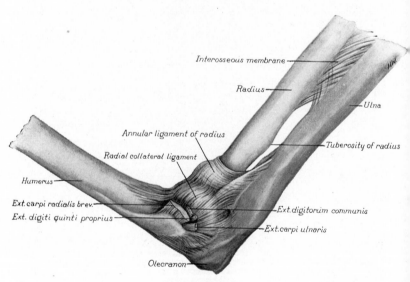

Fig. 101.—Lateral view of right elbow joint.   (W.R.U. 3168, male, Negro, aged 53 years.)

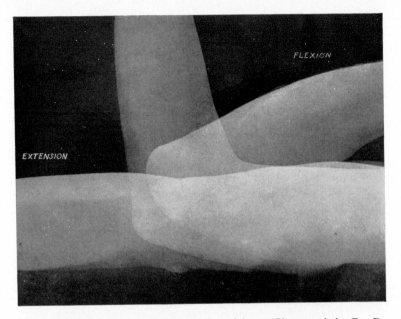

Fig. 102.—Flexion and extension at elbow joint. (Photograph by Dr. D. R. L. Duncan.)

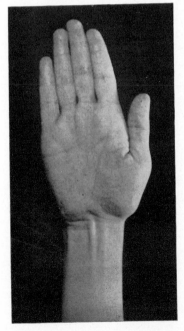

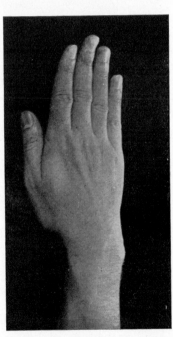

Fig. 103.—Hand in position of supination.

Fig. 104.—Hand in position of pronation.

(Photographs by Dr. D. R. L. Duncan.)

lateral to that bone. During pronation the radius moves in front of the head of the ulna, passing from the lateral side to occupy a position medial to the ulna. During supination and pronation the ulna does not move.

The distal radioulnar joint is separated from the wrist joint by a triangular articular disc of fibrocartilage attached at its apex to the styloid process of the ulna and at its base to the radius. The joint cavity is separate from that of the wrist joint.

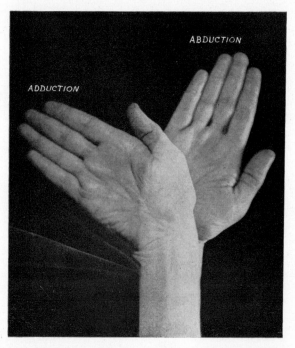

Fig. 105.—Adduction (ulnar deviation) and abduction (radial deviation) with reference to the midplane of the body when the arms are in anatomical position. Considered in relation to the long axis of the forearm both movements shown are abduction. (Photograph by Dr. D. R. L. Duncan.)

Wrist Joint.—The wrist joint is an articulation between the distal end of the radius and the triangular articular disc proximally and the navicular, lunate, and triquetral bones distally. The tendons of the flexor and extensor muscles of the wrist and hand strengthen the joint, and the capsular ligament is further re-enforced by volar and dorsal carpal ligaments (flexor and extensor retinacula).   Movements of the wrist joint are in two planes, abduction-adduction in the frontal plane and flexion-extension in the sagittal plane.

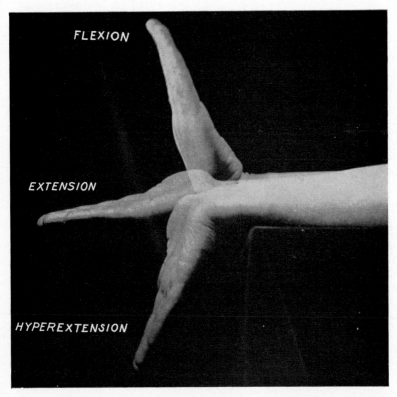

Fig. 106.—Flexion and extension of the hand.   The position of full extension is frequently termed hyperextension and the midposition, extension.   (Photograph by Dr. D. R. L. Duncan.)

Carpal Joints.—The carpal joints are all gliding joints.   The joint between the pisiform and triquetral bones is separate; the cavities between the other carpal bones communicate.   There are numerous intercarpal ligaments on the volar and dorsal aspects of the wrist and also interosseous ligaments between most of the bones.   The various bands are quite strong and hold the carpal bones firmly together.   The joints are further re-enforced by the volar and dorsal carpal ligaments and the long flexor and extensor tendons which pass over the wrist on their way to be attached on the finger bones. The range of movement between any two carpal bones is not great.

Hand Joints.—The joint between the base of the first metacarpal and the greater multangular bones permits the thumb to be flexed and extended, abducted and adducted, and rotated and opposed. Much of the dexterity of the human hand is due to the great freedom of movement of this digit.

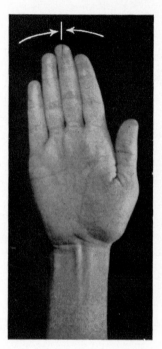
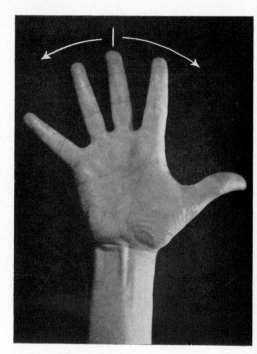

Fig. 107.—Adduction of the fingers.   Fig. 108.—Abduction of the fingers.

(Photographs by Dr. D. R. L. Duncan.)

The remaining metacarpal and the metacarpophalangeal joints permit flexion and extension and a limited amount of abduction and adduction. It must be remembered that adduction of the fingers is a movement toward the midline of the middle finger and abduction movement away from the same line. The interphalan-

Table 6
*Joints of Upper Extremity**

NAME	TYPE	BONES INVOLVED	ACCESSORY LIGAMENTS
Sternoclavicular	Gliding	Sternum and medial end of clavicle	Articular disc of fibrocartilage
Acromioclavicular	Gliding	Lateral end of clavicle and acromion of scapula	Articular disc of fibrocartilage
Shoulder	Ball and socket	Glenoid cavity of scapula and head of humerus	Coracoacromial; coracohumeral; transverse humeral
Elbow			
Humeroradial	Gliding	Lower end of humerus, head of radius, and	Radial collateral; ulnar collateral; annular radial; interosseous membrane of fore-
Humeroulnar	Hinge	upper end of ulna	arm
Proximal radioulnar	Pivot		
Distal radioulnar	Gliding	Lower end of radius and ulna	Articular disc of fibrocartilage; interosseous membrane of forearm
Wrist	Biaxial	Lower end of radius and articular disc with navicular, lunate, and triquetrum	Articular disc of fibrocartilage; volar carpal; dorsal carpal
Carpal	Gliding	Carpus; joint between pisiform and triquetrum is separate; the others communicate	Various interosseous; volar carpal; dorsal carpal
Metacarpal	Gliding	Bases of four medial metacarpals	Transverse
Carpometacarpal of thumb	Biaxial	Base of first metacarpal with greater multangular	
Carpometacarpal of fingers	Gliding	Bases of four medial metacarpals with distal row of carpals	Interosseous
Metacarpophalangeal of thumb	Hinge	Distal end of first metacarpal with base of proximal phalanx	
Metacarpophalangeal of fingers	Ball and socket	Distal ends of metacarpals with bases of proximal phalanges	
Phalangeal	Hinge	Phalanges	

*From Francis, Carl C., and Farrell, Gordon L.: Integrated Anatomy and Physiology, ed. 3, St. Louis, 1957, The C. V. Mosby Co.

geal joints are hinge joints and the only movements are flexion and extension.

Sacroiliac Joint.—The sacroiliac joint is classed as a diarthrosis, but the joint cavity may become more or less obliterated after middle life. The sacrum fits like a wedge between the two iliac bones and is thus adapted to support the weight of the trunk; the joint is not primarily constructed for movement. The capsular ligament is re-enforced by a very strong interosseous sacroiliac ligament, by long and short posterior sacroiliac ligaments, by the

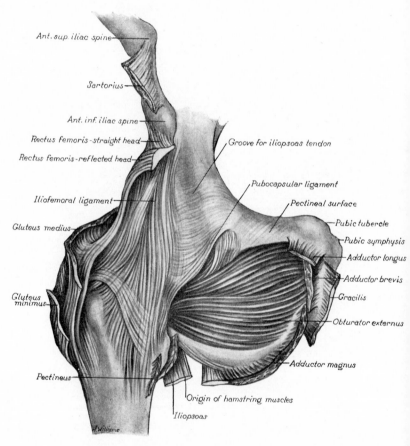

Fig. 109.—Anterior view of right hip joint.   (W.R.U. 3654, male, white, aged 62 years.)

sacrotuberous ligament running from sacrum to ischial tuberosity, and by the sacrospinous ligament running from sacrum to the spine of the ischium.

Pubic Symphysis.—The pubic symphysis is an amphiarthrosis, but there is frequently a slitlike vertical cavity in the disc of fibrocartilage interposed between the two pubic bones. It is not lined with synovial membrane. The joint is strengthened on all sides by thickenings of fibrous tissue.

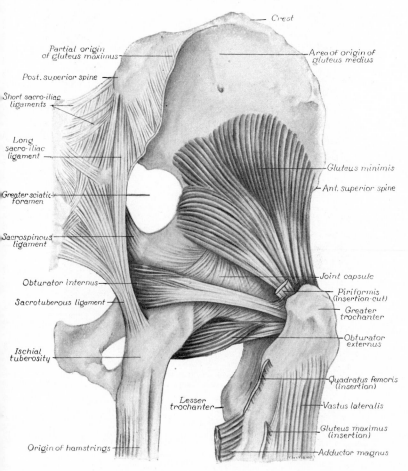

Fig. 110.—Posterior view of right hip joint.   (W.R.U. 3700, male, Negro, aged 57 years.)

There is very little movement either in the sacroiliac joints or in the pubic symphysis, but during the later months of pregnancy the investing ligaments become somewhat softer, thus permitting more movement and occasionally causing much discomfort.

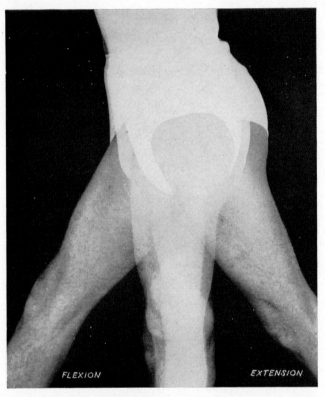

Fig. 111.—Flexion and extension of hip joint. (Photograph by Dr. D. R. L. Duncan.)

Hip Joint.—The articulation between the head of the femur and the acetabulum of the hip bone is the best example in the human body of a ball and socket joint. It permits movements of flexion-extension, abduction-adduction, medial and lateral rotation, and circumduction.

The capsular ligament has three fairly well-defined thickenings: the iliofemoral ligament which resembles an inverted Y and is attached above to the ilium and below to the intertrochanteric line of the femur, the pubofemoral ligament which passes from the pubic bone into the capsule, and the ischiofemoral ligament which passes from the ischium into the capsule. The iliofemoral and ischiofemoral ligaments increase the stability of the joint in the standing position, and the pubofemoral ligament prevents ex-

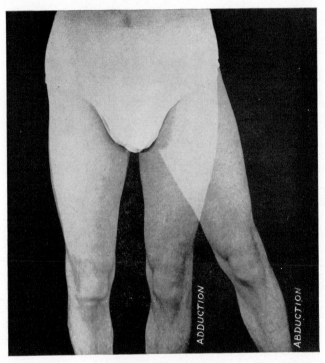

Fig. 112.—Abduction and adduction at the hip joint.   (Photograph by Dr. D. R. L. Duncan.)

cessive abduction of the femur. All three limit medial rotation of the femur. The iliofemoral ligament is one of the strongest ligaments in the body. There is occasionally a strong fibrous band running from the tendon of origin of the reflected head of the rectus femoris muscle to the lateral side of the great trochanter which may be regarded as an accessory ligament.

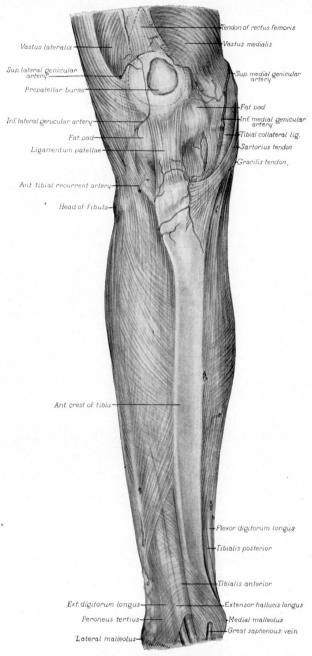

Vastus lateralis

Sup. lateral genicular artery

Prepatellar bursa

Inf. lateral genicular artery

Fat pad

Ligamentum patellae

Ant. tibial recurrent artery

Head of fibula

Ant. crest of tibia

Ext. digitorum longus

Peroneus tertius

Lateral malleolus

Tendon of rectus femoris

Vastus medialis

Sup. medial genicular artery

Fat pad

Inf. medial genicular artery

Tibial collateral lig.

Sartorius tendon

Gracilis tendon

Flexor digitorum longus

Tibialis posterior

Tibialis anterior

Extensor hallucis longus

Medial malleolus

Great saphenous vein

Fig. 113.—Anterior view of right knee joint and deep fascia of leg.
(W.R.U. 3333, male, white, aged 62 years.)

The ligament of the head of the femur (ligamentum teres) lies within the joint cavity, running from a pit in the central portion of the head of the femur to the margin of the acetabular notch. Its function is not clearly understood.

Knee Joint.—The knee joint between the lower end of the femur and the upper end of the tibia is the largest articulation in the body. The main movements are extension and flexion, but there is also a slight degree of medial and lateral rotation of the tibia.

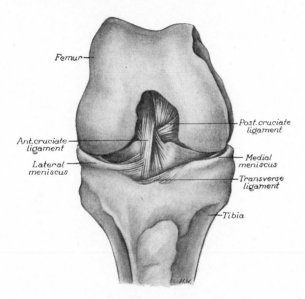

Fig. 114.—Anterior view of right knee joint. The tibia is flexed on the femur and the anterior portion of the capsule has been removed to show the cruciate ligaments and menisci. (W.R.U. 3700, male, Negro, aged 57 years.)

When the macerated bones are moved one against the other, this joint appears to be very insecure, but in reality during life it is an unusually stable joint. Externally the joint capsule is strengthened by muscle tendons. Anteriorly the tendon of the quadriceps femoris muscle is fused with the capsule. The patella lies within this tendon, and the thickened central portion passing from the lower edge of the patella to the tibial tuberosity is known as the patellar ligament. In complete extension the back of the patella articulates with the lower end of the femur, but when the knee is completely flexed, it occupies the deep groove between the two condyles. The patella never articulates with the tibia.

Behind and on either side the articular capsule of the knee joint is further strengthened by muscle tendons and tendinous expansions. The tibial and fibular collateral ligaments are bands of dense fibrous tissue on either side of the joint.

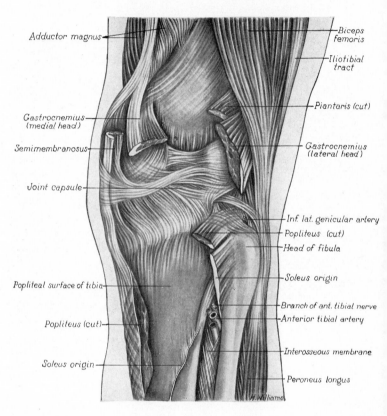

Adductor magnus

Gastrocnemius (medial head)

Semimembranosus

Joint capsule

Popliteal surface of tibia

Popliteus (cut)

Soleus origin

Biceps femoris

Iliotibial tract

Plantaris (cut)

Gastrocnemius (lateral head)

Inf. lat. genicular artery

Popliteus (cut)

Head of fibula

Soleus origin

Branch of ant. tibial nerve

Anterior tibial artery

Interosseous membrane

Peroneus longus

H. Williams

Fig. 115.—Posterior view of right knee joint. (W.R.U. 3654, male, white, aged 62 years.)

Within the joint capsule are the anterior and posterior cruciate ligaments attached above to the sides of the intercondylar fossa of the femur and below to the intercondylar eminence of the tibia. They are so named because they cross each other between their attachments.   The anterior ligament is more tense in extension and the posterior in flexion, and both prevent excessive antero-posterior movement.

The semilunar menisci are two C-shaped fibrocartilages, one placed on the upper surface of each tibial condyle.   Each cartilage is thick at its outer rim and becomes thinner toward the center, thus producing a concave depression into which the respective femoral condyles fit.

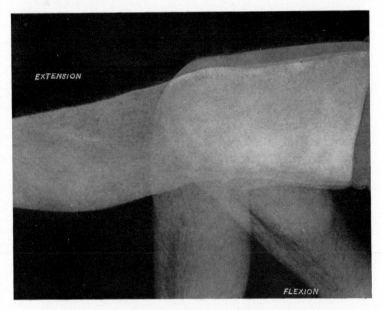

Fig. 116.—Flexion and extension at the knee joint.   (Photograph by Dr. D. R. L. Duncan.)

There are numerous synovial bursae about the knee joint, and some of the deeper ones communicate with the joint cavity. Synovial tissue also invests the tendon of origin of the popliteus muscle.

Tibiofibular Joints.—The upper tibiofibular joint is a gliding joint between the head of the fibula and an articular facet on the under surface of the lateral condyle of the tibia.

The lower tibiofibular joint is a syndesmosis, and a very strong interosseous ligament joins the lower ends of the two bones.   This

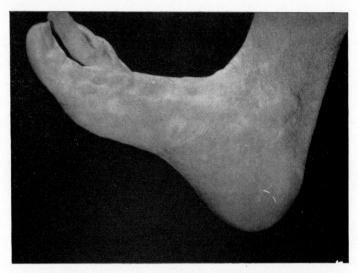

Fig. 117.—Dorsiflexion at the ankle joint. (Photograph by Dr. D. R. L. Duncan.)

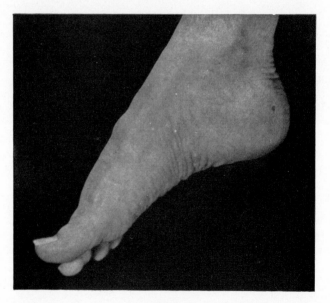

Fig. 118.—Plantar flexion at the ankle joint. (Photograph by Dr. D. R. L. Duncan.)

ligament is the thickened distal portion of the interosseous membrane of the leg.

There is very little movement between the tibia and fibula and none which is comparable to supination and pronation in the forearm.

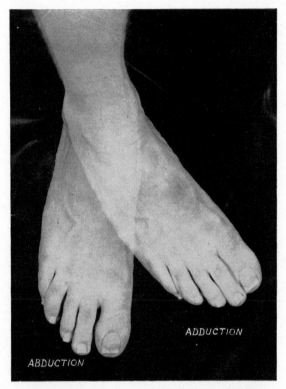

Fig. 119.—Abduction and adduction of the foot.   (Photograph by Dr. D. R. L. Duncan.)

Ankle Joint.—The lower ends of the tibia and fibula form a socket into which the upper portion of the talus fits, forming a hinge joint, and the movements are dorsiflexion and plantar flexion.

The capsular ligament is re-enforced by strong medial and lateral thickenings, and the long tendons of the foot muscles give additional support.   The medial re-enforcement is called the deltoid ligament and is attached above to the medial malleolus and below to the navicular, talus, and calcaneus.

Foot Joints.—The foot is a weight-bearing structure, and the muscles, ligaments, and joints are arranged to support the weight of the body when standing and during locomotion. The joints between the tarsal bones are gliding joints. Movement is lim-

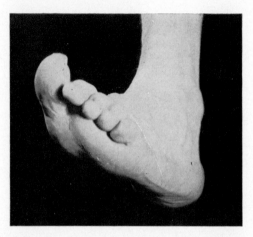

Fig. 120.—Dorsiflexion and inversion of the foot.   (Photograph by Dr. D. R. L. Duncan.)

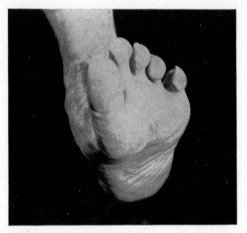

Fig. 121.—Dorsiflexion and eversion of the foot.   (Photograph by Dr. D. R. L. Duncan.)

Table 7
*Joints of Lower Extremity**

NAME	TYPE	BONES INVOLVED	ACCESSORY LIGAMENTS
Sacroiliac	Gliding	Sacrum and ilium	Interosseous; long posterior sacroiliac; short posterior sacroiliac; sacrotuberous; sacrospinous
Pubic symphysis	Amphiarthrosis	Pubes	Disc of fibrocartilage
Hip	Ball and socket	Acetabulum with head of femur	Iliofemoral; pubofemoral; ischiofemoral; round
Knee	Hinge	Lower end of femur with patella and with upper end of tibia	Patellar; tibial collateral; fibular collateral; anterior cruciate; posterior cruciate; medial meniscus; lateral meniscus; transverse
Proximal tibiofibular	Gliding	Head of fibula with lateral condyle of tibia	Interosseous membrane of leg
Distal tibiofibular	Syndesmosis	Lower end of tibia and fibula	Interosseous membrane of leg
Ankle	Hinge	Talus with lower end of tibia and fibula	Deltoid; anterior talofibular; posterior talofibular; calcaneofibular
Tarsal	Gliding	Tarsus	Interosseous; long plantar; short plantar; plantar calcaneonavicular; bifurcate
Tarsometatarsal	Gliding	Bases of metatarsals with distal tarsals	Interosseous
Metatarsal	Gliding	Bases of metatarsals	
Metatarsophalangeal	Ball and socket	Distal ends of metatarsals with bases of proximal phalanges	
Phalangeal	Hinge	Phalanges	

*From Francis, Carl C., and Farrell, Gordon L.: Integrated Anatomy and Physiology, ed. 3, St. Louis, 1957, The C. V. Mosby Co.

ited, but is rather free between talus and calcaneus and at the so-called transverse tarsal joint of Chopart between the talus and calcaneus behind the navicular and cuboid in front. Actually there are two distinct joints: a medial one between talus and navicular and a lateral one between calcaneus and cuboid. Usually the joint cavity between each two tarsal bones is closed, and the various joints do not communicate with each other.

The joints of the bases of the metatarsals permit very little motion. The metatarsophalangeal joints permit flexion and extension of the toes and a limited amount of abduction and adduction. In the toes, movement toward the midline of the *second* toe is adduction and in the opposite direction is abduction. The interphalangeal joints permit only flexion and extension.

Inversion of the foot turns the sole medially and eversion turns the sole laterally. This movement occurs largely at the talocalcaneal joint, but other foot joints are involved. Adduction of the foot turns the toes toward the midline of the body and abduction turns the toes outward.

The foot bones are held in position partly by capsular and interosseous ligaments and partly by powerful ligaments in the sole of the foot and by the tendons of the long flexor muscles. The interosseous ligament between the talus and calcaneus is particularly strong, and it is very unusual to see a dislocation occurring between these two bones. The long plantar ligament is attached behind to the under surface of the calcaneus and passes forward to attach to the plantar surface of the cuboid and to the bases of the three lateral metatarsal bones. Deeper than this ligament is a short, broad, and very strong band of fibers, running from calcaneus to cuboid, called the plantar calcaneocuboid or short plantar ligament. The plantar calcaneonavicular ligament, the spring ligament, is a very strong band of fibers extending from the anterior end of the calcaneus to the navicular and supporting the anterior end of the talus and is an important factor in maintaining the medial longitudinal arch of the foot. The bifurcate ligament is a U-shaped fibrous band attached behind to the calcaneus and in front one arm goes to the lateral side of the navicular and the other arm to the cuboid.

Review Questions

1. Define each of the following: synarthrosis, amphiarthrosis, and diarthrosis.
2. Give an example of each of the above articulations.
3. What are the main differences between a suture, a syndesmosis, and a synchondrosis?   Give an example of each.
4. List five types of diarthrodial joints and give an example of each.
5. What movements are possible in diarthroses?
6. What are the distinguishing features of a diarthrodial joint?
7. Describe the capsular ligament of a diarthrodial joint.
8. What movements occur in the mandibular joint?
9. At what joints do nodding movements of the head occur?   Where do rotatory movements of the head occur?
10. Describe briefly the bones and movements involved in supination and pronation of the hand.
11. What are the important ligaments which strengthen the capsular ligament of the hip joint?
12. Name four structures which increase the stability of the knee joint.
13. With what other bones does the femur articulate?

CHAPTER 6

MUSCLES

||||||||||||||||||||||||||||||||||||||||||||||||||||||||||||||||||||||||||||||||||||||||||||||||||||||||||||||||||||||||||||||||||||||||||||||||||||||||||||||||||||||||||||||||||||||||

Movements of the body are produced by muscular action. The histologic distinctions between smooth, striate, and cardiac muscle and the differences between voluntary and involuntary muscles have already been discussed in Chapter 3. In this chapter voluntary muscles are described. The muscular coats of the heart and viscera will be considered later with their respective organs.

Muscles which are under the control of the will are referred to as voluntary muscles, but no action is brought about by the action of a single muscle. A person voluntarily wills a certain motion, and various muscles act in harmony to produce the desired result. When we refer to voluntary muscles, we really mean muscles concerned in voluntary action. In the description of the individual muscles one or two principal actions will be given, but many other muscles of the area are also contracting to a greater or lesser degree at the same time. For example, a man desires to raise his arm laterally (abduction). This is done primarily by contraction of the deltoid muscle. At the same time the entire shoulder girdle must be firmly fixed in order that the head of the humerus may move against the glenoid of the scapula. This fixation is produced by tensing such muscles as the trapezius, serratus anterior, pectoralis minor, and rhomboids.

A muscle has two areas of attachment; that nearer the center of the body is usually described as the origin, and that more peripherally situated is generally termed the insertion. Usually the origin is from a relatively immovable structure and the insertion is into a relatively movable structure In this text the conventional origin and insertion of the various muscles have been described. In many activities the area which is conventionally called the origin really becomes the functional insertion and

the insertion becomes the origin.   For example, the pectoralis
major muscle is described as originating from the chest wall and
as being inserted into the humerus.   This is true in a freely swing-
ing arm, but in the exercise of chinning on a horizontal bar the
arms are fixed on the bar and the body is drawn upward.   Therefore the area of attachment on the humerus becomes the functional origin and the attachment on the chest wall the functional
insertion.   Of course many other muscles are involved in this exercise, and many are acting in the same way.   Bones carry the
majority of muscular attachments, but there are some muscles
affixed to the costal cartilages and some to the cartilages of the
larynx and air passages.   Muscles have attachments also to the

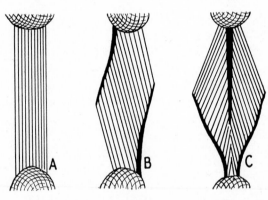

Fig. 122.—Fiber arrangement in muscle.   *A,* Fibers parallel to the long
axis; *B,* pennate arrangement of muscle fibers; *C,* bipennate arrangement
of muscle fibers.   (After Murk Jansen.)

fibrous tissue surrounding them and to the prolongations of their
sheaths.   Finally, there are small muscles in the actual substance
of the skin as well as in the subcutaneous tissue beneath it.   The
fleshy portion of a muscle is occasionally attached directly to the
bone, but the attachment is usually made by means of fibrous
tissue, tendon, or aponeurosis.   A tendon is a narrow ribbon-
like band of dense connective tissue; an aponeurosis is a broad
flat sheet.

The constituent fibers of a muscle are parallel to the long axis
of the muscle when extent of contraction rather than power is the
main requirement.   Where power is needed, muscle fibers are

short, are arranged in a penniform fashion, and are attached to tendons or fibrous bands penetrating the substance of the muscle.

Each muscle is supplied with at least one nerve which transmits impulses from the central nervous system, causing the muscle to contract. A single motor nerve fiber innervates a number of muscle fibers, and it has been found that muscles performing very delicate movements have a smaller number of muscle fibers per nerve fiber than do the muscles used in gross movements. It has been reported that in the extrinsic muscles which move the eyeball there are from six to twelve muscle fibers for each nerve fiber, but that in the semitendinosus, a large muscle of the thigh, there are about fifty muscle fibers per nerve fiber. A motor nerve fiber with the muscle fibers it innervates is called a motor unit. Sensory impulses are carried by nerves from the muscle to the central nervous system, giving information on the degree and strength of contraction.

During infancy, muscles have a small amount of connective tissue, and frequently the muscle fibers attach directly to bone without any intervening tendon or aponeurosis. With increasing age the amount of connective tissue and of elastic fibers increases. This is the only definite age change which occurs in muscles, and there is some evidence that the lessened strength of later years is due to changes within the central nervous system or to vascular changes rather than to changes in the muscles themselves. Muscles have no definite or fixed rate of growth but grow in accordance with the structures to which they are attached and with use. The eye and ear muscles grow very little, whereas the large muscles of the lower extremity increase greatly.

MUSCLES OF EXPRESSION

There are many small muscles beneath the skin of the face, particularly around the eyes and mouth. It is through these that facial expression is effected. Other muscles under the scalp and about the ears belong also to this group. All the muscles described in this section are innervated by branches of a single nerve, the seventh cranial or facial nerve. When this nerve is paralyzed, the face becomes masklike, and the lower eyelid falls away from the eyeball and the lower lip hangs loosely due to paralysis of the muscles.

The orbicularis oculi muscle is añ oval sphincter lying in the subcutaneous tissue of the eyelids and of the forehead. It keeps the lids closely applied to the eyeball, closes the eyes, and draws down the eyebrows. The corrugator supercilii muscle lies between the eyebrows and when contracted, as in frowning, produces vertical folds in the skin of the forehead.

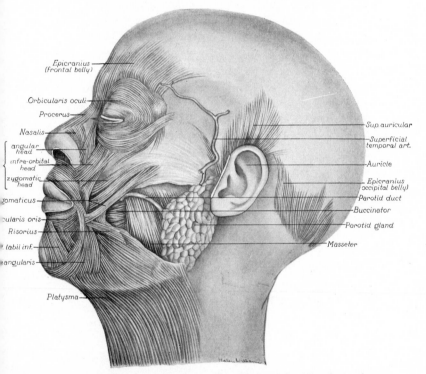

Fig. 123.—Muscles of expression. View of the left side of the face. The lateral portion of the capsule of the parotid gland has been removed. (Dissection by Dr. Frank Vecchio.) (W.R.U. 3489, male, Negro, aged 40 years.)

The orbicularis oris surrounds the lips and is the sphincter of the mouth. The quadratus labii superioris, caninus, and zygomaticus arise from the zygoma and maxilla and are inserted into the upper lip and prevent the corners of the mouth from drooping. The quadratus labii inferioris, the mentalis, and the triangularis arise from the mandible and pass upward to be inserted into the lower lip. They pull the mouth and lower lip down.

The buccinator muscle arises from the side of the maxilla above, from the inner surface of the mandible below, and from the pterygomandibular raphe which is a dense band of the deep fascia of the pharynx. The buccinator thus constitutes the essential muscular coat of the cheek and is inserted into the corner of the mouth. The buccinator aids in chewing movements by keeping the cheek more firmly in contact with the teeth, thus preventing food from being pocketed between teeth and cheek.

The platysma muscle arises from the deep surface of the skin in the upper chest wall and passes within the subcutaneous tissue of the neck to be attached to the lower lip and corner of the mouth. The platysma acts particularly on the skin of the lower lip and neck. The risorius is a small muscle extending laterally from the corner of the mouth. It is more or less intermingled with the platysma, as are all of the muscles which converge to this point.

The epicranius muscle has four bellies, two anterior bellies in the deep fascia of the forehead and two posterior bellies in the fascia over the back of the head, and a strong intervening fibrous sheet, the galea aponeurotica, stretched tightly over the dome of the skull. Contraction of the anterior bellies pulls the scalp forward, raises the eyebrows, and wrinkles the forehead. Contraction of the posterior bellies pulls the scalp backward.

MUSCLES OF UPPER EXTREMITY

The upper extremity in man is specialized for grasping. Its very powerful muscles which give it strength are arranged in the shoulder, upper arm, and forearm; the many smaller muscles used for precision are situated in the hand.

Muscles of Pectoral Region.—The pectoralis major arises from clavicle, sternum, and adjacent costal cartilages and from the sheath of the superficial muscle of the abdominal wall. From this broad origin the fibers converge at their insertion into the upper and anterior part of the humerus. The muscle draws the arm across the chest in such actions as chopping wood and is a powerful adductor. The clavicular portion has a nerve supply and a lymphatic drainage separate from those of the other part of the muscle and from the breast. In radical amputation of the breast the costosternal portion of the pectoralis major is removed along with the pectoralis minor, but the clavicular part of the muscle, which is inserted relatively low on the humerus is occasionally left. Since the lower fibers of the pectoralis major are attached high up on the humerus, there is an overlapping of the tendon of insertion, the lower fibers lying behind the upper or clavicular fibers. The overlapping produces the rounded contour of the anterior axillary border.

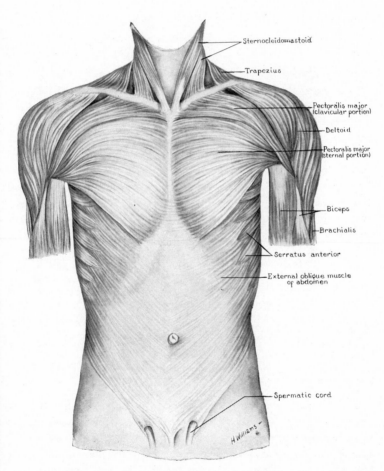

Fig. 124.—Muscles of front of thorax. (W.R.U. 2936, male, white, aged 65 years.)

The pectoralis minor arises from the second, third, and fourth ribs and is inserted into the coracoid process of the scapula. It assists in pulling the shoulder downward and forward. It has the same nerve supply as the pectoralis major (the medial and lateral anterior thoracic nerves, also known as medial and lateral pectoral nerves). The pectoralis minor is removed in radical breast amputations.

The serratus anterior arises from the lateral chest wall from the second to the eighth or ninth rib and is inserted into the vertebral margin of the scapula on the costal surface. The portion arising from each rib is a distinct muscle belly which gives a serrated or saw-tooth appearance to the line of origin, and hence the name. The serratus draws the scapula forward over the thoracic wall. The long thoracic nerve is its nerve supply.

Muscles of Back Attached to Scapula.—The trapezius is a large triangular muscle arising from the occipital bone, from the ligamentum nuchae, and from the spines of the vertebrae from the seventh cervical to the twelfth thoracic inclusive. The ligamentum nuchae, by its attachment to the spines of the cervical vertebrae, separates from each other the two muscular columns of the back of the neck. The trapezius is inserted into the lateral third of the clavicle and the spine of the scapula. It is used in bracing and raising the shoulders and in rotating the scapula. It is innervated by the accessory nerve.

The latissimus dorsi is a large muscle arising from the spines of the lower six thoracic vertebrae, from a short layer of fascia in the loin known as the lumbodorsal fascia, from the iliac crest, and occasionally also from the lower angle of the scapula. It is inserted into the humerus medial to the pectoralis major. The thick lateral margin of the muscle forms the posterior wall of the axilla. This muscle is a very powerful adductor and extensor of the arm and is the main muscle used in sweeping the arm down and back during swimming. It is supplied by the thoracodorsal nerve.

The levator scapulae, rhomboideus major, and rhomboideus minor are three flat muscles beneath the trapezius which arise from the transverse processes of cervical and upper thoracic vertebrae and are inserted on the vertebral margin of the scapula. The levator and rhomboids draw the scapula back and up and help to steady that bone during movements of the arm.

Muscles of Shoulder.—The deltoid is a large and powerful muscle arising from the lateral end of the clavicle and from the acromion and spine of the scapula and is inserted into the deltoid tuberosity, a prominence midway down the outer surface of the humerus. It is innervated by the axillary (circumflex) nerve and is the chief abductor of the humerus.

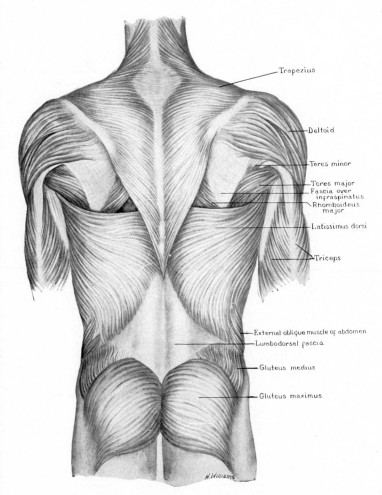

Fig. 125.—Superficial muscles of back. (W.R.U. 2936, male, white, aged 65 years.)

The supraspinatus arises from the superficial surface of the scapula above the spine and passes over the shoulder joint to be inserted at the top of the greater tuberosity of the humerus. The infraspinatus arises from the superficial surface of the scapula below the spine and passes back of the shoulder joint to be inserted at the greater tuberosity below the supraspinatus. The supra- and infraspinatus muscles are supplied by the suprascapular

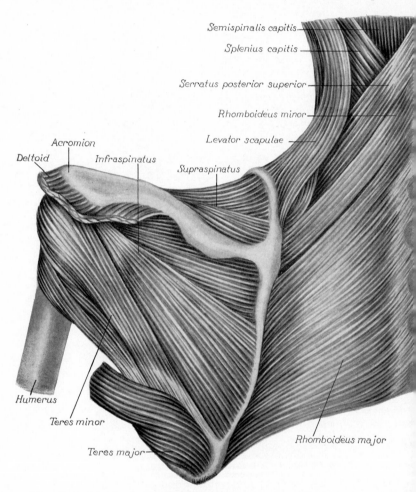

Fig. 126.—Muscles beneath the trapezius attached to scapula. (W.R.U. 3824, male, white, aged 62 years.)

nerve. The teres minor arises from the upper portion of the axillary margin of the scapula and passes back of the humerus below the infraspinatus to be inserted at the greater tuberosity of the humerus below the infraspinatus. It is supplied by the axillary (circumflex) nerve. The teres major arises from the axillary border of the scapula below the teres minor and passes forward to be inserted on the humerus medial to the latissimus dorsi. It is supplied by the lower subscapular nerve. The subscapularis muscle arises from the deep surface of the scapula and is inserted into the lesser tuberosity of the humerus. It is supplied by both subscapular nerves. The combined action of the muscles just described steadies the shoulder girdle in movements of the entire arm. The supraspinatus is an abductor of the arm, the others are adductors; the infraspinatus and teres minor rotate the humerus outward, and the teres major and subscapularis rotate the humerus inward.

It is convenient to remember that the four great superficial muscles of the chest and shoulder, the pectoralis major, trapezius, deltoid, and latissimus dorsi, are all triangular in outline. The fibers of each converge from a widespread origin to a small insertion. Small portions of each muscle are capable of functioning separately; for example, the fibers of the deltoid which arise from the spine of the scapula pull the arm backward and those which arise from the clavicle pull the arm forward, but when the muscle acts as a whole, it becomes an abductor of the humerus.

The action of many individual muscles can be demonstrated easily in a living human being, and movements at the shoulder joint illustrate this fact. The abducting action of the deltoid muscle can be palpated in anyone. The assisting action of the supraspinatus muscle is difficult to demonstrate. The opposite movement of adduction of the arm is brought about by two very powerful muscles, the pectoralis major in front and the latissimus dorsi behind. The accessory adductors, which have been mentioned, are less easily palpated in order to demonstrate their activity.

Muscles of Upper Arm.—On the front of the upper arm are the following muscles: (1) the coracobrachialis which arises from the coracoid process of the scapula and is inserted into the medial border of the humerus; (2) the biceps which arises by two heads, one from the coracoid and the other from the tubercle overhanging

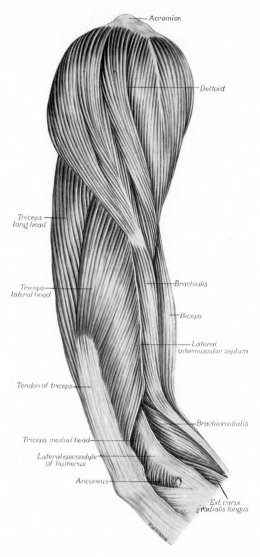

Fig. 127.—Muscles of upper arm, lateral view.   (W.R.U. 3824, male, white, aged 62 years.)

the glenoid surface of the scapula, and is inserted into the tuberosity of the radius and deep fascia of the forearm (lacertus fibrosus) ; and (3) the brachialis which arises from the lowest portion of the front of the humerus and is inserted into and below the coronoid process of the ulna. All are supplied by the musculocutaneous nerve. The biceps is the most superficial of the three and causes the bulge of the lower part of the front of the arm when the elbow is powerfully flexed.

The biceps is a supinator and flexor of the supinated forearm. The brachialis is the flexor of the pronated forearm. The brachioradialis (a muscle of the forearm) innervated by the radial nerve is also a flexor of the forearm in the semisupinated, semipronated position. Flexion of the elbow is therefore possible after paralysis of the musculocutaneous nerve.

The triceps is the only important muscle of the back of the upper arm. It arises from a prominence immediately below the glenoid surface of the scapula, from the back of the humerus above and below the radial groove, and is inserted into the upper end of the ulna. This muscle is the extensor of the elbow joint and is innervated by the radial nerve.

After injuries to the radial nerve as it passes around the shaft of the humerus, active extension of the forearm is possible because the long head of the triceps is innervated by the nerve immediately beyond its emergence from the brachial plexus. After fractures of the olecranon the triceps pulls the proximal fragment upward, and this pull must be overcome to bring about reduction and must be counteracted during healing.

Muscles of Forearm.—The superficial muscles, namely, the flexor carpi radialis, palmaris longus, flexor carpi ulnaris, flexor digitorum sublimis (superficialis), and pronator teres, all arise by a common tendon of origin from the medial epicondyle; the latter three have additional origins from the ulna. After fracture of the medial epicondyle these muscles pull the fragment downward.

The flexor carpi radialis is inserted into the base of the second and third metacarpal bones, the flexor carpi ulnaris into the pisiform and base of the fifth metacarpal, and the palmaris longus into the apex of the palmar aponeurosis. These three muscles flex the wrist joint and aid in steadying that joint during movements

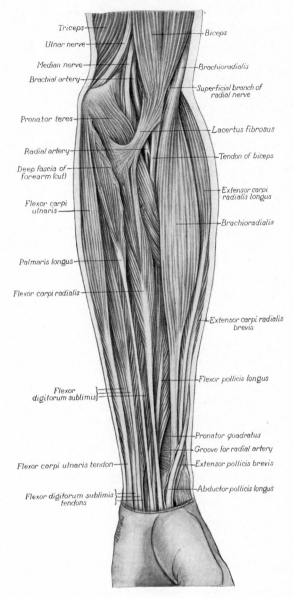

Triceps

Ulnar nerve

Median nerve

Brachial artery

Pronator teres

Radial artery

Deep fascia of forearm (cut)

Flexor carpi ulnaris

Palmaris longus

Flexor carpi radialis

Flexor digitorum sublimis

Flexor carpi ulnaris tendon

Flexor digitorum sublimis tendons

Biceps

Brachioradialis

Superficial branch of radial nerve

Lacertus fibrosus

Tendon of biceps

Extensor carpi radialis longus

Brachioradialis

Extensor carpi radialis brevis

Flexor pollicis longus

Pronator quadratus

Groove for radial artery

Extensor pollicis brevis

Abductor pollicis longus

Fig. 128.—Superficial muscles of volar aspect of left forearm.   (W.R.U. 3320, male, white, aged 68 years.)

of the fingers. The radial flexor abducts the hand and the ulnar
flexor adducts the hand. The pronator teres is inserted into the
midportion of the shaft of the radius on the lateral side.

The flexor digitorum profundus and pronator quadratus have
origins from the volar (front) aspect of the ulna. The flexor
pollicis longus arises from the volar aspect of the radius. The
flexors profundus and pollicis also have origins from the interosseous membrane. These three muscles lie deeper than the superficial group.

The tendons of the long flexors of the fingers pass beneath the
transverse carpal ligament (flexor retinaculum) into the palm and
out along the fingers. The tendons of the flexor digitorum sublimis are inserted into the base of the middle phalanges of the four
medial fingers, and the tendons of the flexor digitorum profundus
are inserted into the base of the terminal phalanges of the same
fingers. The flexor pollicis longus is inserted into the base of the
terminal phalanx of the thumb. The pronator quadratus is inserted
into the lower one fourth of the anterior surface of the radius.

In the forearm, the flexor carpi ulnaris and the ulnar portion
of the flexor profundus are innervated by the ulnar nerve; all
other muscles on the volar aspect of the forearm are innervated
by branches of the median nerve.

On the back of the forearm there is a superficial group of muscles, namely, the brachioradialis, anconeus, extensors carpi radialis
longus and brevis, extensor digitorum communis, extensor digiti
quinti proprius, and extensor carpi ulnaris. These arise from the
lateral epicondyle of the humerus. There is likewise a deep
group, namely, the supinator, extensors pollicis longus and brevis,
abductor pollicis longus, and extensor indicis proprius. These
arise from the dorsal aspect of the bones of the forearm and interosseous membrane—the supinator, extensor pollicis longus, and
extensor indicis proprius from the ulna; the extensor pollis brevis
from the radius; and the abductor pollicis longus from both bones.
All are supplied by branches of the radial nerve. After fracture
of the lateral epicondyle the extensor muscles pull the fragment
downward.

The brachioradialis is inserted into the lower end of the radius
on the lateral side. The anconeus is inserted into the ulna in common with the triceps muscle and may be regarded as an extra part

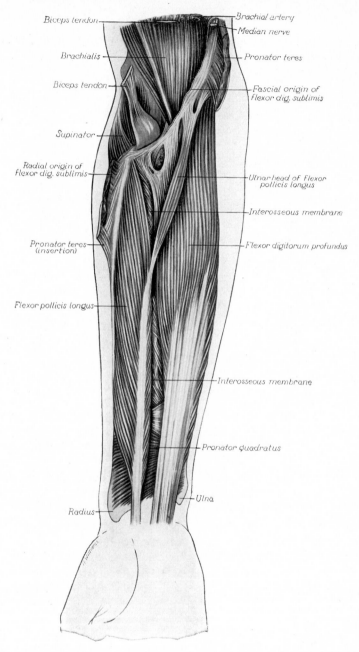

Fig. 129.—Deep muscles of volar aspect of right forearm. (W.R.U. 3700, male, Negro, aged 57 years.)

of that muscle. The extensor carpi radialis longus is inserted into the base of the second metacarpal bone on the dorsal surface and the extensor carpi radialis brevis is inserted similarly into the third metacarpal. The extensor carpi ulnaris is inserted into the base of the fifth metacarpal. The muscles just mentioned produce extension of the wrist joint. The radial extensors assist in movement of the hand to the thumb side (radial deviation), whereas the ulnar extensor assists in movement to the side of the little finger (ulnar deviation). The extensors of the fingers all become tendinous before reaching the wrist joint and pass beneath the extensor retinaculum on to the back of the hand to be inserted into the back of the various fingers by tendinous expansions. The supinator wraps around the lateral side of the upper portion of the radius and is inserted into the anterior aspect of that bone. The abductor pollicis longus is inserted into the lateral side of the base of the first metacarpal.

In thinking of the large number of complicated muscles of the forearm, one will find it helpful to remember a few general facts. The superficial flexor muscles arise from the region of the medial epicondyle of the humerus, and the muscle bundles pass downward into the forearm; at or near the wrist they become tendinous and are inserted into the various bones of the hand. These muscles are re-enforced by a deeper set which arise from the volar aspect of radius, ulna, and interosseous membrane. The flexor carpi ulnaris and part of the flexor digitorum profundus are supplied by the ulnar nerve, all the others by the median nerve.

The superficial extensor muscles arise from the region of the lateral epicondyle, their muscle bundles pass down the back of the forearm to become tendinous at the wrist, and are inserted into hand and finger bones. They are also re-enforced by deeper muscles arising from the dorsal aspect of the bones and interosseous membrane of the forearm. All are innervated by the radial nerve.

A very helpful way to associate the twelve muscles of the dorsal aspect of the forearm is to divide them into four functional groups of three each. There are three muscles, the anconeus, supinator, and brachioradialis, which are inserted into the bones of the forearm and act on the elbow joint. There are three muscle, the extensor carpi ulnaris and extensors carpi radialis longus and brevis, which are inserted into the metacarpal bones and are primarily ex-

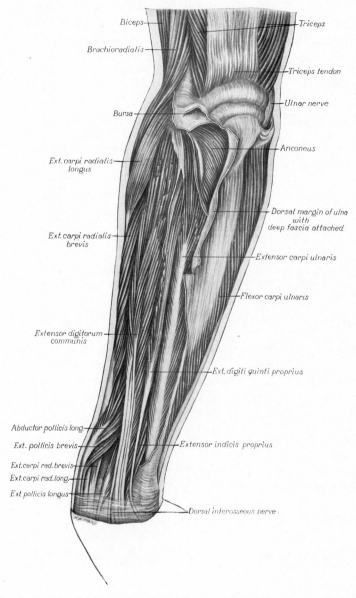

Fig. 130.—Superficial muscles of dorsal aspect of left forearm. (W.R.U. 3320, male, white, aged 68 years.)

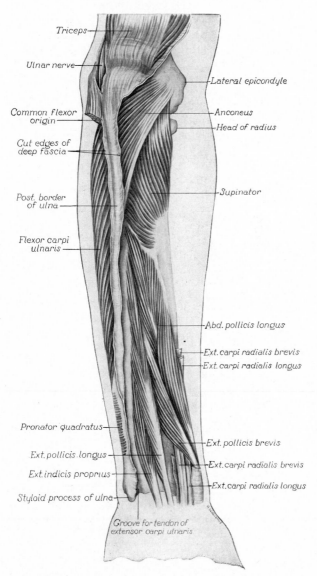

Fig. 131.—Deep muscles of dorsal aspect of right forearm. (W.R.U. 3700, male, Negro, aged 57 years.)

tensors of the wrist joint. There are three muscles, the abductor pollicis longus and extensors pollicis longus and brevis, which go to the thumb. There are three muscles, the extensors digitorum communis, indicis proprius, and digiti quinti proprius, which are inserted into the fingers and act primarily as extensors of the metacarpophalangeal joints.

The flexor muscles flex the wrist and fingers and associated with them are the pronators. The extensors extend the wrist and fingers and associated with them are the supinators.

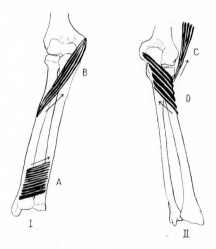

Fig. 132.—Pronation and supination. *I*, Principal muscles used in pronating the forearm; *A*, pronator quadratus muscle; *B*, pronator teres muscle. *II*, Principal muscles used in supinating the forearm; *C*, biceps brachii muscle; *D*, supinator muscle.

The muscles of the upper arm and the forearm have been described separately because of their natural anatomical grouping. However, in many movements of the upper extremity, muscles from each of these two large groups act together. This is especially true in the very important movement of supination of the forearm. The supinating action of the biceps brachii muscle can be demonstrated by palpating the muscle belly of the muscle while supinating the hand. The action of the supinator muscle itself cannot be felt. It is also difficult to palpate the muscles which bring about the opposite movement of pronation.

On the anterior surface of the wrist the volar carpal ligament (flexor retinaculum) is a strong band of connective tissue attached on either side to carpal bones. Beneath this ligament the flexor tendons of the forearm pass into the palm. On the dorsal surface of the wrist the dorsal carpal ligament (extensor retinaculum) forms a strong band under which the extensor tendons pass on to the back of the hand.

Muscles of Hand.—There are nineteen small muscles in the hand. Those for the thumb form the thenar eminence and include the abductor pollicis brevis, the opponens pollicis, the flexor pollicis brevis, and the adductor pollicis. There are also four muscles in the hypothenar eminence, the palmaris brevis, the abductor digiti quinti, opponens digiti quinti, and flexor digiti quinti brevis. There are four lumbrical muscles which arise in the palm from the tendons of the flexor digitorum profundus muscle and are inserted into the capsules of the metacarpophalangeal articulations of the four fingers.

In the spaces between the metacarpal bones are three volar and four dorsal interosseous muscles. Each volar interosseous muscle arises by a single head from a metacarpal bone and each dorsal arises by two heads, one from each bone bounding an intermetacarpal space. Each interosseous muscle is inserted into the back of the base of a finger.

The abductor pollicis brevis, the opponens pollicis, the flexor pollicis brevis, and the two lateral lumbricals are supplied by branches of the median nerve. All the other muscles of the hand are supplied from branches of the ulnar nerve.

Certain distinctive functions of the muscles of the hand should be remembered. The lumbricals flex the fingers at the metacarpophalangeal joints and extend them at the interphalangeal joints. The long extensors extend the wrist, the metacarpophalangeal joints of the fingers, and the joints of the thumb. The dorsal interossei abduct the fingers from the midline of the middle finger and the volar interossei adduct to the midline of the middle finger. The long flexors flex the wrist, metacarpophalangeal joints, and finger joints.

Palmar Aponeurosis.—The palmar aponeurosis is a dense sheet of fibrous connective tissue placed in the palm beneath a superficial fatty layer of connective tissue and above the tendons of the

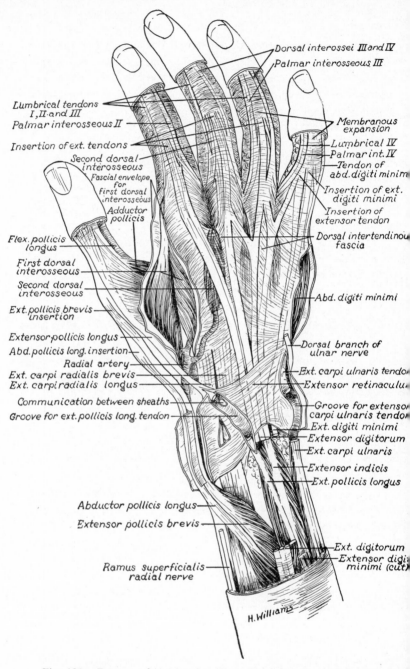

Dorsal interossei III and IV

Palmar interosseous III

Lumbrical tendons I, II and III
Palmar interosseous II

Insertion of ext. tendons

Second dorsal interosseous

Fascial envelope for first dorsal interosseous

Adductor pollicis

Flex. pollicis longus

First dorsal interosseous

Second dorsal interosseous

Ext. pollicis brevis insertion

Extensor pollicis longus

Abd. pollicis long. insertion

Radial artery

Ext. carpi radialis brevis

Ext. carpi radialis longus

Communication between sheaths

Groove for ext. pollicis long. tendon

Abductor pollicis longus

Extensor pollicis brevis

Ramus superficialis radial nerve

Membranous expansion

Lumbrical IV

Palmar int. IV

Tendon of abd. digiti minimi

Insertion of ext. digiti minimi

Insertion of extensor tendon

Dorsal intertendinous fascia

Abd. digiti minimi

Dorsal branch of ulnar nerve

Ext. carpi ulnaris tendon

Extensor retinaculum

Groove for extensor carpi ulnaris tendon

Ext. digiti minimi

Extensor digitorum

Ext. carpi ulnaris

Extensor indicis

Ext. pollicis longus

Ext. digitorum

Extensor digiti minimi (cut)

H. Williams

Fig. 133.—Dorsum of the hand. (From Brickel: Surgical Treatment of Hand and Forearm Infections, St. Louis, 1939, The C. V. Mosby Co.) (W.R.U. 3084, male, Negro, aged 50 years.)

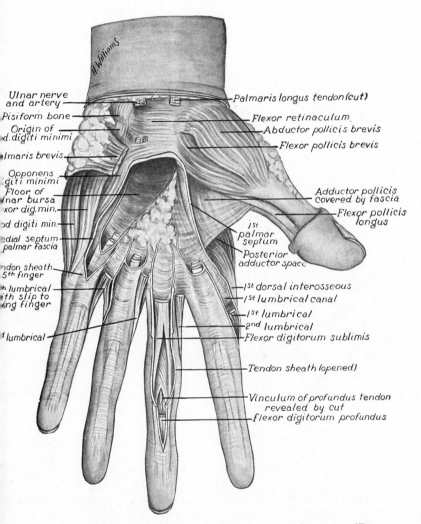

Ulnar nerve and artery

Pisiform bone

Origin of d. digiti minimi

Imaris brevis

Opponens giti minimi

Floor of lnar bursa xor dig. min.

od digiti min.

edial septum palmar fascia

ndon sheath 5th finger

h lumbrical ith slip to ing finger

d lumbrical

Palmaris longus tendon (cut)

Flexor retinaculum

Abductor pollicis brevis

Flexor pollicis brevis

Adductor pollicis covered by fascia

Flexor pollicis longus

1st palmar septum

Posterior adductor space

1st dorsal interosseous

1st lumbrical canal

1st lumbrical

2nd lumbrical

Flexor digitorum sublimis

Tendon sheath (opened)

Vinculum of profundus tendon revealed by cut

flexor digitorum profundus

Fig. 134.—Muscles of thenar and hypothenar eminences. (From Brickel: Surgical Treatment of Hand and Forearm Infections, St. Louis, 1939, The C. V. Mosby Co.) (W.R.U. 3226, male, white, aged 65 years.)

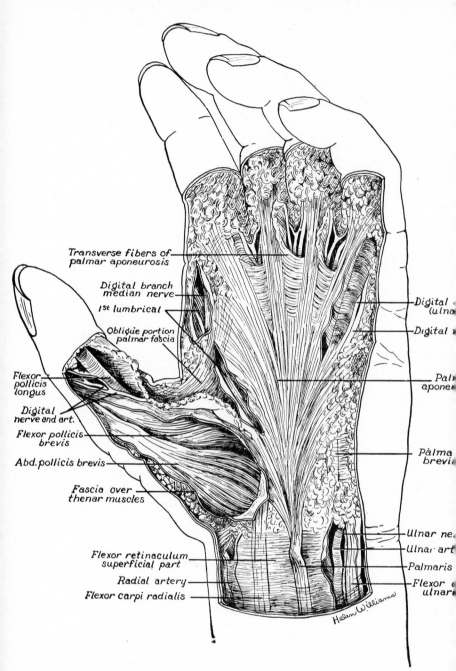

Transverse fibers of
palmar aponeurosis

Digital branch
median nerve

1st lumbrical

Oblique portion
palmar fascia

Flexor
pollicis
longus

Digital
nerve and art.

Flexor pollicis
brevis

Abd. pollicis brevis

Fascia over
thenar muscles

Flexor retinaculum
superficial part

Radial artery

Flexor carpi radialis

Digital
(ulna

Digital

Pal
apone

Palma
brevi

Ulnar ne

Ulnar art

Palmaris

Flexor
ulnar

Helen Williams

Fig. 135.—The palmar fascia. (From Brickel: Surgical Treatment of
Hand and Forearm Infections, St. Louis, 1939, The C. V. Mosby Co.)
(W.R.U. 2961, male, Negro, aged 42 years.)

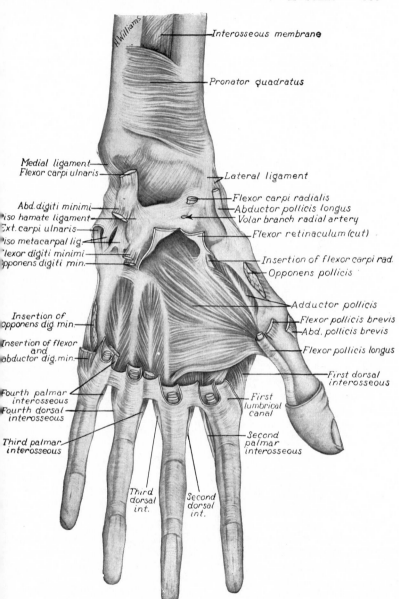

Fig. 136.—Deep muscles and ligaments of volar aspect of hand and wrist. (From Brickel: Surgical Treatment of Hand and Forearm Infection, St. Louis, 1939, The C. V. Mosby Co.) (W.R.U. 3245, male, Negro, aged 50 years.)

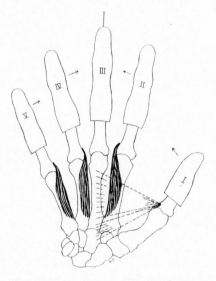

Fig. 137.—Diagram showing action of the intrinsic muscles of the hand which adduct the fingers and thumb. The three volar interosseous muscles are indicated by the heavy lines. The adductor pollicis is indicated by dotted outline. All are supplied by the ulnar nerve.

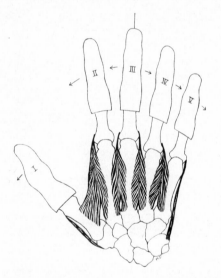

Fig. 138.—Diagram showing action of the intrinsic muscles of the hand which abduct the fingers and thumb. All are supplied by the ulnar nerve except the abductor pollicis brevis which is supplied by the median nerve.

long flexor muscles and the lumbrical and interosseous muscles. This aponeurosis is triangular in shape, with the apex toward the wrist and the base at the base of the fingers. The apex is continuous with the lower end of the tendon of the palmaris longus muscle and with some of the fibers of the volar carpal ligament. At its base the fibers of the aponeurosis fan out, and slips pass to each of the four medial metacarpophalangeal joints and blend with the capsules of these joints. There are septa which pass from the undersurface of the aponeurosis deeply into the palm, fusing with the fascia about the interosseous muscles. The palmar aponeurosis adds greatly to the strength of the hand.

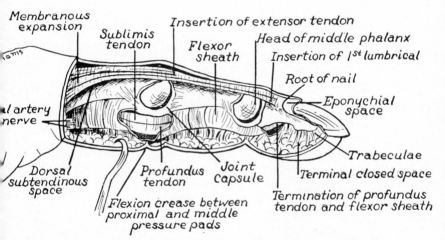

Fig. 139.—Left index finger. (From Brickel: Surgical Treatment of Hand and Forearm Infections, St. Louis, 1939, The C. V. Mosby Co.) (W.R.U. 3098, male, white, aged 59 years.)

MUSCLES OF LOWER EXTREMITY

The lower extremity in man is specialized for locomotion. This important function involves approximately one-half the total muscular mass of the body.

Muscles of Front of Thigh.—These muscles lie beneath the fascia lata and are separated on the medial side from the adductor group by the medial intermuscular septum and from the hamstring group laterally by the lateral intermuscular septum.

The sartorius, the longest muscle in the body, arises from the anterior superior iliac spine and passes distally and medially across the front of the thigh to be inserted high up on the medial surface of the tibial shaft.   This is literally the tailor's muscle, and the position a tailor assumes when seated on the floor illustrates the functions of the muscle, that is, to flex the hip and knee joints, and to turn the thigh outward.

The quadriceps femoris forms the great bulk of the anterior aspect of the thigh and has four separate parts.   The rectus femoris arises from the anterior inferior iliac spine and from the ilium above the acetabulum.   The three vasti muscles (vastus medialis vastus lateralis, and vastus intermedius) arise from the femur and ensheathe the lower two thirds of the bone except for its linea aspera and condyles.   The four parts of the quadriceps are usually described as being inserted into the patella, but the patella is really a sesamoid bone developed within the central portion of the tendon by which the compound muscle is attached to the tuberosity of the tibia.   There are expansions of insertion by aponeurotic fibers into the upper end of both condyles of the tibia. The central tendon and its expansions, also known as retinacula, replace to some extent the proper capsule of the knee joint.   The articularis genu muscle consists of few fibers which arise from the lower part of the front of the femur and are inserted into the capsule of the knee joint.

The quadriceps is a very powerful extensor of the knee and is brought into function in such movements as rising from a sitting position, kicking a football, and swimming.   The articularis genu pulls the upper part of the joint capsule upward during extension and thus prevents pinching of the synovial membrane between the joint surfaces.

The iliopsoas is a compound muscle, the iliac portion arising from the medial surface of the iliac blade, and the psoas major arising from the anterior surface of the lowest thoracic and the upper four lumbar vertebrae and intervening fibrocartilaginous discs.   The iliac and psoas portions unite and pass beneath the inguinal ligament lateral to the femoral nerve to be inserted into the lesser trochanter.   A large bursa is present beneath this muscle as it passes over the pubis and hip joint.   The iliopsoas is the main flexor of the hip joint, and when the femur is fixed, it acts as a

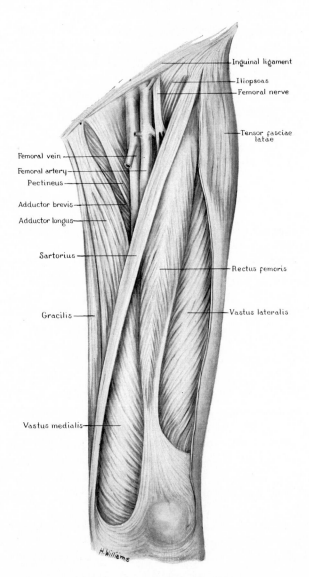

Fig. 140.—Muscles of front of left thigh. The knee has been laterally rotated to show the adductor muscles. (W.R.U. 2792, male, white, aged 64 years.)

flexor of the trunk. In the latter function it is assisted by the portion of the rectus femoris which arises from the ilium.

The pectineus muscle arises from the upper surface of the superior pubic ramus and is inserted into the back of the femur just below and behind the lesser trochanter. This muscle is an adductor and flexor of the hip joint.

The sartorius, quadriceps, iliacus, and pectineus muscles are supplied by branches of the femoral nerve. The psoas muscle is supplied directly from the lumbar nerves.

Muscles of Inner Side of Thigh.—These muscles include the gracilis, the three adductors, and the obturator externus.

The gracilis is a long, flat muscle which arises from the pubis just below the symphysis and is inserted by a strong tendon into the upper end of the tibia behind the sartorius and in front of the semitendinosus.

The adductor longus arises from the body of the pubis just lateral to the symphysis and is inserted into the middle two fourths of the medial lip of the linea aspera. The adductor brevis arises from the inferior ramus and body of the pubis lateral to the gracilis and is inserted into the femur below the pectineus and into the upper end of the linea aspera behind the adductor longus. The adductor magnus is the largest of the adductors. It arises from the lower part of the inferior ramus of the pubis, from the ramus of the ischium and from the tuberosity of the ischium. It is inserted into the posterior portion of the femur on the entire length of the linea aspera, into the adductor tubercle, and medial to the insertion of the quadratus femoris. The portion which arises from the ischial tuberosity and is inserted into the adductor tubercle is really not an adductor, but a part of the hamstring group.

The obturator externus arises from the lateral surface of the obturator membrane and adjacent portion of the hip bone. The fibers pass behind the hip joint, and the tendon is inserted into the trochanteric fossa of the femur.

The name of this group of muscles indicates their main function, adduction at the hip joint; in addition, the obturator externus is a lateral rotator of the femur and the gracilis flexes the knee joint.

The adductors and the obturator externus are supplied by the obturator nerve, except the hamstring portion of the adductor magnus which is supplied by the sciatic nerve.

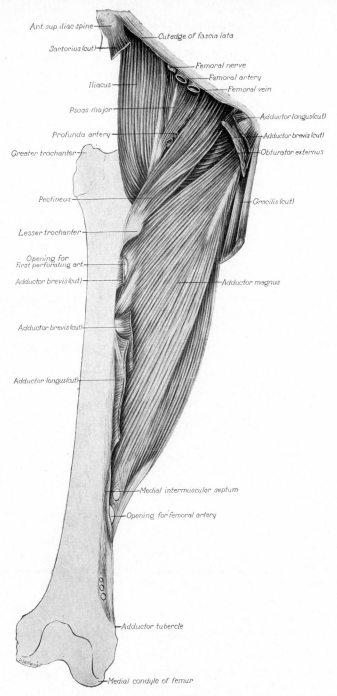

Fig. 141.—Deep muscles of medial side of right thigh. (W.R.U. 3700, male, Negro, aged 57 years.)

The femoral triangle is a large triangular space bounded above by the inguinal ligament, laterally by the sartorius, and medially by the adductor longus. The more important structures in this area are the first part of the femoral artery and accompanying vein, the femoral nerve, numerous lymph nodes, and the terminal portion of the long saphenous vein. Below, the femoral vessels pass beneath the sartorius muscle into a tunnel known as the sub-sartorial or Hunter's canal.

Muscles of Buttock.—This group of muscles includes the three glutei, the tensor fasciae latae, and a group of small muscles known as lateral rotators, including the obturator internus, the piriformis, quadratus femoris, and the two gemelli.

The gluteus maximus arises from the posterior portion of the iliac blade, the dorsal surface of the sacrum and coccyx, the sacro-tuberous ligament, and the lumbodorsal fascia. It is inserted into the back of the iliotibial tract and also into the gluteal tuberosity of the femur. Through the iliotibial tract it receives an indirect attachment to the tibia. This muscle has coarser fibers than any other muscle of the body. It is a very powerful extensor of the hip joint.

The tensor fasciae latae arises from the lateral anterior portion of the iliac crest and is inserted into the anterior portion of the iliotibial tract; it acts mainly as a flexor of the hip joint. The iliotibial tract is a wide, strong band of longitudinal fibers of the deep fascia attached above to the iliac crest and below to the lateral condyle of the tibia and capsule of the knee joint. In its upper portion it is split into two sheets which enclose the tensor fasciae latae muscle; below that muscle the two sheets fuse. Functionally the tract is the aponeurosis of the tensor fasciae latae and of the gluteus maximus.

The gluteus medius and minimus arise from the lateral surface of the iliac blade beneath the gluteus maximus and are inserted into the greater trochanter. These muscles are abductors of the femur and aid in stabilizing the pelvis on the femora during walking. The gluteus minimus is a medial rotator of the femur.

The gluteus maximus is supplied by the inferior gluteal nerve and the tensor fasciae latae and the gluteus medius and minimus by the superior gluteal nerve.

The obturator internus arises from the inner surface of the obturator membrane and the adjoining bone. Its fibers converge to the lesser sciatic foramen, and the tendon passes behind the hip joint to be inserted into the medial side of the greater trochanter above the fossa. This muscle is a lateral rotator of the femur.

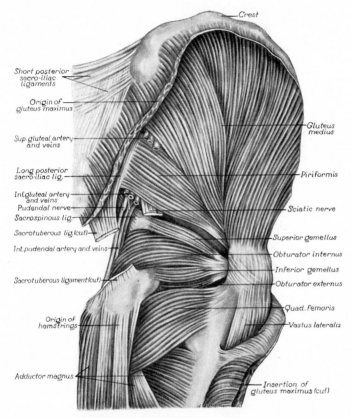

Fig. 142.—Deep muscles of right buttock. (W.R.U. 3678, male, Negro, aged 33 years.)

The superior gemellus muscle arises from the spine of the ischium; the inferior gemellus from the ischial tuberosity. The tendon of each gemellus muscle blends with that of the obturator internus and is inserted in common with that muscle. The quadratus femoris arises from the lateral margin of the ischial tuberosity and is inserted into the upper portion of the shaft of the femur. The piriformis arises from the front of the second, third, and fourth sacral vertebrae and passes through the greater sciatic notch to be inserted into a pit on the medial aspect of the greater trochanter.

Hamstring Muscles.—The hamstring muscles are the biceps femoris, the semitendinosus, semimembranosus, and the ischial portion of the adductor magnus. They are primarily flexors of the knee joint, and when the knee is fixed, they aid in extension of the hip joint.

The biceps femoris has a long head which arises in common with the semitendinosus from the medial portion of the ischial tuberosity and an additional origin or short head from the lateral lip of the linea aspera. The biceps is inserted into the head of the fibula and lateral condyle of the tibia. The semitendinosus arises with the long head of the biceps and is inserted into the upper end of the tibia behind the sartorius and below the gracilis. The semimembranosus arises from the lateral facet of the ischial tuberosity and is inserted into a groove on the back of the medial condyle of the tibia and into the deep fascia about the medial and posterior portions of the knee joint. The muscles of this group are innervated by the nerve to the hamstrings, a portion of the sciatic nerve.

The muscles of the thigh may be divided into three large groups: (1) an anterior knee extensor group innervated by the femoral nerve, (2) a medial hip adductor group innervated by the obturator nerve, and (3) a posterior knee flexor group innervated by a portion of the sciatic nerve. Each group has complex origins from the femur and from the pelvic girdle; therefore each group is capable of moving the hip joint as well as the knee joint. Movements of abduction, medial rotation, and lateral rotation of the thigh are produced by a number of deeply placed muscles.

Muscles of Front of Leg.—These muscles lie in front of the interosseous septum and between the lateral surface of the tibia and the anterior peroneal septum. They are the tibialis anterior, extensor digitorum longus, peroneus tertius, and extensor hallucis longus. All of these are supplied by the deep peroneal nerve and all are dorsiflexors of the foot. In addition, the tibialis anterior acts as an invertor of the foot and the peroneus tertius as an evertor.

The tibialis anterior arises from the upper lateral portion of the tibia and lateral intermuscular septum, and is inserted into the medial aspect of the first cuneiform and base of the first metatarsal. It is the most medial tendon in front of the ankle joint. The extensor digitorum longus arises from the lateral condyle of the tibia and the upper portion of the fibula and is inserted into the second, third, fourth, and fifth toes by tendons which are plainly

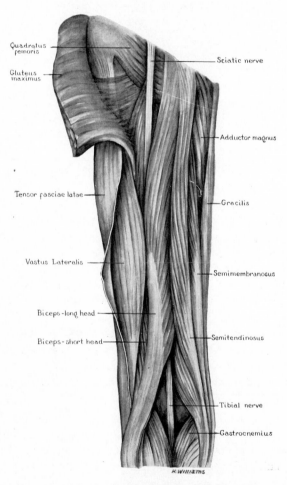

Fig. 143.—Muscles of back of left thigh. (W.R.U. 2792, male, white, aged 64 years.)

visible on the dorsum of the foot. The peroneus tertius arises
from the lower part of the fibula and is inserted into the dorsal aspect of the base of the fifth metatarsal. This muscle is not separated at its origin from the extensor digitorum longus. The extensor hallucis longus arises from the fibula deeper than the other
muscles. At the ankle its tendon becomes superficial and runs
laterally to that of the tibialis anterior to its insertion into the base
of the terminal phalanx of the first toe.

Muscles of Outer Side of Leg.—The peroneus longus arises
from the lateral condyle of the tibia and from the head and upper
part of the lateral surface of the fibula. Its tendon passes behind
the lateral malleolus, crosses the sole, and is inserted into the first
cuneiform and base of the first metatarsal. The peroneus brevis
arises from the lower part of the lateral surface of the fibula, passes
behind the lateral malleolus, and is inserted into the tuberosity of
the fifth metatarsal. The peroneus longus and brevis are supplied
by the superficial peroneal nerve. They are plantar flexors of the
ankle joint and evertors of the foot.

Muscles of Back of Leg.—The muscles of the superficial group
are the soleus, gastrocnemius, and plantaris, all inserting into the
calcaneus and all acting as plantar flexors of the foot. The gastrocnemius arises from the back of the condyles of the femur and
from the posterior surface of the capsule of the knee joint. The
soleus arises from the back of the fibula and tibia and arches over
the popliteal vessels. Both of these muscles join in a common
tendon of insertion, the tendo Achillis or tendo calcaneus, into
the back of the calcaneus. The plantaris is relatively unimportant,
arising from the back of the lateral condyle of the femur deeper
than the gastrocnemius. By means of a long slender tendon it
is inserted into the tendo calcaneus or directly into the calcaneus.
The deep muscles of the back of the leg are the popliteus, flexor
digitorum longus, flexor hallucis longus, and tibialis posterior.

The popliteus arises from the lateral side of the lateral epicondyle of the femur, passes behind the knee joint, and is inserted
into the upper medial posterior surface of the tibia. The flexor
digitorum longus arises from the back of the tibia, passes behind the
medial malleolus beneath the laciniate ligament, and is inserted into
the base of the terminal phalanges of the second, third, fourth,
and fifth toes. The flexor hallucis longus arises from the posterior

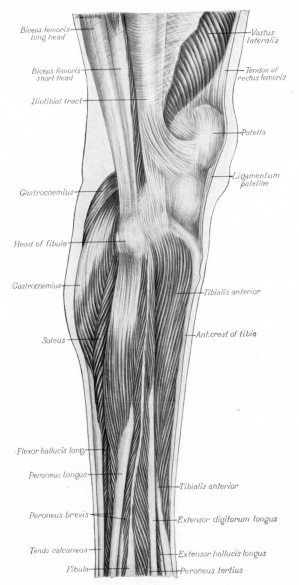

Biceps femoris long head

Biceps femoris short head

Iliotibial tract

Gastrocnemius

Head of fibula

Gastrocnemius

Soleus

Flexor hallucis long.

Peroneus longus

Peroneus brevis

Tendo calcaneus

Fibula

Vastus lateralis

Tendon of rectus femoris

Patella

Ligamentum patellae

Tibialis anterior

Ant.crest of tibia

Tibialis anterior

Extensor digitorum longus

Extensor hallucis longus

Peroneus tertius

Fig. 144.—Muscles of lateral aspect of right leg. This dissection shows the close relationship of the muscle tendons around the knee to the joint capsule. (W.R.U. 3654, male, white, aged 62 years.)

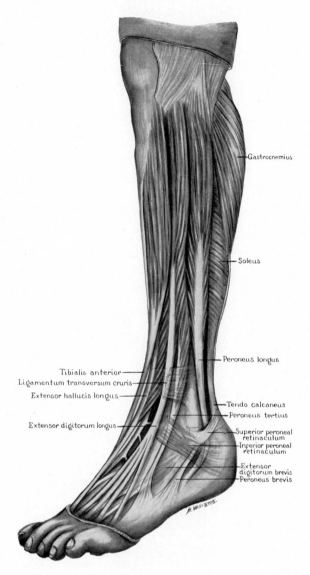

Fig. 145.—Muscles of lateral aspect of left leg.   (W.R.U. 2792, male, white, aged 64 years.)

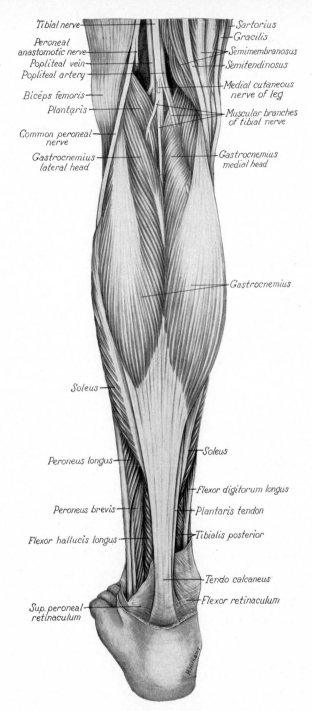

Fig. 146.—Superficial muscles on back of left leg. (W.R.U. 3555, male, white, aged 62 years.)

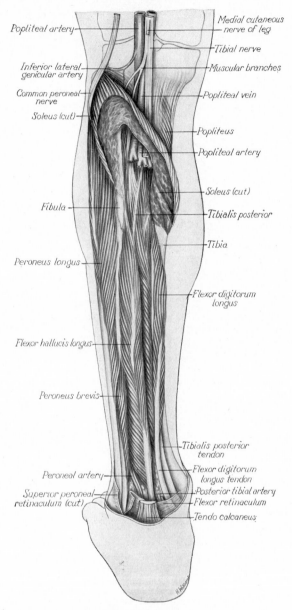

Fig. 147.—Deep muscles of back of left leg.   (W.R.U. 3555, male, white, aged 62 years.)

surface of the fibula and passes into the sole deeper than the tendon of the flexor digitorum longus to be inserted into the base of the terminal phalanx of the great toe. The tibialis posterior arises from the back of the tibia and fibula and the back of the interosseous membrane. The tendon passes behind the medial malleolus and spreads out in the sole of the foot to an insertion into the second, third, and fourth metatarsals and into all the tarsals except the talus; its greatest insertion is into the navicular. All of the muscles of the back of the leg are supplied from branches of the tibial nerve.

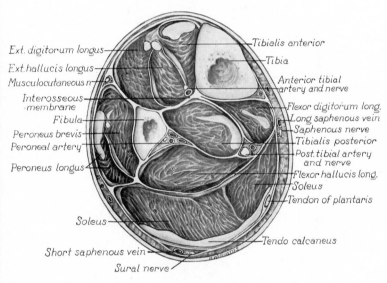

Fig. 148.—Cross section through upper third of left calf. Section passes through junction of upper and middle thirds.

The popliteus aids in flexion of the knee joint. The remaining deep muscles of the back of the leg are plantar flexors at the ankle joint and flexors of the toes. The tibialis posterior, working with the tibialis anterior, inverts the foot. The deep fascia overlying the muscle tendons at the ankle has certain definite thickenings which strengthen the ankle joint and hold tendons in place. On the outer side of the ankle are the superior and inferior peroneal retinacula passing from the lateral malleolus to the calcaneus and binding down the tendons of the peroneal muscles. In front is the transverse ligament of the ankle (superior extensor retinaculum) stretching between the two malleoli, and lower down is the cruciate ligament of the ankle (inferior extensor retinaculum). On the inner side of the ankle is the laciniate ligament (flexor retinaculum) attached to the medial malleolus and the calcaneus and stretched over the tendons of the long flexor muscles of the foot.

In studying the lower extremity it is helpful to remember how frequently the number three is associated with the structures. There are three main nerves: the obturator, the femoral, and the sciatic. The latter, in turn, has three main branches: the nerve to the hamstrings, the tibial nerve, and the peroneal nerve.

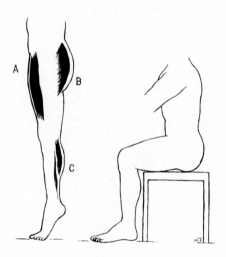

Fig. 149.—Diagram of the great extensor muscles of the lower extremity. *A,* The quadriceps femoris muscle; *B,* the gluteus maximus muscle; *C,* the gastrocnemius and soleus muscles.

The muscles of the thigh are divided into three groups: the knee extensors, the adductors, of which there are three main ones, and the knee flexors or hamstrings, of which there are three. The muscles of the leg attached to tarsal bones are divided into three groups: the tibialis anterior and posterior on the inner side, the three peroneal muscles on the outer side, and the three muscles attached to the calcaneus behind, soleus, gastrocnemius, and plantaris. Three muscles which arise from points on the os coxae, the sartorius, gracilis, and semitendinosus, are inserted together into the tibia. There are also three gluteal muscles. At the ankle the tendons of three muscles pass beneath the extensor retinaculum, and the tendons of three muscles pass behind the medial malleolus beneath the flexor retinaculum.

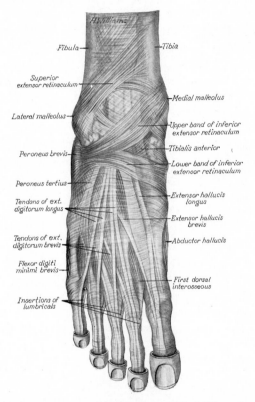

Fig. 150.—Dorsal aspect of right foot. (W.R.U. 3475, male, white, aged 51 years.)

At the beginning of this discussion it was stated that one half of the muscle bulk of the body in man is located in the lower extremities. The muscles which are especially large are the gluteus maximus, the quadriceps femoris, the gastrocnemius, and the soleus. In order for man to assume and maintain an erect posture these muscles must be very powerful. He uses them particularly to push the body weight upward when arising from a seated position, to climb stairs, and to stand on tiptoe.

Muscles of Foot.—There are eighteen small muscles in the plantar aspect of the foot: the quadratus plantae, four lumbricals, abductor hallucis, flexor digitorum brevis, abductor digiti quinti, flexor hallucis brevis, adductor hallucis, flexor digiti quinti brevis, four dorsal interossei, and three volar or plantar interossei.

There is much less freedom of motion in the foot than in the hand, but the actions of the muscles are similar to those of the corresponding muscles in the hand. In the foot the midline anatomically is the middle of the *second* toe. The quadratus plantae is an accessory flexor arising from the under surface of the calcaneus and strengthening the action of the long flexors of the toes; the flexor digitorum brevis has an action similar to that of the flexor digitorum sublimis of the hand. The abductor hallucis strengthens the medial longitudinal arch of the foot, and the abductor digiti quinti does the same for the lateral longitudinal arch.

The first lumbrical, the abductor hallucis, the flexor digitorum brevis, and the flexor hallucis brevis are supplied by the medial plantar branch of the tibial nerve. The remaining small muscles of the sole of the foot are supplied by branches of the lateral plantar nerve from the tibial nerve.

On the dorsum of the foot the extensor digitorum brevis muscle arises from the upper surface of the calcaneus and is inserted by four tendons into the four medial toes. The most medial muscle bundle and tendon is sometimes called the extensor hallucis brevis. The nerve supply comes from a branch of the peroneal nerve.

Plantar Aponeurosis.—In the sole there is a sheet of dense connective tissue called the plantar aponeurosis. At the back it is attached to the under surface of the calcaneus; in front the fibers fan out, and small branches pass to the metatarsophalangeal articulations and blend with the capsular ligaments. Other fibers pass from the deep surface of the aponeurosis between the small muscles of the foot and the long flexor tendons of the sole to attach to the deep fascia below the bones. The plantar aponeurosis helps in maintaining the stability of the foot.

Functions of Lower Limb Muscles in Standing and Walking.— In an active standing position, the gravity line of the body usually falls slightly in front of the hip joint, slightly behind the knee joint, and several centimeters in front of the ankle joint. The

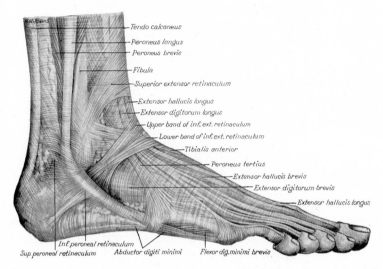

Fig. 151.—Lateral aspect of right foot. (W.R.U. 3475, male, white, aged 51 years.)

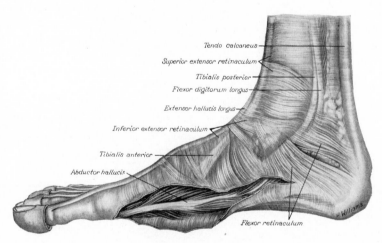

Fig. 152.—Medial aspect of right foot. (W.R.U. 3475, male, white, aged 51 years.)

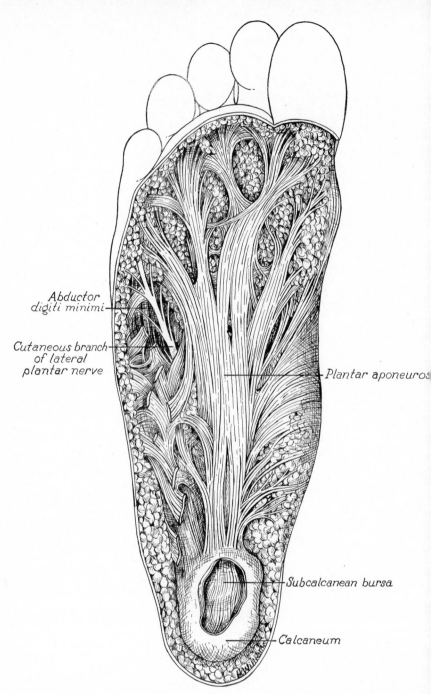

Fig. 153.—The plantar aponeurosis. (W.R.U. 3482, male, white, aged 55 years.)

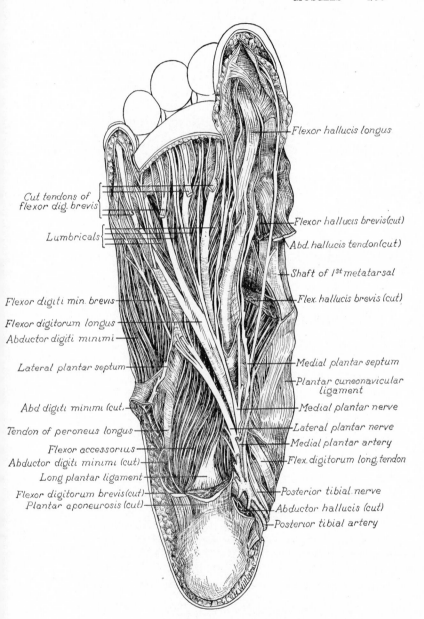

Cut tendons of
flexor dig. brevis

Lumbricals

Flexor digiti min. brevis
Flexor digitorum longus
Abductor digiti minimi

Lateral plantar septum

Abd digiti minimi (cut.

Tendon of peroneus longus

Flexor accessorius
Abductor digiti minimi (cut)
Long plantar ligament
Flexor digitorum brevis (cut)
Plantar aponeurosis (cut)

Flexor hallucis longus

Flexor hallucis brevis (cut)
Abd. hallucis tendon (cut)

Shaft of 1st metatarsal

Flex. hallucis brevis (cut)

Medial plantar septum
Plantar cuneonavicular
ligament
Medial plantar nerve
Lateral plantar nerve
Medial plantar artery
Flex. digitorum long. tendon

Posterior tibial nerve
Abductor hallucis (cut)
Posterior tibial artery

Fig. 154.—Plantar aspect of the left foot. (W.R.U. 3482, male, white,
aged 55 years.)

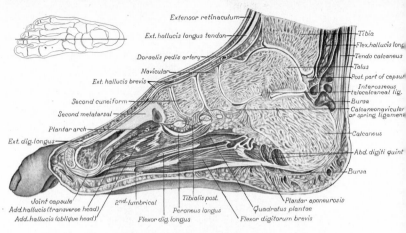

Fig. 155.—Longitudinal section through right foot. The small diagram shows the plane of the section. The drawing is of the medial surface of the lateral portion of the foot. (W.R.U. museum specimen N2.)

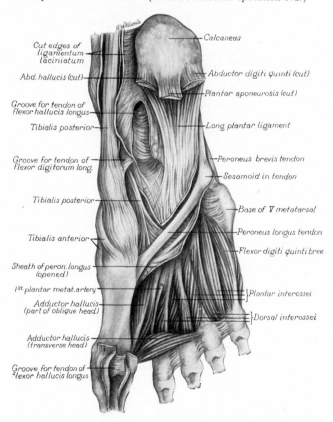

Fig. 156.—Deep muscles and ligaments of plantar aspect of right foot. (W.R.U. 3692, female, Negro, aged 45 years.)

tendency for the weight of the body to cause flexion in these joints is opposed by the pull of the extensor muscles of the hip, knee, and ankle joint. This pull is not a constant one; rather there is alternate yielding and shortening which causes the body to sway forward and backward over the base of support. Lateral balance, when both feet are on the ground, is due to the interplay of the hip joint abductors and the peroneal muscles on the outer side of the right and left legs. When the weight is supported on only one foot, the leg is stabilized on the foot by the interplay of the medial and lateral groups of lower leg muscles.

Walking involves weight-bearing and a backward-downward thrust of the propelling leg, a forward swing of the free leg, and a checking of momentum as the advanced leg strikes the floor. The propelling phase calls for contraction of the extensors of the hip, knee, and ankle joint and of the abductors of the hip joint. During this phase the force of gravity causes the body to fall forward and slightly medialward. Meanwhile the forward swing of the free leg, started by the hip joint flexors and the force of gravity, has been completed. Then the hip, knee, and ankle joint extensors and the peroneal muscles again become active in checking momentum. The hip joint abductors on the side of the advanced foot become active when the rear foot leaves the ground.

MUSCLES OF ABDOMINAL WALL

The muscles in the abdominal wall are the external oblique, internal oblique, transversus, rectus, pyramidalis, and quadratus lumborum. Together they complete that portion of the abdominal wall not formed by bone.

The external oblique muscle is a broad, thin sheet arising from the external surface of the lower eight ribs. The fibers pass downward and forward. Then the muscle fibers give way to dense fibrous tissue which forms an aponeurosis. The lower border of the muscle is attached to the iliac crest, to the anterior superior iliac spine, and to the pubic tubercle. Between the spine and the tubercle the lower border has no bony attachment but forms a dense, strong band called the inguinal (Poupart's) ligament. Above the pubis the fibers of the aponeurosis of the external oblique of each side meet in the midline to form the linea alba. . This is a white band of interlacing fibers extending from the pubis upward to the xiphoid process, thus helping to form a dense sheath covering the rectus abdominis muscle.

The umbilicus or navel is a scar in the midline, halfway between the xiphoid and symphysis pubis. At this point the umbilical cord of the fetus was attached. The fibers of the linea alba strengthen this area.

The internal oblique muscle arises from the hinder part of the iliac crest and the deep fascia of the back and from the lateral half of the inguinal ligament. Its fibers pass upward at right angles to the direction of the fibers of the external oblique. It has a fanlike, tendinous insertion into the pubic bone, the linea alba, and the lower ribs and becomes a part of the sheath for the rectus abdominis muscle. A few fibers from the inferior border of the internal oblique form loops extending downward over the spermatic cord to become the cremaster muscle.

The transversus abdominis lies deeper than the internal oblique and arises from the iliac crest, from the inguinal ligament, from the deep fascia of the back, and from the lower ribs. Its fibers pass directly forward around the abdominal wall. Below it is inserted into the pubis together with the internal oblique. This blended insertion of the two muscles is called the falx aponeurotica inguinalis (conjoined tendon). The transversus is also inserted into the linea alba and helps to form the sheath of the rectus.

The pyramidalis is inconstant and unimportant.

It is obvious that these three muscles form a triple muscular wall for the abdomen and since the fibers run in three different directions, the wall is greatly strengthened. In an appendectomy the surgeon is careful to split each muscle layer parallel to the direction of its fibers in order that the strength of the wall may be maintained (McBurney's incision).

The rectus abdominis arises from the upper border of the pubis and passes upward as a strong, heavy column of muscle to be inserted into the xiphoid and fifth, sixth, and seventh costal cartilages. There are three or four transverse bands of fibrous tissue (inscriptiones tendineae) interrupting the muscular bundles which, therefore, do not extend the full length of the muscle itself.

The sheath of the rectus abdominis muscle requires some further description. The aponeurosis of the external oblique forms a complete anterior investment. When the aponeurosis of the in-

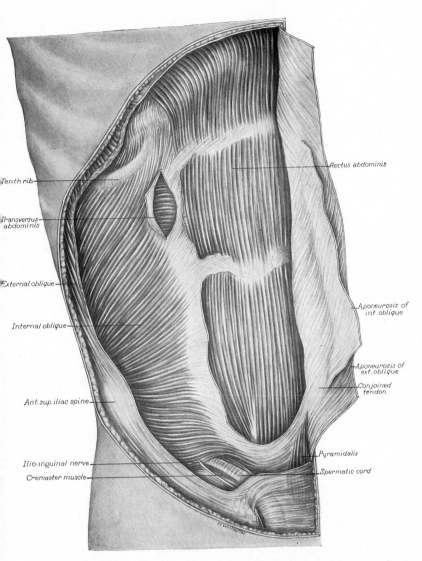

Fig. 157.—Muscles of abdominal wall.   (W.R.U. 3700, male, Negro, aged 57 years.)

ternal oblique reaches the lateral border of the rectus, it splits, and the anterior sheet blends with the aponeurosis of the external oblique and the posterior sheet passes behind the rectus to form a posterior investment. The aponeurosis of the transversus abdominis helps to form the posterior portion of the sheath. However, the superior part of the rectus lies directly upon the anterior chest wall, and there are no aponeurotic investments posteriorly. In the lowest one fourth of the rectus the entire aponeurosis of the internal oblique and transversus passes in front of the rectus and the only structure forming the posterior sheath is the anterior fascia outside the peritoneum (transversalis fascia).

The quadratus lumborum is a short, strong column of muscle arising from the hinder part of the iliac crest and transverse processes of the lower lumbar vertebrae and is inserted above into the twelfth rib and transverse processes of the upper lumbar vertebrae.

The quadratus lumborum is innervated from branches of the upper three or four lumbar nerves; the anterior muscles of the abdominal wall are innervated from the lower six thoracic nerves.

Inguinal Canal.—The inguinal canal is an oblique channel through the lower part of the anterior abdominal wall just above the inguinal ligament. In a male the spermatic cord passes through the canal, and in a female the round ligament of the uterus lies in this channel. An inguinal hernia is an outpouching of the parietal peritoneum into this canal. The pouch is gradually lengthened and finally descends into the scrotum (or labium majus). Some portion of the abdominal organs, usually the omentum or a loop of the intestine, may also be pushed downward in this peritoneal tube. In an operation for repair of inguinal hernia the surgeon re-places these structures into the abdomen and attempts to obliterate the peritoneal pouch and strengthen the abdominal wall by overlapping the ligaments, fascia, and muscles that form the canal.

As the spermatic cord passes from the anterior abdominal wall into the scrotum, it receives three investments: (1) the external spermatic fascia derived from the aponeurosis of the external oblique muscle, (2) the cremasteric fascia and cremaster muscle derived from the internal oblique muscle, and (3) the internal spermatic fascia which is continuous with the transversalis fascia.

The opening in the transversalis fascia through which the spermatic cord leaves the abdominal cavity is the internal or abdominal inguinal ring, and the opening in the inguinal ligament is the external or subcutaneous inguinal ring. In a healthy man the subcutaneous ring is barely large enough to admit the tip of the little finger.

The inguinal canal is the site where there is most frequently weakening of the abdominal wall, and hence inguinal hernias are relatively common. However, areas of weakness are occasionally found about the umbilicus, in the linea alba above the umbilicus, in the femoral canal medial to the femoral vein, and in the lumbar region in the triangle between the iliac crest, latissimus dorsi, and external oblique, in the substance of the diaphragm, and beside the obturator artery as it leaves the pelvic cavity. A hernia may occur at any of these sites.

DEEP MUSCLES OF BACK

The deep muscles of the back are very numerous and variable. They consist of overlapping series of muscular columns arising from the sacrum and lower vertebrae and inserted into higher vertebrae. Some have long fibers and extend for long distances upward; others are short and connect adjacent bones. The muscles of the back are usually divided into four groups or layers. All are innervated by the posterior rami of the spinal nerves. They extend the spinal column and produce various twisting and lateral movements of the trunk.

The first group consists of the serratus posterior superior, the serratus posterior inferior, and the splenius. The superior serratus arises from the spines of the last cervical and upper thoracic vertebrae and the fibers pass down and out to be inserted into the third, fourth, and fifth ribs. The inferior serratus arises from the spinous processes of the last two thoracic and first two lumbar vertebrae and the fibers pass laterally to be inserted into the last four ribs. These two muscles are usually very poorly developed. The splenius is a broad, flat muscle arising from the ligamentum nuchae and the spines of the upper thoracic vertebrae. The fibers radiate upward and outward to be inserted into the superior nuchal line of the occipital bone and the transverse processes of the upper cervical vertebrae.

The second layer consists of the sacrospinalis (erector spinae) which is subdivided into the iliocostalis, the longissimus, and the spinalis dorsi. The various fibers of these muscles originate near the midline and are directed up and out to be inserted into some portion of the axial skeleton above and usually extend over several intervening bones.

The third group consists of the semispinalis and the multifidus. The fibers of these muscles are shorter than those of the second group and are directed upward and inward from origin to insertion.

The fourth and deepest group consists of the obliquus capitis superior and inferior, the rectus capitis posterior major and minor, the rotatores, the interspinales, and the intertransversarii. These muscles have short fibers which originate from one member of the axial skeleton and usually pass directly upward to be inserted into the next bone above. The muscles of this group attached to the skull are also included in the next section.

MUSCLES WHICH MOVE THE HEAD

Certain of the deep muscles of the neck and upper part of the back are inserted into the occipital bone behind the foramen magnum. The more important of these are the semispinalis, rectus capitis posterior major, rectus capitis posterior minor, and obliquus capitis superior muscles. These muscles produce extension of the head on the atlas, lateral movements of the head, and rotation of the atlas on the second cervical vertebra and therefore rotation of the head from side to side.

The sternocleidomastoid muscle must also be discussed here. This muscle arises from the anterior surface of the manubrium of the sternum and from the medial portion of the clavicle and is inserted into the mastoid portion of the temporal bone. One muscle acting alone rotates the head to the opposite side and both acting together flex the head on the atlas and flex the cervical spine against resistance. The muscle is supplied from the accessory nerve.

MUSCLES OF THE PELVIS AND PERINEUM

If one studies an articulated skeleton, he sees that the sacrum and the two hip bones form a heavy ring of bone which has a large central opening.   In life the outlet of the pelvis is spanned by two fibromuscular sheets; the upper one is the pelvic diaphragm which is attached to the inner aspect of the bones forming the pelvic girdle, and the lower one is the urogenital diaphragm which is attached on either side to the conjoined ramus of pubis and ischium.

The pelvic diaphragm contains the paired levator ani and coccygeus muscles.   The levator ani muscle has two portions; the pubococcygeal part arises from the inner surface of the pubis and passes directly backward to be inserted into the coccyx, and the iliococcygeal part arises from the fascia covering the inner aspect of the obturator internus muscle and the inner surface of the spine of the ischium and is inserted into the coccyx.   The coccygeus is a fan-shaped muscle which arises from the inner surface of the ischial spine and is inserted into the side of the sacrum and coccyx.

The connective tissue above these muscles and outside the peritoneum is quite dense and contains some smooth muscle fibers. In the space between the two pubococcygeus muscles, the diaphragm is pierced by the urethra and the anal canal, and in a female, there is a third opening, the vagina.   As these structures pass through the diaphragm, each tube receives attachments from the muscles and dense fascia.   These attachments are a major support of the pelvic viscera; in addition, the muscles have a sphincteric action on the anal canal and vagina.

An understanding of the perineum is necessary in order to visualize the urogenital diaphragm.   The perineum, the lowest portion of the trunk, is a diamond-shaped area bounded on either side by the inner aspect of the thigh and extending from the symphysis of the pubis in front to the coccyx behind.   It is subdivided into an anal triangle behind and a urogenital triangle in front. The anus is located in the central portion of the anal triangle, and on either side is a pyramidal-shaped space called the ischiorectal fossa.   The lateral wall of the fossa is the fascia covering the inner surface of the obturator internus muscle; the medial wall is the fascia covering the outer or lateral surface of the levator ani muscle; the posterior wall is the fascia covering the gluteus maximus muscle.   In life the fossa is filled with fat and contains the pudendal vessels and nerves.   The sphincter ani externus is the voluntary anal sphincter surrounding the lower portion of the anal canal and anus. Some of its fibers blend with those of the levator ani, some pass into the central portion of the perineum, and others are attached to the tip of the coccyx.

The urogenital triangle contains the external genitalia and the urogenital diaphragm and is subdivided into two spaces by layers of fascia. The superior fascia of the diaphragm is just below the levator ani muscle. The inferior fascia of the diaphragm (perineal

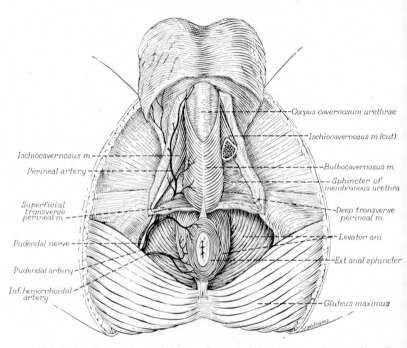

Fig. 158.—The male perineum. On the right the posterior portion of the right crus of the penis and the perineal membrane (inferior fascia of the urogenital diaphragm) have been removed to show the muscles of the urogenital diaphragm within the deep pouch. (Dissection by Dr. Frank Vecchio.)

membrane) is attached on either side to the conjoined ramus. The potential space thus formed is the deep perineal pouch and contains the deep group of perineal muscles. This group of muscles, together with the layer of fascia above and below, forms the urogenital diaphragm.

The deeper layer of fascia of the anterior abdominal wall is continued downward beneath the skin of the urogenital triangle as a thin fibrous sheet known as Colles' fascia. This sheet has firm attachments to the bone on either side and into the posterior edge of the urogenital diaphragm; it invests the scrotum and penis. The potential space between the inferior fascia of the urogenital diaphragm above and Colles' fascia below is the superficial perineal pouch. This space contains the proximal portions of the penis or clitoris and associated muscles.

The muscles of the urogenital diaphragm (in the deep pouch) are the sphincter urethrae membranaceae and transversus perinei profundus. The muscles in the superficial pouch are the transversus perinei superficialis, bulbocavernosus, and ischiocavernosus.

The sphincter of the membranous urethra arises from the inferior ramus of the pubis. Its fibers are directed inward and surround the urethra, forming the voluntary sphincter. The deep transverse perineal muscle arises from the ramus of the ischium and is inserted into the central portion of the perineum. These two muscles are not well separated from each other.

The superficial transverse perineal muscle is a small bundle which arises from the medial aspect of the ischial tuberosity and is inserted into the central point of the perineum. In a female it is usually very poorly formed. The bulbocavernosus arises from the central portion of the perineum and in a male sweeps laterally surrounding the bulb of the urethra and the corpus cavernosum urethrae to be inserted into the base of the penis. By its contraction it aids in emptying the urethra. In the female it is separated into two halves by the vagina, covers the bulb of the vestibule on either side, and acts as a sphincter of the vaginal opening. The ischiocavernosus arises from the tuberosity of the ischium, passes forward over the crus of the penis, and is inserted into the pubis and corpus cavernosum penis. In the female this muscle has the same relations but is smaller.

The muscles of the pelvis and perineum are innervated by branches from the pudendal nerve.

Other Groups of Muscles.—The muscles of the eyeball are discussed with that organ. The muscles of breathing and those associated with the larynx are discussed in the chapter on respiration; the muscles of chewing and swallowing, with the digestive system.

Table 8 contains a summary of the more important muscles. If the function of each is opposed so that it contracts against re-

Table 8
Important Muscles

NAME	ORIGIN	INSERTION	NERVE SUPPLY	FUNCTION
Sternocleido-mastoid	Clavicle and sternum	Occiput	Spinal accessory	Flexes head
Pectoralis major	Clavicle and chest wall	Humerus	Anterior thoracic	Flexes and adducts arm
Serratus anterior	Chest wall	Scapula	Long thoracic	Draws scapula forward
Trapezius	Upper vertebrae	Scapula and clavicle	Spinal accessory	Braces shoulder
Latissimus dorsi	Lower vertebrae and ilium	Humerus	Thoracodorsal	Extends and adducts arm
Deltoid	Clavicle and scapula	Humerus	Axillary	Abducts arm
Triceps brachii	Humerus and scapula	Ulna	Radial	Extends forearm
Biceps brachii	Scapula	Radius	Musculocutaneous	Flexes and supinates forearm
Flexors of forearm	Medial epicondyle of humerus, radius and ulna	Wrist and fingers	Median (and ulnar)	Flex wrist and fingers
Extensors of forearm	Lateral epicondyle of humerus, radius and ulna	Wrist and fingers	Radial	Extend wrist and fingers
Quadriceps femoris	Ilium and femur	Tibia	Femoral	Extends leg
Iliopsoas	Ilium and lumbar vertebrae	Femur	Femoral	Flexes thigh
Adductors of thigh	Ilium and pubis	Femur and tibia	Obturator	Adduct thigh
Gluteus maximus	Sacrum and ilium	Femur	Inferior gluteal	Extends thigh
Tensor fasciae latae	Ilium	Tibia	Superior gluteal	Abducts thigh
Hamstring group	Ischial tuberosity	Tibia and fibula	Sciatic	Flexes leg
Peroneus longus and brevis	Tibia and fibula	Foot	Peroneal	Plantar flex foot
Anterior tibial group	Tibia and fibula	Foot	Peroneal	Dorsiflexes foot
Posterior tibial group	Tibia and fibula	Foot	Tibial	Plantar flexes foot
Rectus abdominis	Pubis	Sternum and costal cartilages	Lower thoracic	Flexes trunk
Sacrospinalis	Vertebrae	Vertebrae and ribs	Spinal	Extends trunk

sistance, the entire muscle will become firm and may be palpated beneath the skin from origin to insertion. Nearly all the muscles in the table may be identified in this manner, and the student should study their action in his own body.

Review Questions

1. Name four large superficial muscles of the chest wall and shoulder; give one important function of each.
2. What are the bony attachments of the biceps brachii muscle? What function does this muscle perform?
3. What is the main action of the triceps brachii muscle? What is its innervation?
4. Name four muscles on the volar aspect of the forearm. What does each do? What is the innervation of each?
5. Name four muscles on the dorsal aspect of the forearm. What does each do? What is the nerve supply?
6. What muscles abduct the fingers? What muscles adduct the fingers?
7. Describe the palmar aponeurosis.
8. What is the action of the iliopsoas muscle?
9. Describe briefly the quadriceps femoris muscle. What is its most important action?
10. Name the muscles which are located on the inner aspect of the thigh. What is their nerve supply?
11. Describe briefly the gluteus maximus muscle. What is its most important action?
12. What muscles are found in the hamstring group?
13. What are the three important muscles of the front of the leg? What is their nerve supply? Give one action which is common to all three.
14. Describe briefly the gastrocnemius muscle. Why is it so large in man?
15. Name the muscles which form the abdominal wall.
16. What is the inguinal canal? What passes through it in a male? What passes through it in a female?
17. What forms the pelvic diaphragm?

unit 3   **INTEGRATIVE MECHANISMS**

1, What constituted the
   nervous system?

2, Define autonomic N.S.
   Central N.S.; Peripheral N.S.

3, Describe Atypical Nerve

4, Tell difference between
      a motor Nerve &
      Sensory Nerve.

Where is the peripheral
   Nerve, Siatic N,
   Vagus N.

Name sub-division of
   brain.

What is one important
   function of
      cerebellum,

Where is the gray matter
   of cord located.

In an adult the spinal
cord extends between what
two vertebal levels,

CHAPTER 7

THE NERVOUS SYSTEM

The nervous system consists of the brain, spinal cord, and peripheral nerves. There are thirty-one pairs of spinal nerves and twelve pairs of cranial nerves. These connect all areas of the body with the central system. Certain branches of these forty-three nerves are connected through outlying collections of nerve cells or ganglia with the viscera, glands, and smooth muscle of blood vessels. These ganglia and their nerve fibers form the autonomic nervous system.

PERIPHERAL NERVOUS SYSTEM

In early fetal life the spinal cord occupies the entire length of the spinal canal. A nerve trunk passes out on each side through a corresponding intervertebral foramen. To the seven cervical nerves thus identified is added one which passes out on each side between the occiput and the first cervical vertebra; hence, there are eight pairs of cervical nerves. There are twelve thoracic, five lumbar, and five sacral nerves on either side. With the addition of the single pair of coccygeal nerves the total is thirty-one. That portion of the cord which corresponds and gives origin to a pair of nerves is known as a segment. There are therefore thirty-one segments in all.

During later fetal life and in childhood the vertebral canal lengthens much more than the spinal cord, so that ultimately the spinal cord terminates at the level of the disc between the first and second lumbar vertebrae.

In the upper cervical region the spinal nerves run horizontally from the cord to the intervertebral foramina, but because of the disparity in length between the spinal cord and spinal canal, the lower nerves pass obliquely from the cord to the foramina. Below the disc between the first and second lumbar vertebrae, the spinal cord having terminated, the lowest nerves form a sheaf called, because of its resemblance to a horse's tail, the cauda equina.

In a lumbar puncture the operator pushes the needle through the ligaments between the neural arches of the third and fourth, or fourth and fifth, lumbar vertebrae. This site is chosen because it is below the level of the spinal cord, and there is a comparatively wide space between the successive laminae. Furthermore, the puncture is made in the midline where the available interlaminar space is greatest.

A Typical Nerve.—All spinal nerves are constructed upon a common plan: two roots on each side, an anterior root and a posterior root, attach the nerve to the spinal cord. The posterior or dorsal root possesses a small swelling or ganglion containing nuclei of sensory nerve cells. The anterior or ventral root has no ganglion.

The anterior root of every spinal nerve is composed of motor nerve fibers coming from nerve cells which lie within the spinal cord. Such a cell body with its processes is an efferent neuron. These fibers carry motor impulses to the muscles innervated by that nerve. The posterior root contains sensory nerve fibers which pass from the nerve cells in the dorsal ganglion, and these are afferent pathways. These fibers carry impulses from the peripheral distribution of that nerve whether it be skin or underlying tissues. Sensory receptors for temperature, touch, and pain are located in the skin. Sensory receptors in the deeper structures such as muscles and tendons, and joint capsules are for vibration, pain, position, and tension. The sensations which arise from stimuli within the body are just as important as those arising from external stimuli, although we are not usually as conscious of them. All sensory impulses enter the cord through the dorsal root and ganglion. The two roots unite in the intervertebral foramen to form a common trunk. Just outside the foramen the trunk divides into a posterior ramus and an anterior ramus. The anterior ramus is usually much the larger. The posterior ramus divides into medial and lateral divisions or branches. The anterior ramus also divides into lateral and medial divisions or branches.

A nerve trunk contains both sensory and motor fibers. The cutaneous branches are typically sensory; the muscular branches must carry motor fibers but, in addition, include many sensory fibers conveying sense of position and muscle tension.

The spinal nerves, from the second thoracic to the twelfth thoracic inclusive, follow the pattern of a typical nerve. They lie in the substance of the body wall between the ribs and send motor branches to intercostal muscles and sensory branches to the skin.

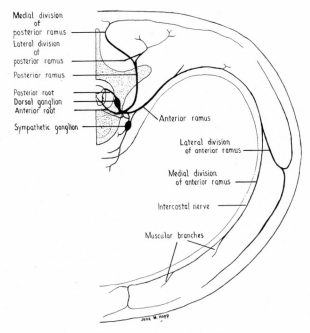

Fig. 159.—A typical spinal nerve.

The remaining spinal nerves require further description. The anterior rami of the upper four cervical nerves (cervical plexus) innervate the anterior region of the neck; the anterior rami of the lower four cervical and first thoracic nerves (brachial plexus) are reserved for the innervation of the upper extremity; the anterior rami of the lumbar and upper four sacral nerves (lumbosacral plexus) are used for the innervation of the lower extremity; the anterior rami of the fifth sacral and coccygeal nerves (coccygeal plexus) innervate the perineal region.

Cervical Plexus.—The anterior rami of the first four cervical nerves form the cervical plexus from which the following three groups of nerves arise:

1. Three ascending sensory branches: the lesser occipital, the great auricular, and the anterior cutaneous nerve of the neck.

2. Three descending sensory branches: the anterior, middle, and posterior supraclavicular nerves.

3. Branches to numerous neck muscles: communicating branches to phrenic, vagus, accessory, and hypoglossal nerves.

Fig. 160 is a simple diagram of the cervical plexus. The first cervical nerve usually has no sensory fibers and therefore no dorsal ganglion. The second and third cervical nerves carry sensory fibers from the back of the scalp, from the region behind and below the ear, and from the front of the neck below the mandible. The fourth cervical nerve has sensory fibers from the lower portions of the neck down to the level of the collar bone and from the skin of the upper portion of the shoulder. Fibers arise from the anterior rami and go directly to the deep muscles lying in front of the cervical vertebrae. Some fibers also go to the sternocleido-mastoid and trapezius muscles, but the chief nerve supply for these two muscles is from the accessory nerve. From a loop between the first and second cervical nerves motor fibers go to the rectus capitis lateralis and rectus capitus anterior. Other fibers from this loop are, for a time, incorporated within the sheath of the hypo-glossal nerve and therefore are known as the descendens hypoglossi. This nerve is motor to the geniohyoid and thyrohyoid muscles and sends fibers to the ansa hypoglossi. From a loop between the second and third cervical nerves comes the descendens cervicalis which unites with the descendens hypoglossi to form the ansa hypoglossi from which are innervated the sternohyoid, sternothyroid, and omohyoid muscles. Some nerve fibers from the upper cervical segments of the cord pass upward through the foramen magnum into the skull and back out through the jugular foramen as the spinal portion of the eleventh cranial nerve.

The phrenic nerve supplies the diaphragm, which in early embryonic life lies in the cervical region. This nerve arises from the third, fourth, and fifth cervical nerves but derives most of its fibers from the fourth.   In the neck it lies upon the anterior scalene muscle and is accessible to the surgeon in this position, where he may cut or remove the nerve in order to paralyze the diaphragm in treatment of certain diseases of the chest.

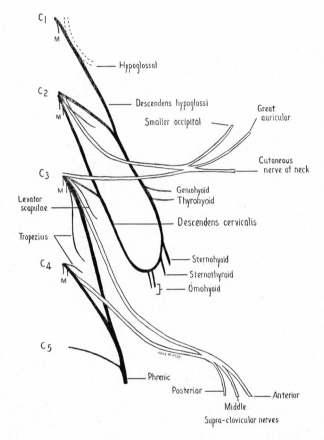

Fig. 160.—Left cervical plexus.   The cutaneous branches are drawn in black outline and the muscular branches in solid black.   Fibers labeled *M* go to deep muscles of neck.

The posterior rami of the upper four cervical nerves supply the deep muscles of the back of the neck.   The second, third, and fourth have sensory fibers from the back of the neck and skull in the greater and third occipital nerves.

Brachial Plexus.—The four lower cervical nerves and the first thoracic nerve supply the arm. After their emergence from the intervertebral foramina, anterior rami of these five nerves undergo an interweaving, known as the brachial plexus, from which originate the various nerves supplying the shoulder and arm. In Fig. 161 is shown a diagram of this plexus. There are three cords, named from their relation to the brachial artery, one lateral, one medial, and one posterior.

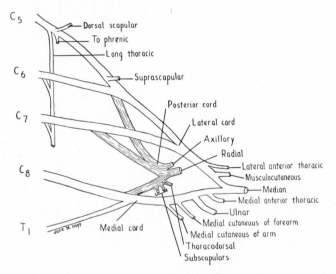

Fig. 161.—Left brachial plexus. The posterior cord and branches are shaded.

The nerves arising from the brachial plexus are the following:

1. The suprascapular and dorsal scapular nerves course over the scapula to supply muscles attached to the superficial aspect of that bone.

2. The medial and lateral anterior thoracic nerves, penetrating the costocoracoid membrane or the pectoralis minor, supply that muscle and the pectoralis major.

3. The long thoracic nerve runs down the anterior chest wall to the serratus anterior muscle.

4. The thoracodorsal nerve and two subscapular nerves pass downward and backward through the armpit (axilla). The former

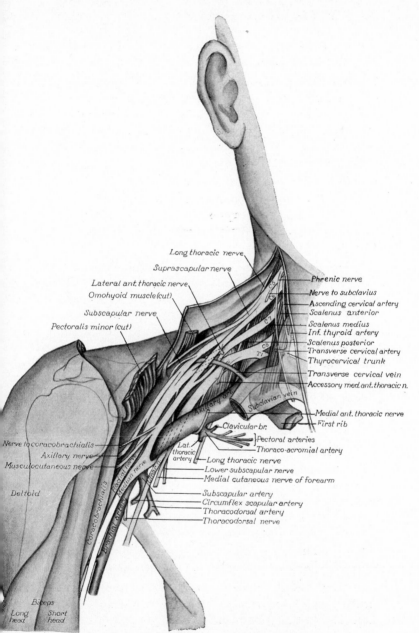

Fig. 162.—Right brachial plexus. In this specimen there were two medial anterior thoracic nerves; no medial cutaneous nerve of the arm could be found. Minor variations from the typical pattern are very common. (W.R.U. 3320, male, white, aged 87 years).

supplies the latissimus dorsi muscle and the latter supply the sub-scapularis and the teres major muscles.

5. The axillary (circumflex) nerve supplies the deltoid and teres minor muscles and is also distributed to the skin over the deltoid muscle. After the axillary nerve arises from the posterior cord of the brachial plexus it passes backward around the shaft of the humerus just below the tuberosities, enters the deltoid on the deep surface of the muscle, and is accompanied by the posterior humeral circumflex artery.

6. The musculocutaneous nerve supplies the muscles of the front of the upper arm, the biceps brachii, coracobrachialis, and brachialis. It is the sensory supply for the skin on the outer side of the forearm.

7. The ulnar nerve supplies the flexor carpi ulnaris and part of the flexor digitorum profundus in the forearm. It supplies the muscles of the hand except the lumbricals for the second and third fingers, and the opponens, flexor, and abductor of the thumb. It is sensory to the medial side of the hand, the little finger, and the medial (ulnar) half of the fourth finger. The ulnar nerve is rather superficial where it passes behind the medial epicondyle of the humerus and when hit in this position gives rise to a sensation of pin and needle pricks in the area of its sensory distribution.

8. The median nerve supplies the remaining muscles of the front of the forearm and hand. Its cutaneous fibers are distributed to the volar surface of the thumb, index, and middle fingers.

9. The radial nerve winds around the back of the humerus, supplying the triceps in its course. It also supplies all the muscles on the back of the forearm and sends sensory branches to the skin on the back of the forearm and hand. As the radial nerve passes around the humerus, it is accompanied by the profunda artery of the arm. The nerve lies very close to the humerus and may be seriously injured in fracture of the midshaft of the bone.

10. The medial cutaneous nerve of the upper arm and the medial cutaneous nerve of the forearm have sensory fibers for the inner side of the upper arm and forearm respectively.

In Fig. 163 the distribution of these nerves is portrayed in outline drawings of the upper extremity. The cutaneous branches which bring impulses giving rise to sensations of pain, touch, and

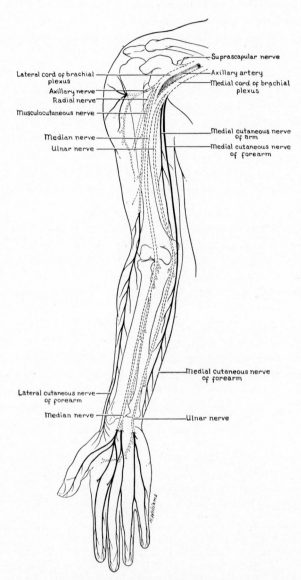

Fig. 163.—Nerves of the right arm. Cutaneous branches are shown in solid black; deeper branches are shown in dotted outline.

temperature pass inward to the cord; the muscular branches carry nerve impulses outward from the cord to the muscles. They do, however, also bring to the cord sensory impulses for pressure, position, vibration and muscle tension.

The posterior rami of the lower four cervical nerves and the first thoracic nerve are smaller than the anterior rami and send branches to the deep muscles of the upper part of the back and to the skin over them.

Lumbosacral Plexus.—The anterior rami of the five lumbar and upper four sacral nerves form a plexus which gives rise to nerves supplying the lower limb and perineum (Fig. 164).

The following are the nerves originating in the lumbosacral plexus:

1. The iliohypogastric nerve is sensory to the anterior abdominal wall and sends motor fibers to muscles of the same area.

2. The ilioinguinal nerve is sensory to the anterior abdominal wall and external genitalia and has motor fibers for muscles of the abdominal wall. The iliohypogastric and ilioinguinal nerves may be fused.

3. The genitofemoral nerve is sensory to the skin of the inguinal area and the external genitalia.

4. The lateral cutaneous nerve of the thigh is sensory to the outer side of the thigh.

5. The femoral nerve is motor to the quadriceps, sartorius, pectineus, and iliacus muscles and sensory both to the front of the thigh and to the inner side of the leg below the knee (saphenous nerve).

6. The obturator nerve is motor to the adductor muscles of the inner or medial portion of the thigh.

7. The tibial nerve (medial popliteal) is motor to the muscles and sensory to the skin of the calf of the leg and to the sole of the foot.

8. The peroneal nerve (lateral popliteal) is motor to the muscles which evert and dorsiflex the foot and sensory to the outer side of the leg and dorsal surface of the foot. The peroneal nerve is quite near the surface as it passes lateral to the neck of the fibula; it is frequently injured when a person falls sideways and may be severely damaged in this location by pressure from a plaster cast which is too tight.

The sural or medial cutaneous nerve of the leg is formed from sensory branches of the tibial and peroneal nerves and is sensory to the calf of the leg and lateral side of the foot.

9. The nerve to the hamstring muscles is motor to the muscles of the back of the thigh.

The three nerves just named, tibial, peroneal, and nerve to the hamstrings, are usually enclosed in a common sheath in the upper thigh. Thus is constituted the sciatic nerve which emerges through

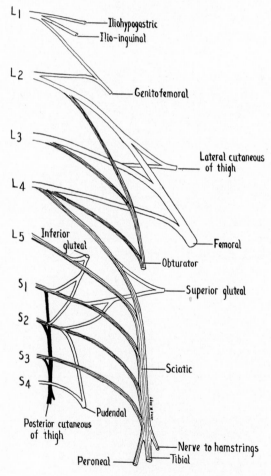

Fig. 164.—Left lumbosacral plexus.

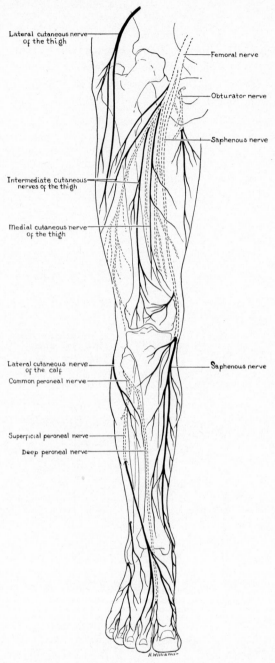

Lateral cutaneous nerve of the thigh

Femoral nerve

Obturator nerve

Saphenous nerve

Intermediate cutaneous nerves of the thigh

Medial cutaneous nerve of the thigh

Lateral cutaneous nerve of the calf

Common peroneal nerve

Saphenous nerve

Superficial peroneal nerve

Deep peroneal nerve

H. Williams.

Fig. 165.—Nerves of front of right lower extremity. Cutaneous branches are shown in solid black; deeper branches are shown in dotted outline.

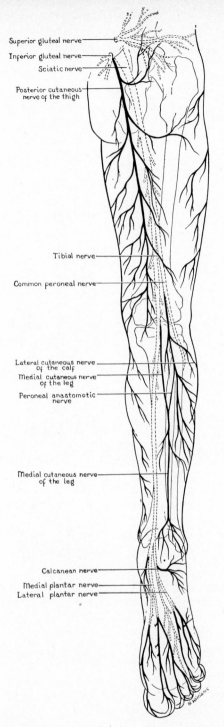

Superior gluteal nerve

Inferior gluteal nerve

Sciatic nerve

Posterior cutaneous
nerve of the thigh

Tibial nerve

Common peroneal nerve

Lateral cutaneous nerve
of the calf

Medial cutaneous nerve
of the leg

Peroneal anastomotic
nerve

Medial cutaneous nerve
of the leg

Calcanean nerve

Medial plantar nerve

Lateral plantar nerve

Fig. 166.—Nerves of back of right lower extremity. Cutaneous branches
are shown in solid black; deeper branches are shown in dotted outline.

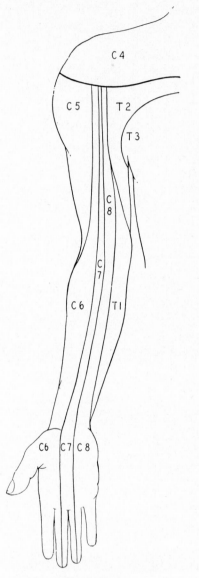

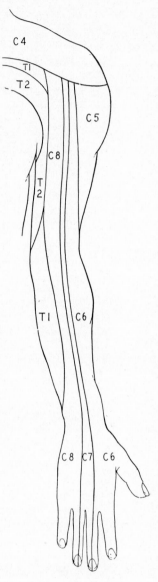

Fig. 167.—Segmental sensory distribution to front of arm. *C*, Cervical segments; *T*, thoracic segments. (After Collier and Purves-Stewart.)

Fig. 168.—Segmental sensory distribution to back of arm. *C*, Cervical segments; *T*, thoracic segments. (After Collier and Purves-Stewart.)

the greater sciatic foramen and passes down the back of the thigh for a short distance before splitting into its component parts.   The sciatic is the largest nerve of the body.

10. The superior and inferior gluteal nerves are motor to the muscles of the buttock and the tensor fasciae latae muscle.

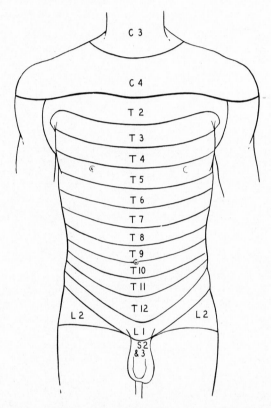

Fig. 169.—Sensory distribution to front of torso. *C,* Cervical; *T,* thoracic; *L,* lumbar; *S,* sacral segments.   (After Collier and Purves-Stewart.)

11. The posterior cutaneous nerve of the thigh is sensory to the skin of the buttock, back of thigh, and leg.

12. The pudendal nerve is motor to the muscles and sensory to the skin of the perineum.

Figs. 165 and 166 are outlines of the lower limb to show the distribution of the nerves.

236 INTEGRATIVE MECHANISMS

Frequently for purposes of description the lumbosacral plexus is divided into three parts: the lumbar, sacral, and pudendal. The lumbar plexus includes the anterior rami of the upper three lumbar nerves and that part of the anterior ramus of the fourth lumbar nerve that goes to the femoral and obturator nerves. The sacral plexus is formed from the rest of the anterior ramus of the fourth lumbar nerve, the anterior rami of the fifth lumbar and first sacral nerves, and part of the anterior rami of the second and

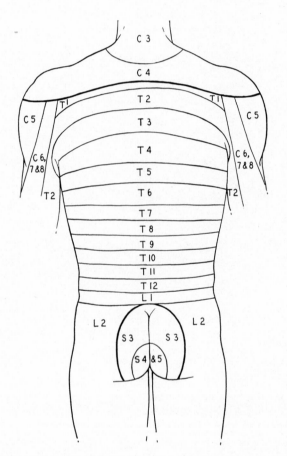

Fig. 170.—Sensory distribution to nerves of back of torso. *C,* Cervical segments; *T,* thoracic segments; *L,* lumbar segments; *S,* sacral segments. (After Collier and Purves-Stewart.)

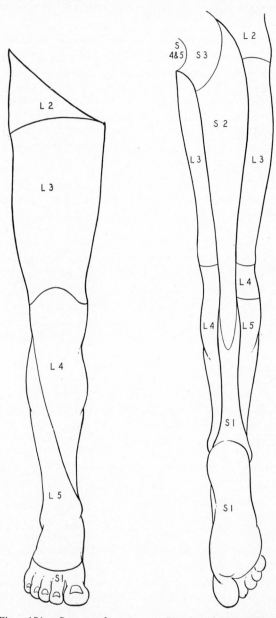

Fig. 171.—Segmental sensory distribution to front of lower extremity. *L*, Lumbar segments; *S*, sacral segments. (After Collier and Purves-Stewart.)

Fig. 172.—Segmental sensory distribution to back of lower extremity. *L*, Lumbar segments; *S*, sacral segments. (After Collier and Purves-Stewart.)

third sacral nerves. The remaining parts of the anterior rami of the second and third sacral nerves and part of the anterior ramus of the fourth sacral nerve form the pudendal plexus.

Coccygeal Plexus.—The coccygeal plexus is formed from the anterior rami of the fifth sacral and the coccygeal nerves and a part of the anterior ramus of the fourth sacral nerve. It sends fibers to the coccygeus and levator ani muscles and receives fibers from the skin over the coccyx.

The posterior rami of the lumbar, sacral, and coccygeal nerves supply the deep muscles of the lower part of the back, the skin of the small of the back, and the medial portion of the buttocks.

Segmental Sensory Distribution.—All of the sensory nerves from a given skin area ultimately come into a specific segment of the spinal cord, although they may pass inward from the surface along more than one nerve. This fact is of great importance when a physician is attempting to determine the exact site of an injury to or a disease of the spinal cord. The segmental distribution of the various segments of the spinal cord is shown in Figs. 167 to 172.

CRANIAL NERVES

There are twelve pairs of nerves attached to the brain stem. These emerge through special foramina in the skull. Named in order, beginning with the most anterior, they are:

1. Olfactory nerve—sensory
2. Optic nerve—sensory
3. Oculomotor nerve—motor (parasympathetic)
4. Trochlear nerve—motor
5. Trigeminal nerve—motor, sensory
6. Abducent nerve—motor
7. Facial nerve—motor, sensory (parasympathetic)
8. Acoustic nerve—sensory
9. Glossopharyngeal nerve—motor, sensory (parasympathetic)
10. Vagus nerve—motor, sensory (parasympathetic)
11. Accessory nerve—motor
12. Hypoglossal nerve—motor

Olfactory Nerve.—The nerve of smell arises by a number of fine bundles from the olfactory area situated in the nasal cavity, partly on the upper portion of the septum and partly on the superior concha or turbinate. In each nostril there are about twenty nerve bundles which pass through the cribrifrom plate of the ethmoid bone into the olfactory bulb. Relays of fibers carry sensory impulses back along the olfactory tract to the substance of the cerebrum.

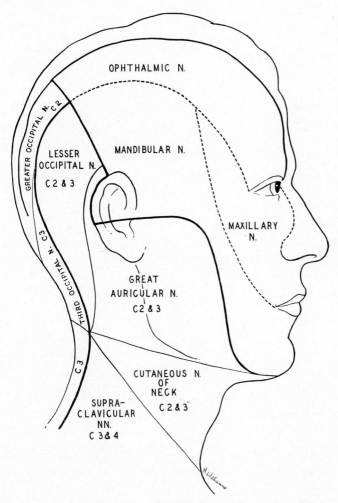

Fig. 173.—Sensory distribution to head and face, side view. *C,* Cervical segments.

Optic Nerve.—The nerve of sight arises from cells in the retina of the eye. The nerve emerges from the back of the eyeball and passes into the skull through the optic foramen, after which it joins the nerve from the other eye at the optic chiasm. Here the fibers from the nasal half of each retina cross over to the other side. The fibers from the temporal half of each retina do not cross

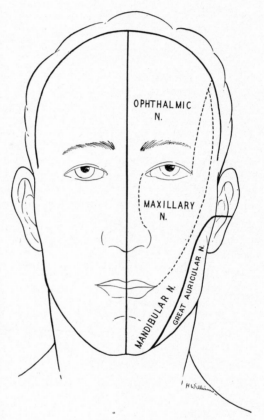

Fig. 174.—Sensory distribution to face, front view.

but continue in the optic tract of the same side. From the chiasm the optic tracts carry the sensory impulses of vision to the brain stem, and eventually the fibers reach the visual cortex at the back of the occipital lobe. In reality the retina is an outgrowth of a portion of the brain wall, and the optic nerve is the distal part of a brain tract whose cells of origin lie in the retina and whose fibers end in the brain stem.   The optic nerve is covered by three sheaths derived from the three coverings of the brain.   The outer sheath, which is a prolongation of the dura mater, is quite dense and fibrous, and blends with the sclera of the eyeball.

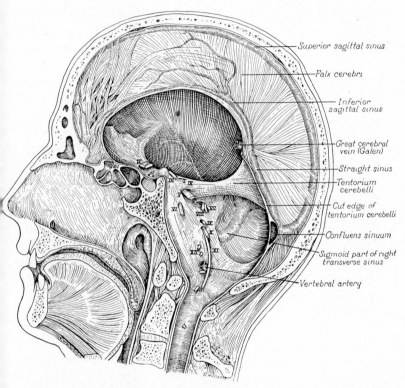

Fig. 175.—Sagittal section of head showing medial aspect of right half of skull.   The brain and spinal cord have been removed but the dura mater has been left intact.   Cranial nerves II to XII are shown at their point of exit from the cranial cavity.

Oculomotor Nerve.—The oculomotor nerve arises from the under surface of the brain stem in front of the pons, passes forward into the orbit through the superior orbital fissure, and supplies the levator palpebrae superioris muscle, superior rectus, medial rectus, inferior rectus, and inferior oblique muscles of the eyeball.   If this nerve is damaged, the upper lid droops, and the eyeball has a downward and outward cast; inward, upward, and directly downward movements of the eyeball are impossible. The oculomotor nerve also supplies the smooth muscles of the iris and ciliary body (cranial autonomic outflow). If these fibers are destroyed, the pupil remains widely dilated and there is difficulty in accommodation for near and far vision.

Trochlear Nerve.—The trochlear nerve arises from the dorsal surface of the midbrain, passes around the side of the brain stem and then forward into the orbit through the superior orbital fissure to supply the superior oblique muscle of the eye. If this muscle is paralyzed, the eyeball has an upward and outward cast.

Trigeminal Nerve.—The trigeminal nerve has two roots, a sensory and a motor, attached close together to the side of the pons. On the sensory root as it passes laterally into the middle fossa of the skull there is a large ganglion called the semilunar (Gasserian) ganglion. There are three large sensory branches bringing fibers into this ganglion: (1) the ophthalmic, bringing sensory impressions from the orbit, upper eyelid, bridge of the nose, and scalp as far as the crown of the head; (2) the maxillary, bringing sensory impressions from the lower eyelid, the lower portions of the nose, the cheek, upper lip, jaw, and palate; and (3) the mandibular, bringing sensory impressions from the lower lip and jaw, tongue, lower part of the face, and front of the ear. The ophthalmic nerve passes through the superior orbital fissure, the maxillary through the foramen rotundum, and the mandibular through the foramen ovale.

The motor root of the trigeminal lies beneath the semilunar ganglion and is continued into the mandibular nerve as it emerges through the foramen ovale. The motor fibers go to the muscles of mastication, namely, the internal and external pterygoid muscles, the masseter muscle, and the temporal muscle. For this reason the motor part of the trigeminal is frequently called the masticator nerve. The motor root also supplies two muscles in the neck, the anterior belly of the digastric and the mylohyoid, and the tensor veli palatini and tensor tympani muscles in the pharynx. The latter two are supplied by fibers from the branch going to the internal pterygoid muscle.

The fifth nerve carries sensory fibers for heat, cold, pain, and touch but not for taste.

Abducent Nerve.—This nerve arises from the under surface of the brain stem just behind the pons, and passes forward through the superior orbital fissure to supply the lateral rectus muscle of the eyeball. If this nerve is damaged, there is an internal squint (toward the nose).

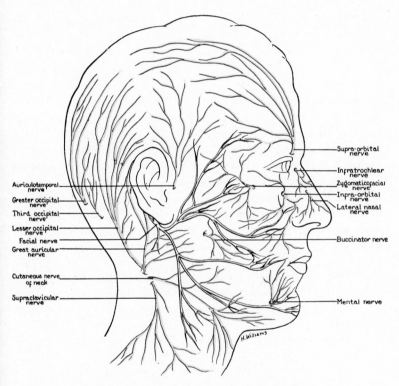

Auriculotemporal nerve

Greater occipital nerve

Third occipital nerve

Lesser occipital nerve

Facial nerve

Great auricular nerve

Cutaneous nerve of neck

Supraclavicular nerve

Supra-orbital nerve

Infratrochlear nerve

Zygomaticofacial nerve

Infra-orbital nerve

Lateral nasal nerve

Buccinator nerve

Mental nerve

H. Williams

PLATE 5.—Nerves of the face and head. Sensory nerves in yellow; facial nerve in black outline.

Facial Nerve.—This nerve arises from the side of the brain stem just behind the pons very close to the origin of the eighth nerve. Together with the latter, the seventh nerve enters the internal acoustic meatus. It then continues through the facial canal, passes over the inner ear, changes its direction to course downward in the mastoid process, and emerges through the stylomastoid foramen. Its fibers are then distributed to the muscles of expression.

If the facial nerve is damaged, paralysis of muscles on that side of the face results in a masklike expression. The eyelid on the affected side cannot be closed voluntarily and the corner of the mouth droops. The facial nerve is also motor to the posterior belly of the digastric muscle, the stylohyoid muscle, and the stapedius muscle.

Within its sheath the facial nerve, essentially motor, also carries sensory fibers from the taste buds of the anterior two-thirds of the tongue. These sensory fibers have their nuclei in the geniculate ganglion which is a small oval swelling present on the facial nerve in the facial canal. The sensory fibers reach the nerve in the facial canal by a branch called the chorda tympani, which crosses the middle ear cavity in its course from the mandibular nerve to the facial. The fibers leave the facial nerve by the pars intermedia to join the eighth nerve at its entrance to the brain stem. Pars intermedia and chorda tympani are successive parts of a single visceral nerve conveying secretory fibers (cranial autonomic outflow) to the submaxillary and sublingual salivary glands in addition to sensory fibers from the taste buds. Other secretory fibers of the pars intermedia reach the lacrimal gland and glands of the nasal mucosa by a complicated pathway.

Acoustic Nerve.—The acoustic nerve has two distinct sensory parts: vestibular and auditory. Vestibular fibers arise in cells located within the semicircular canals which are organs of balance intimately associated with the inner ear and located within the petrous part of the temporal bone. The auditory fibers arise from the hair cells of the organ of Corti which is the essential receptive organ of hearing located within the cochlea of the inner ear. These two parts, enclosed in a single sheath, form the acoustic nerve which emerges from the petrous portion of the temporal bone and reaches the brain stem behind the pons.

Glossopharyngeal Nerve.—The glossopharyngeal nerve joins the side of the medulla just behind the eighth nerve and in front of the tenth nerve. It passes out of the skull through the jugular foramen into the neck. The trunk has two swellings, the jugular (superior) and petrous (inferior) ganglia, which are analogous to the dorsal root ganglia of spinal nerves. It carries motor fibers to the stylopharyngeus. Fibers from the ninth, tenth, and eleventh cranial nerves and from the superior cervical ganglion of the sympathetic send branches to the side wall of the pharynx where the pharyngeal plexus is formed. All the muscles of the pharynx and soft palate (except stylopharyngeus, tensor tympani, and tensor veli palatini) are innervated from this plexus. It also carries sensory fibers from the mucosa of the pharynx and back of the tongue. There is a component conveying sensory fibers from the taste buds of the back of the tongue and secretory fibers to the parotid gland (cranial autonomic outflow). This nerve receives important sensory fibers by way of the carotid ramus, from the carotid sinus and carotid body; these fibers are very important in reflexes controlling blood pressure.

Vagus Nerve.—The vagus nerve arises from the side of the medulla just behind the ninth nerve and leaves the skull through the jugular foramen. There are two ganglia, the jugular (superior) and nodose (inferior), which are analogous to the dorsal root ganglia of spinal nerves. Immediately after it enters the neck it is joined by a large branch from the eleventh cranial nerve carrying motor fibers which are distributed to muscles of the larynx and pharynx (pharyngeal plexus). The vagus has sensory fibers from the mucosa of the larynx and also a few from the external ear. The visceral fibers of the vagus are distributed to the heart, lungs, bronchi, esophagus, stomach, and intestine (cranial autonomic outflow).

Accessory Nerve.—The accessory nerve has two portions: the cranial arising from the medulla behind the vagus, and the spinal from the upper five or six cervical segments in the cord. The nerve passes through the jugular foramen where its cranial portion joins the vagus and is distributed to the muscles of the larynx and pharynx (pharyngeal plexus).

The spinal portion forms a nerve trunk which passes through the foramen magnum to enter a common sheath with the part arising from the medulla. On emerging through the jugular foramen the spinal fibers are distributed to the sternocleidomastoid and trapezius muscles.

Hypoglossal Nerve.—The hypoglossal nerve arises from the medulla posterior to the eleventh nerve, leaves the skull through the hypoglossal canal, and supplies the muscles of the tongue.

AUTONOMIC NERVOUS SYSTEM

The innervation of smooth muscle, cardiac muscle, and glands has been discussed under various names which include autonomic, vegetative, visceral, involuntary, and sympathetic systems. Its special features are ganglia, nerve trunks, and plexuses. The ganglia of the autonomic nervous system are an integral part of the involuntary outflow from the central nervous system and must be differentiated from the dorsal root ganglia described earlier, which are sensory. Structurally and functionally the autonomic nervous system consists of two portions, a craniosacral part and a thoracolumbar part. The craniosacral involuntary outflow is frequently called the parasympathetic system, and the thoracolumbar outflow the sympathetic system (in its restricted sense).

Thoracolumbar Outflow.—On each side of the vertebral column there lies a chain of ganglia connected with each other by short nerve trunks. The chain begins below the base of the skull, with the large, superior cervical ganglion, and extends downward through the neck, thoracic cavity, and abdominal cavity into the pelvic cavity where each chain ends by joining its fellow in a very small ganglion, the ganglion impar, lying on the anterior surface of the coccyx. There are usually three cervical ganglia on each side, but in the thoracic, lumbar, and sacral regions there is typically a ganglion associated with each spinal nerve. However in the lumbar and sacral regions the number of ganglia is quite variable. The entire chain is frequently called the paravertebral ganglionated trunk.

A typical thoracic nerve is connected with its autonomic ganglion by means of white and gray rami. In the white ramus are myelinated nerve fibers which come from cells located within the spinal cord and are known as preganglionic fibers. The preganglionic fibers synapse with the processes of nerve cells located in the autonomic (sympathetic) ganglion. The gray ramus contains fibers which come from the ganglion cells and are known as postganglionic fibers. The thoracic spinal nerves and the upper two lumbar spinal nerves have white rami, and since the white rami come only from these segments of the spinal cord, this part of the autonomic nervous system is called the thoracolumbar outflow.

However not all the white rami associated with a given spinal nerve end in the autonomic ganglion attached to that nerve. In the upper thoracic region many white rami turn upward in the ganglionated chain to synapse in the cervical ganglia. In the middle and lower thoracic regions many white rami pass out along certain nerve trunks, the splanchnic nerves, to ganglia located in

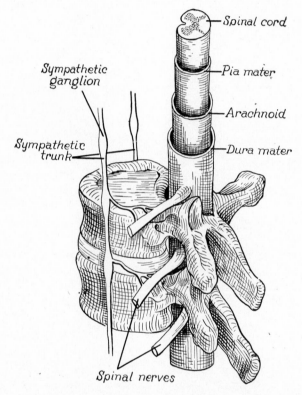

Fig. 176.—Diagram of the spinal cord showing its coverings and connections with sympathetic ganglia. (From Anthony: Textbook of Anatomy and Physiology, St. Louis, 1946, The C. V. Mosby Co.)

plexuses near the origin of the great arteries which supply the abdominal viscera. These are the celiac ganglion, the superior mesenteric ganglion, and the inferior mesenteric ganglion, or collectively, the collateral ganglia. From the lower thoracic and lumbar regions certain other white rami turn down in the ganglionated chain to synapse in the lower lumbar and sacral ganglia.

All the ganglia give rise to many gray rami. The gray rami from
a single paravertebral ganglion may go to several peripheral
nerves, either spinal or cranial. Also gray rami frequently travel
along the course of blood vessels; this is particularly true of the
superior cervical ganglion which sends rami along the branches of
the carotid artery, and of the rami from the collateral ganglia
which travel along the visceral arteries within the abdomen.

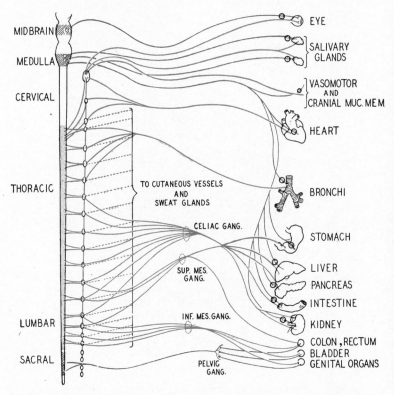

PLATE 6.—The autonomic nervous system. Craniosacral outflow in blue
lines. Thoracolumbar outflow to cutaneous vessels and sweat glands in dotted red lines and to other structures in solid red lines. (After Meyer and
Gottlieb.)

A single white ramus bringing efferent impulses from a cell in a
given spinal segment of the spinal cord synapses with a number
of ganglion cells located in one or more autonomic (sympathetic)
ganglia, and in turn the gray rami from these cells have a wide-

spread distribution. For example, impulses originating in the first thoracic segment of the spinal cord go to sweat glands, pilomotor muscles, and the smooth muscle of blood vessels of the head, as well as to certain specific smooth muscles within the eyeball.

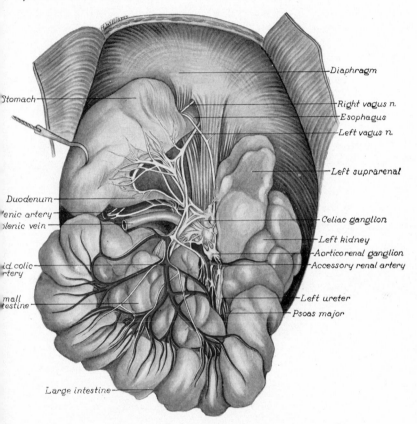

PLATE 7.—Celiac plexus. The stomach has been turned up and to the right and the transverse colon has been pulled downward. (Dissection by Dr. R. W. Machamer.) (W.R.U. E1946, term fetus.)

The distribution of the thoracolumbar outflow is shown by red lines in Plate 6.

From the cervical ganglia many nerve fibers pass to the blood vessels associated with the head, thus forming numerous small plexuses. From the thoracic ganglia, fibers are given off which form esophageal, pulmonary, and cardiac plexuses. Many fibers from the vagus nerve are intermingled in the thoracic plexuses.

The superficial cardiac plexus is small and is located below the arch of the aorta. The deep cardiac plexus is larger and has two halves, one lying on either side of the aorta and trachea. The pulmonary and coronary plexuses are a continuation of the deep cardiac plexus. Below the deep cardiac plexus the two vagus

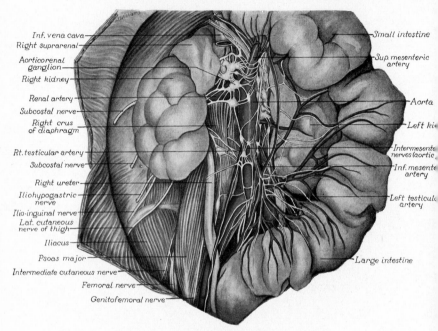

Inf. vena cava
Right suprarenal
Aorticorenal ganglion
Right kidney
Renal artery
Subcostal nerve
Right crus of diaphragm
Rt. testicular artery
Subcostal nerve
Right ureter
Iliohypogastric nerve
Ilio-inguinal nerve
Lat. cutaneous nerve of thigh
Iliacus
Psoas major
Intermediate cutaneous nerve
Femoral nerve
Genitofemoral nerve

Small intestine
Sup. mesenteric artery
Aorta
Left ki[]
Intermesente[] nerves (aortic[]
Inf. mesente[] artery
Left testicul[] artery
Large intestine

PLATE 8.—Inferior and superior mesenteric plexuses. The posterior parietal peritoneum and inferior vena cava have been removed. (Dissection by Dr. R. W. Machamer.) (W.R.U. E1946, term fetus.)

nerves leave the plexus and pass down on either side of the esophagus but soon subdivide to form the esophageal plexus. At the esophageal opening of the diaphragm two nerve bundles are formed, the anterior and posterior vagal trunks.

There are large networks of nerves lying about the collateral ganglia, forming the celiac, superior mesenteric, inferior mesenteric, hypogastric, and pelvic plexuses. The gastric, hepatic, splenic, phrenic, adrenal, and renal plexuses are derived from the celiac. The vagus nerves send many fibers to the celiac and mesenteric plexuses, and the sacral nerves send fibers to the more distal plexuses. The intermesenteric nerves are downward continuations of the celiac plexus on either side of the aorta. There are some intermediate strands, but there is no true aortic plexus. The intermesenteric nerves send fibers to the inferior mesenteric and hypogastric plexuses.

The greater splanchnic nerve receives fibers from the fifth to the ninth or tenth sympathetic ganglia, and its fibers pass to the

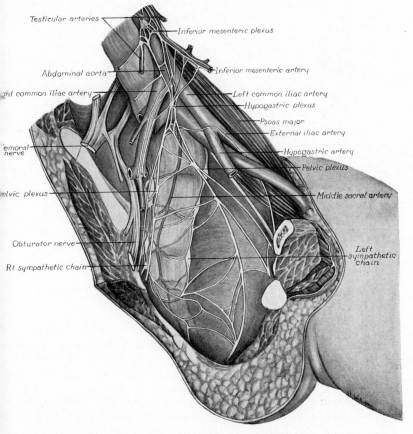

Fig. 177.—Pelvic nerve plexuses. The parietal peritoneum has been stripped away and the right os coxae has been removed by an oblique cut. (Dissection by Dr. R. W. Machamer.)   (W.R.U. E1946, term fetus.)

celiac ganglion.   The lesser splanchnic nerve arises from the ninth
to the eleventh ganglia, and its fibers pass to the aorticorenal
ganglion.   The lowest splanchnic nerve arises from the last
thoracic ganglion and its fibers pass to the renal plexus.   The
splanchnic nerves contain involuntary motor fibers passing from
the thoracic cord to the viscera and also many afferent fibers
carrying sensory impulses to the spinal cord.   The afferent fibers
make their way into the cord by way of the dorsal roots.

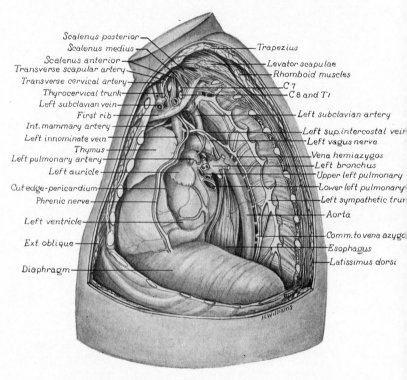

Fig. 178.—Left mediastinal wall. The left thoracic chain of sympathetic ganglia is well shown. (Dissection by Dr. N. W. Ingalls.) (W.R.U.
museum specimen C410, term fetus.)

The thoracolumbar outflow is characterized by (a) being the
involuntary outflow from the thoracic and lumbar regions of the
central nervous system, (b) having ganglia relatively near the
central nervous system, and (c) having short preganglionic fibers
(white) and long postganglionic fibers (gray).

Craniosacral Outflow.—The craniosacral outflow is the involuntary outflow coming from the two ends of the central nervous system. From the brain are fibers passing out with the third, seventh, ninth, and tenth cranial nerves; from the second, third, and fourth sacral nerves is an outflow to the pelvic region. In Plate 6 the craniosacral division is indicated in blue lines.

The ganglia of the craniosacral outflow are always located in or very close to the organ innervated. The preganglionic fibers come from cells located within the central nervous system, and the postganglionic fibers arising in the ganglia go to the particular structure innervated. With the cranial nerves are the following four autonomic ganglia:

1. The ciliary ganglion of the third nerve that gives visceral motor fibers to the ciliary muscle and the sphincter muscle of the iris.

2. The sphenopalatine (pteryopalatine) ganglion of the seventh nerve that gives visceral motor fibers to the lacrimal gland and to glands located in the nasal and pharyngeal mucosa.

3. The otic ganglion of the ninth nerve that sends visceral motor fibers to the parotid gland.

4. The submaxillary (submandibular) ganglion of the seventh nerve that sends visceral motor fibers to the submaxillary (submandibular) and sublingual salivary glands.

Sensory fibers of the trigeminal nerve pass through these ganglia; therefore they are frequently described with the fifth nerve although functionally they are not part of it. Sensory fibers pass through the ciliary ganglion to join the ophthalmic branch. Sensory fibers from the submaxillary and sublingual salivary glands pass through the submaxillary ganglion to the lingual branch of the mandibular division. Sensory fibers from the nasal mucosa pass through the sphenopalatine ganglion to the maxillary division. Sensory fibers from the parotid gland pass through the otic ganglion to the auriculotemporal branch of the mandibular division. Gray rami from the superior cervical ganglion also pass through these ganglia. Only the fibers of the parasympathetic system synapse in the ganglia.

The autonomic fibers of the vagus have a very widespread distribution. In the thorax they go to the heart and smooth muscle of the esophagus and respiratory tract. In the abdominal cavity the fibers are intermingled with the plexuses of the thoracolumbar outflow and go mainly to the glands and smooth muscle of the digestive tube down to about the middle of the transverse colon.

The sacral autonomic outflow comes from sacral nerves two, three, and four, and the fibers are intermingled with the thoracolumbar fibers of the pelvic plexuses. The fibers go to the distal colon, rectum, and pelvic viscera.

The craniosacral outflow is characterized by (a) being the involuntary outflow from the two ends of the central nervous system, (b) having ganglia close to the organ supplied, and (c) having long preganglionic fibers and short postganglionic fibers.

There are other distinctions between the two divisions of the autonomic nervous system. Most structures receive postganglionic fibers from both divisions which functionally have opposite actions.

Some of the more important functional distinctions are presented in Table 9.

Table 9

	CRANIOSACRAL OUTFLOW	THORACOLUMBAR OUTFLOW
Pupil of eye	Constricts	Dilates
Heart rate	Slows	Increases
Bronchi	Constricts	Dilates
Salivary glands	Causes increased flow of thin, watery saliva	Causes a thick viscid saliva
Peristalsis of intestine	Augments	Lessens
Sphincters of intestine	Relaxes	Contracts

Sweat glands, arrector pili (pilomotor) muscles, and peripheral blood vessels are innervated by the thoracolumbar outflow and not by the craniosacral outflow.

In the nerves supplying viscera, glands, and blood vessels are fibers which carry sensory impulses from these structures to the central nervous system. Many of these fibers pass through the various plexuses and ganglia of the autonomic system. They leave the ganglia by passing in the white rami to the dorsal root ganglia and then by way of the posterior roots into the spinal cord. Although these sensory fibers pass through the autonomic nervous system, they do not synapse with any of the cells within that system. Sensory nerve fibers synapse only within the central nervous system. Most of these sensory impulses never reach conscious levels, and those which do are poorly localized and rather indefinite, producing sensations of general discomfort or comfort. Even sensations of pain, which at times may be extremely severe, are not sharply localized. Nevertheless, the sensory impulses arising in the viscera play essential parts in reflexes which control such functions as digestion and heart beat, and the process of childbirth.

CENTRAL NERVOUS SYSTEM

The brain and cord are parts, functionally and structurally, of a continuous organ, but for purposes of description they are best discussed separately.

Spinal Cord

This is a column of nerve tissue extending from the foramen magnum to the upper border of the second lumbar vertebra. It is about eighteen inches long in men and about sixteen inches long in women. It is much shorter than the vertebral canal and is surrounded by several protective coverings. The innermost covering is the thin, delicate pia mater which has many small blood vessels and is closely attached to the surface of the cord. Outside of this is the arachnoid which is a delicate meshwork of fibrous tissue. During life the spaces of the arachnoid are filled with cerebrospinal fluid. The outermost covering is the thick, fibrous dura mater, and outside this there is a cushion of fatty tissue containing numerous veins.

The spinal cord has two indistinct spindle-shaped swellings: a cervical enlargement, extending from the level of the third cervical to that of the second thoracic vertebra and a lumbar enlargement, from the level of the ninth thoracic to that of the first lumbar vertebra. The nerves to the extremities come from these two enlargements. Below the lumbar enlargement the cord quickly decreases in size to a cone-shaped termination from which is prolonged a slender thread, the filum terminale, attached below to the coccyx.

There are eight grooves extending along the cord. The median anterior fissure is deep and distinct for the entire length of the cord. The median posterior sulcus is quite shallow. The posterior lateral sulcus is an indistinct furrow along the line of attachment of posterior roots of the spinal nerves. The anterior lateral sulcus, marking the line of attachment of the anterior roots, is quite indistinct. In the upper segments of the cord there is another line, called the intermediate posterior sulcus, lying between the median sulcus and the posterior lateral sulcus.

If a cross section of the cord is studied immediately after death, one will observe that it is composed of two kinds of tissue—one white and the other grayish pink. The white substance is composed largely of nerve fibers with myelin sheaths; the gray substance is composed of nerve cells, blood vessels, and unmyelinated nerve fibers.

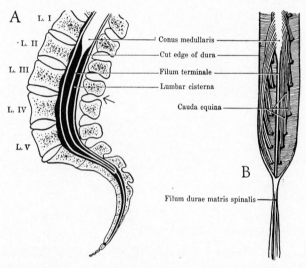

Fig. 179.—Diagram of the lower end of the spinal cord. *A,* Sagittal section of the lower end of the vertebral column. Note the termination of the spinal cord (conus medullaris) at upper border of the second lumbar vertebra, the termination of the dura mater at the second sacral vertebra, and the attachment of the filum terminale to the coccyx. The arrow indicates the point of insertion of a needle in doing a lumbar puncture. *B,* The dural sac opened from behind. (From Mettler: Neuroanatomy, St. Louis, 1948, The C. V. Mosby Co.)

The gray substance in the cord is centrally located and in cross section somewhat resembles the letter H. In each half of the cord the gray substance is a comma-shaped mass united to the mass of the other side by a bar. The larger end of the comma forms the anterior horn and the tail of the comma the posterior

horn.   In a longitudinal section the masses are called anterior
and posterior columns, respectively.   The neuroglial cells of various types form the supporting tissue of the cord.

The central canal of the cord lies within the central bar of gray
matter, extends the entire length of the cord, and is continuous
above with the fourth ventricle of the medulla.   In an adult the
caliber of the canal is extremely small and it is usually blocked
by remnants of cells which originally lined the canal.

The nerve cells in the anterior horn are motor in function, and
their processes form the anterior roots of the spinal nerves.   The
cells in the posterior horn receive sensory impulses which come in
over the posterior roots and relay these impulses to the other parts
of the central nervous system.

The white substance of the cord surrounds the gray and is composed of parallel longitudinal bundles of myelinated fibers.   These
columns in each half of the cord are grouped into three strands
or funiculi.   The posterior funiculus lies between the posterior
median fissure and the posterior lateral sulcus; the lateral funiculus lies between the posterior lateral sulcus and the anterior lateral
sulcus; the anterior funiculus lies between the anterior lateral
sulcus and the median anterior fissure.   The funiculi are also
called columns.

Within the white substance of the cord the fibers are arranged
in definite groups, those having a common origin and ending
being close together.   The more important groups are described.
The fibers in the posterior funiculus arise from cells in the dorsal
ganglion of each spinal nerve and relay certain sensory impulses
to the brain.   It is therefore easy to see why in cross sections of
the cord (Fig. 180) the posterior funiculus increases in size from
below upward.   Sensory impulses, such as sense of position and
vibration, pass up to the brain in the posterior column on the
same side of the body.   Other fibers whose cells of origin are in
the dorsal root ganglia carry the sensory impulses of pain, heat,
and cold.   These pass over to the other half of the spinal cord
as soon as they enter the posterior lateral sulcus and pass upward
to the brain in the lateral funiculus.   The course of the fibers
bearing the sensory impulses of touch is not completely known,
but some pass upward in the anterior funiculus.

Usually a fiber whose cell of origin is in a dorsal root ganglion
does not go all the way up to the brain.   In the course of such

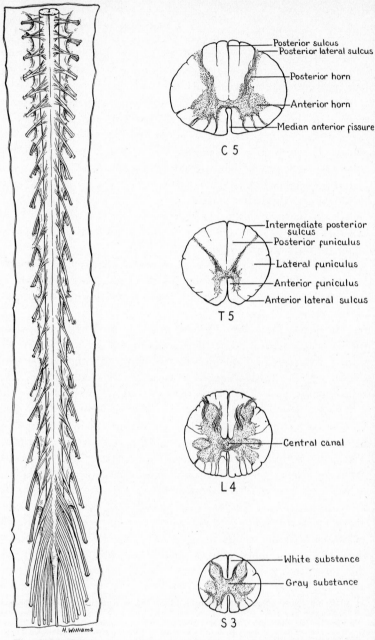

Fig. 180.—Dorsal view of spinal cord. Dura mater split longitudinally and drawn aside. *C* 5, Cross section of spinal cord at level of fifth cervical segment; *T* 5, cross section of spinal cord at level of fifth thoracic segment; *L* 4, cross section of spinal cord at level of fourth lumbar segment; *S* 3, cross section of spinal cord at level of third sacral segment. (W.R.U. museum specimen.)

a sensory fiber there is usually interposed at least one neuron whose cell of origin is in the gray matter of the cord. This intermediate or intercalated neuron also makes connections within the cord itself, thus making many spinal reflexes possible.

In the lateral funiculus is also placed the lateral corticospinal tract, carrying impulses downward from the cerebral cortex to the motor cells in the anterior horn of the gray matter. This is the voluntary motor pathway by means of which we have conscious control over the movements of the body. This pathway is also called the crossed pyramidal tract because the fibers arise in pyramid-shaped cells of the cerebral cortex of one side of the brain, and, as they pass downward, cross over to the other side of the brain to control movements of the opposite side of the body.

There are other bundles of fibers in the lateral and anterior funiculi which carry impulses to and from the brain for involuntary and reflex movements.

Brain

The brain is composed of three main parts—the brain stem, the cerebellum, and the cerebrum.

The brain stem begins at the foramen magnum as the upward continuation of the cervical cord and is a mass of interlacing bundles of nerve fibers and nests or nuclei of cells. It lies in the midline on the floor of the cranial cavity and extends forward to the level of the sella turcica of the sphenoid bone. The brain stem has the following main parts: medulla oblongata, pons, mesencephalon, and diencephalon.

The cerebellum consists of two lateral lobes and a central mass which is indistinctly separated from the lobes. It is placed in the posterior cranial fossa above the medulla and pons and is separated from the posterior portion of the cerebrum above by a fold of dura mater called the tentorium.

The cerebrum consists of two large hemispheres and a connecting bridge, the corpus callosum. In human beings the cerebral hemispheres are so large that they cover the other parts of the brain. When the brain is viewed from above, the cerebrum alone can be seen.

Medulla Oblongata.—This portion of the brain stem extends from the upper end of the spinal cord, just above the origin of the first cervical nerve, to the distinctly defined lower border of the pons. There is no such clear distinction from the spinal cord. The structures present in the cervical cord extend up into the medulla, gradually undergoing rearrangement in their course. The central gray matter is broken up into more or less distinct nests of cells or nuclear masses, with columns of white matter interwoven among the nuclei.

Important nuclei of the medulla are connected with the last four cranial nerves, that is, the ninth to the twelfth inclusive. The taste fibers of the seventh and ninth make important connections in the medulla. On the posterior surface of the lower part of the medulla there are two nuclei on each side, the nucleus

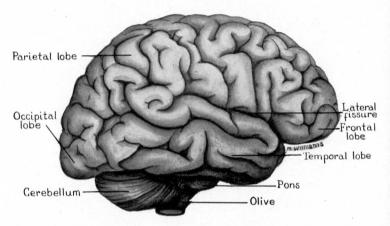

Fig. 181.—Brain, right side.   (W.R.U. 540, male, Negro, aged 45 years.)

gracilis and the nucleus cuneatus. These receive the sensory impulses coming up in the posterior columns of the cord and relay them to the other side of the medulla, whence they pass upward to higher sensory nuclei and to the cerebral cortex. Nearly all sensory impulses received on one side of the body are registered finally on the opposite side of the brain. We have already pointed out that fibers carrying sensory impulses of pain and temperature cross in the cord. In the medulla there are also a number of centers for the regulation of essential activities of the body such as the respiratory center, cardiac center, vasomotor center, and centers for deglutition, vomiting, gastric secretion, and sweating.

On the side of the medulla there is a swelling formed by a nucleus, called, because of its shape, the olive. From the olive a large bundle of fibers arises which passes across the midline through the substance of the medulla and thence to the cerebellum. This bundle, together with some fibers from the nucleus gracilis and nucleus cuneatus, forms the bulk of the inferior cerebellar peduncle or restiform body.

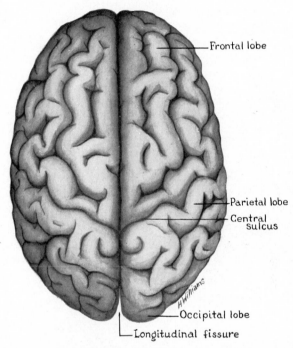

Fig. 182.—Brain, from above. (W.R.U. 540, male, Negro, aged 45 years.)

The dorsal surface of the medulla is at first an upward continuation of the cord, but it soon flattens out. The central canal becomes a widely dilated space called the fourth ventricle, having the main substance of the medulla and pons in front and below, and a thin roof behind and above.

The under surface of the medulla is similar to that of the cord, but the midportion of the median anterior fissure is obliterated by an interlacing mass of crossing fibers known as the decussation of the pyramids. This marks the crossing of the corticospinal tract which arises in the pyramidal cells of the cerebral cortex and ends in the anterior horn cells of the gray matter of the cord.

Pons.—This portion of brain stem lies on the under surface just above the medulla. It is a large bundle of transverse fibers connecting with each half of the cerebellum and is the main mass

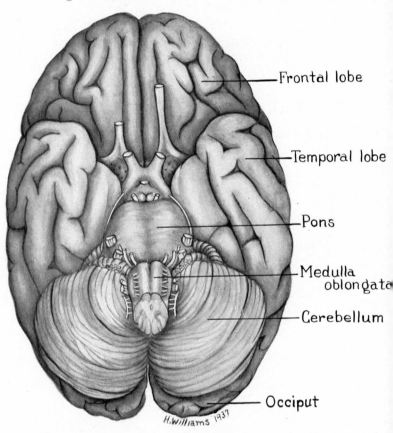

Fig. 183.—Brain, from below. (W.R.U. 540, male, Negro, aged 45 years.)

of the middle cerebellar peduncle. These transverse fibers arise from cells embedded within the substance of the pons and relay impulses from the cerebral cortex to the cerebellum.

Deep in this transverse band and beneath the fourth ventricle there are longitudinal fiber bundles which carry impulses up and down the brain stem. The nuclei of the fifth, sixth, seventh, and eighth cranial nerves are located within the upper part of the pons. Sensory impulses received from the fifth and eighth nerves are relayed through these nuclei in their upward course across the midline. Part of those for hearing and touch eventually reach the cerebral cortex and others make reflex connections within the brain stem.

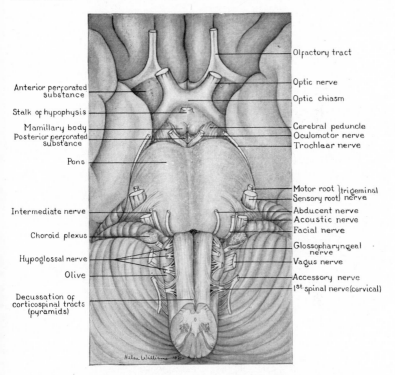

Fig. 184.—Brain stem from below to show attachment of cranial nerves. (W.R.U. 540, male, Negro, aged 45 years.)

Mesencephalon.—This segment of the brain stem is about three-fourths of an inch in length. In its center is the cerebral aqueduct (the aqueduct of Sylvius), a narrow canal connecting the fourth ventricle with the third ventricle.

The longitudinal bundles of the pons are continued upward into the mesencephalon. At its anterior end they form two prominent bands on the under surface of the brain stem, the crura cerebri or cerebral peduncles, which are connected with the cerebral hemispheres. It is within these columns that most of the motor fibers pass down from the cerebrum to the lower parts of the nervous system. Large bundles of sensory fibers passing upward to the thalamus lie deeper than the cerebral peduncles.

The nuclei of the third and fourth cranial nerves are located deep in the mesencephalon. The anterior portion of the nucleus of the fifth nerve is also located there.

The red nucleus is an important mass in the mesencephalon. It is connected with the cerebellum by means of a band of fibers called the brachium conjunctivum cerebelli or superior cerebellar peduncle. Other fibers which pass downward into the cord from the red nucleus are important in certain reflex patterns.

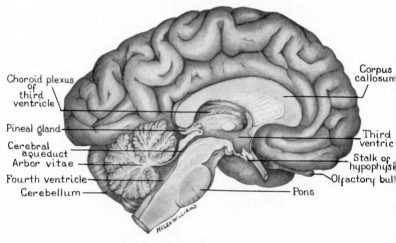

Fig. 185.—Sagittal section of brain, showing medial aspect of left half of brain. (W.R.U. museum specimen.)

On the upper surface of the mesencephalon are two pairs of small round knobs called the colliculi. The inferior colliculi are relay stations for reflexes concerned with hearing, and the superior colliculi for reflexes concerned with sight.

Diencephalon.—The diencephalon is that portion of the brain stem which surrounds the third ventricle. In the intact brain the upper surface is completely hidden by the overlying cerebral hemispheres. The pineal body is a small cone-shaped mass attached by a slender stalk to the upper surface of the diencephalon.

The under surface of the diencephalon may be seen in the narrow space bounded behind by the cerebral peduncles and in front by the optic chiasm. The hypophysis is a small rounded body lying in the sella turcica and attached by a slender stalk to the diencephalon. The mammillary bodies, two small rounded masses seen just behind the stalk of the hypophysis, are, in part, relay stations in the pathway for sensory impulses of smell.

The fibers carrying visual impulses leave the optic chiasm, sweep laterally under the cerebral peduncles, and some pass to the superior colliculi for reflexes involving vision; others turn into the lateral part of the thalamus, where they are relayed up and back through the substance of each cerebral hemisphere to the back of the occipital lobe where visual impulses are registered on the cortex for conscious vision.

A very important nucleus lying within the substance of the diencephalon is the thalamus which eventually receives nearly all the sensory impulses flowing into the central nervous system and relays them on to the cerebral cortex. That portion of the diencephalon lying below and on either side of the third ventricle is called the hypothalamus and has extremely important and diverse reflex functions. Experimental evidence indicates that there are centers here which have to do with the regulation of many essential functions such as temperature control, water and fat metabolism, sleep, sexual activity, and emotional control.

Cerebellum.—The cerebellum is a solid mass of tissue consisting of a core of white matter and a rather thin continuous layer of gray matter on the surface. The gray matter is of uniform thickness and is thrown into a series of more or less parallel folds. In a sagittal section can be seen primary, secondary, and tertiary folds, with branches of white matter projecting into the folds, forming a treelike pattern, thus suggesting the term *arbor vitae*. These folds are also known as laminae.

Buried within the white matter of each cerebellar hemisphere is the dentate nucleus, the most important nuclear mass of the cerebellum.

The cerebellum is connected with the rest of the brain by three pairs of nerve bundles or peduncles already mentioned. The inferior cerebellar peduncle or restiform body brings nerve fibers from the nuclei of the medulla and some from the spinal cord.

The middle cerebellar peduncle or brachium pontis brings nerve fibers from the nuclei of the pons. The superior cerebellar peduncle or brachium conjunctivum cerebelli carries impulses from the dentate nucleus of the cerebellum to the red nucleus of

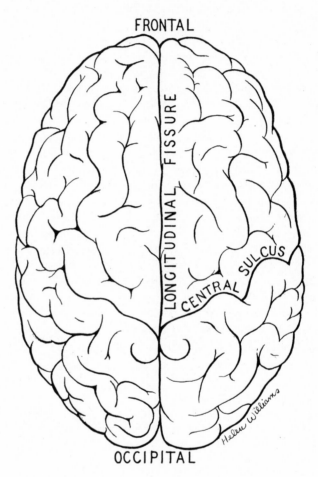

Fig. 186.—Upper surface of brain showing fissures. Same brain as shown in Fig. 182.

the mesencephalon. The cerebellum is a coordination center for muscular activity, particularly for the muscles used in walking.

Cerebrum.—The cerebrum has an outer layer of gray matter, and each hemisphere has a large central cavity called a lateral ventricle. The surface has many complex folds called gyri, separated from each other by depressions called fissures or sulci. The pattern of these folds is fairly stable, but the detail differs greatly from brain to brain and indeed on the two sides of the same brain. There are certain well-marked fissures which may be distinguished in every brain.

The longitudinal fissure separates the two hemispheres. Passing almost at right angles to this fissure outward and downward over the side of each hemisphere is the central sulcus. On the lateral side of the hemisphere, below the end of the central sulcus, is the lateral fissure which begins on the under surface of the brain and passes out and back along the side of the brain.

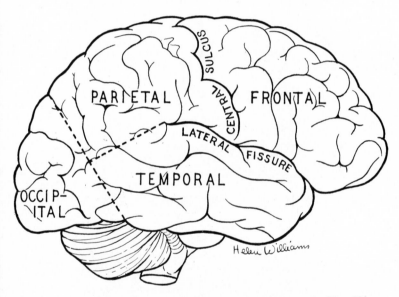

Fig. 187.—Brain showing lobes. Same brain as shown in Fig. 181.

On the under surface of the front of the cerebrum there is the olfactory sulcus in which lies the olfactory tract, and on each side are two long prominent grooves, the collateral and inferior temporal sulci.

On the medial surface of each hemisphere there are two important grooves, the sulcus cinguli curving around the corpus callosum, and posterior to this, the calcarine fissure.

Each hemisphere is arbitrarily divided into several lobes. The frontal lobe lies above the lateral sulcus and in front of the central. Behind the central sulcus lies the parietal lobe, and below the lateral fissure lies the temporal lobe. The posterior pole of the cerebrum is called the occipital lobe and has no anatomic boundary. The calcarine fissure lies on the medial surface of the occipital lobe.

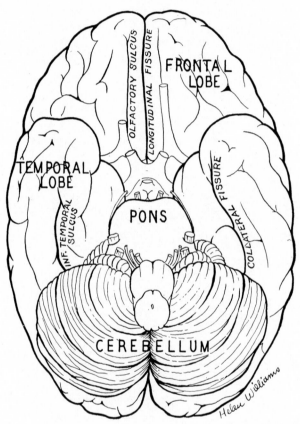

Fig. 188.—Under surface of brain showing fissures. Same brain as shown in Fig. 183.

The interior of the cerebrum contains large bundles of fibers which connect various portions of the same hemisphere, various parts of the two hemispheres with each other by way of the corpus callosum, and the cortex of each hemisphere with sensory and motor nuclei in lower parts of the nervous system. Within the substance of the cerebrum and in close contact with these interlacing bands of fibers are the basal ganglia, or corpus striatum, a group of nuclei which serves as a coordinating center for sensory and motor impulses.

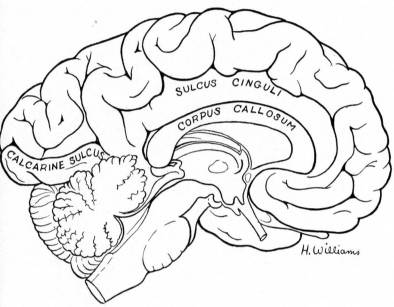

Fig. 189.—Sagittal section of brain.   Same brain as shown in Fig. 185.

Cerebral Localization.—Certain areas of the cerebral cortex are specialized for definite functions. The precentral gyrus or fold of the frontal lobe anterior to the central sulcus is specialized for voluntary motor movements. Each part of the body is represented by groups of pyramidal cells, the order being that illustrated in Fig. 190. The area for the foot is nearest the longitudinal fissure, often actually on the mesial surface of the hemisphere. The rest of the body is represented in order, the face being the last—just above the lateral sulcus. The left cerebral hemisphere governs movements of the right side of the body, and the right hemisphere of the left side of the body.

The motor area governing speech is in the left frontal lobe of right-handed persons in the angle between the central sulcus and lateral fissure. In left-handed persons it is the right frontal lobe which governs speech.

That area of the parietal lobe just behind the central sulcus is set aside for conscious perception of such sensations as touch, heat, and cold. Areas are assigned to the specific parts of the body for sensations just as for movements, and corresponding areas are placed side by side.

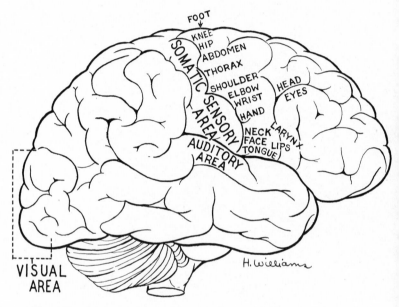

Fig. 190.—Brain showing areas of cerebral localization. Same brain as shown in Fig. 181. Somatic sensory area is the portion of cortex receiving impulses from all parts of the skin.

The occipital cortex on both sides of the calcarine fissure receives impulses of vision (the center of conscious sight).

Auditory impulses are received in the temporal lobe just below the middle of the lateral sulcus (the center of conscious hearing).

In man the portion of the cortex which receives sensations of smell appears small. It is on the under surface of the temporal lobe in a rolled-in convolution of the brain called the hippocampus. This is lateral to the mammillary bodies of the diencephalon where the olfactory tracts reach the brain.

These areas just mentioned, devoted to motor outflow and to sensory reception, occupy only a small portion of the entire cerebral cortex. The rest, the so-called association areas, are devoted to such functions as motor patterns, memory, and attention and to building composite concepts from various sensory impulses. It is probable that the portion of the frontal lobe anterior to the primary motor area is devoted to the motor patterns involved in walking, writing, playing musical instruments, etc. Concepts of word-hearing are in the temporal lobe and of word-seeing in the occipital lobe.

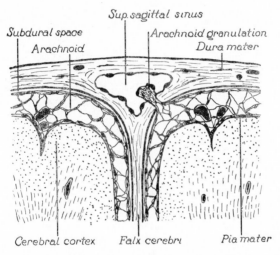

Fig. 191.—Coronal section of skull showing coverings of brain and superior sagittal sinus.   (After Weed.)

Coverings of Brain.—Like the cord the brain has three coverings—the pia mater, arachnoid, and dura mater. The thin and delicate pia is closely applied to the cortex. It passes into the depths of the various sulci or fissures and protrudes into the ventricles. The arachnoid is a thin meshwork between the pia and dura. It bridges over the sulci but does not enter them. The meshes are filled with cerebrospinal fluid. Blood vessels form networks in this layer. The dura is tough and fibrous, and within the cranium it is subdivided into two layers. The outer layer is closely adherent to the inner surface of the brain case. The inner layer, which corresponds to the dura mater of the cord, forms the outermost covering of the brain. It also forms septa: the falx cerebri, which extends downward into the longitudinal fissure between the two hemispheres, the tentorium between the cerebellum and the occipital lobes, and the falx cerebelli between the cerebellar hemispheres.

Between the two layers of dura mater there is a system of blood sinuses which receives venous blood from the brain and empties it into the internal jugular veins in the neck. This system is discussed in Chapter 10, The Circulatory System.

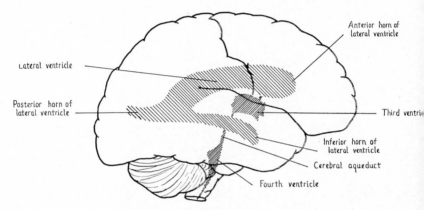

Fig. 192.—Ventricles of brain.

Ventricles of Brain.—The central canal of the cord extends upward into the brain where it undergoes certain changes and enlargements. In each cerebral hemisphere is a large lateral ventricle consisting of a central part with three outpouchings or horns. The anterior horn extends into the frontal lobe, the posterior horn into the occipital lobe, and the inferior horn into the temporal lobe. The central part of each lateral ventricle communicates with the third ventricle by a small opening, the interventricular foramen (foramen of Monro).

The third ventricle is a small cleftlike cavity in the center of the diencephalon. It is continuous behind with the cerebral aqueduct which leads into the fourth ventricle.

The fourth ventricle lies beneath the cerebellum on the upper surface of the pons and front half of the medulla. The fourth ventricle communicates with the spaces of the arachnoid by means

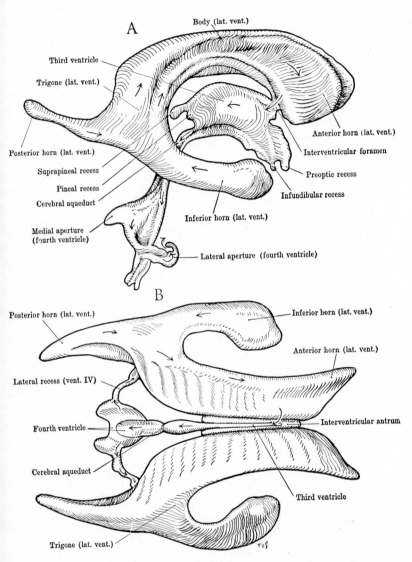

A

Body (lat. vent.)

Third ventricle

Trigone (lat. vent.)

Posterior horn (lat. vent.)

Suprapineal recess

Pineal recess

Cerebral aqueduct

Medial aperture
(fourth ventricle)

Anterior horn (lat. vent.)

Interventricular foramen

Preoptic recess

Infundibular recess

Inferior horn (lat. vent.)

Lateral aperture (fourth ventricle)

B

Posterior horn (lat. vent.)

Lateral recess (vent. IV)

Fourth ventricle

Cerebral aqueduct

Trigone (lat. vent.)

Inferior horn (lat. vent.)

Anterior horn (lat. vent.)

Interventricular antrum

Third ventricle

Fig. 193.—Diagram of the ventricles of the brain. *A,* Lateral view;
B, as seen from above. The arrows show the direction of flow of the cerebrospinal fluid. (After Bailey. From Mettler: Neuroanatomy, St. Louis,
1948, The C. V. Mosby Co.)

of three small openings or foramina. There is one opening in the midline of the posterior part of the roof of the ventricle and one lateral opening from each lateral recess of the ventricle.

There are folds of pia mater, each with a plexus of blood vessels pushing into the ventricles. These folds are called choroid plexuses.

Cerebrospinal Fluid.—The ventricles of the brain and the spaces of the arachnoid between the pia and dura mater are all filled with a clear, colorless fluid. This fluid is formed within the ventricles of the brain from the choroid plexuses. It passes out into the spaces of the arachnoid through the roof of the fourth ventricle and, among other functions, serves as a water cushion for the brain and cord. The fluid is resorbed into the venous sinuses of the dura mater from fingerlike projections (villi, Pacchionian bodies, or arachnoidal granulations) of the arachnoid into the sinuses. Most of the absorption occurs in the superior sagittal sinus.

Growth of Brain.—The brain grows very rapidly during the first few years of life. The cortex, particularly that of the parietal and frontal lobes, grows more rapidly in the first two years, and the pattern becomes increasingly complex up to about six years of age.

Table 10
Volume of the Brain at Different Ages

AGE	APPROXIMATE VOLUME (CC.)
Birth	330
One year	750
Two years	900
Four years	1,000
Twenty years	1,200

The various fiber tracts of the central nervous system do not develop myelin sheaths at the same time. The afferent and efferent fibers of the spinal nerves show myelin after the fifth fetal month, but the corticospinal tracts do not become fully myelinated until the second year of life. This is part of the explanation of the fact that babies have a definite pattern of developmental activity, and we cannot expect them to be able to walk, for example, until the nervous system is mature enough to enable the child to perform that function.

Review Questions

1. Describe briefly a typical nerve.
2. How many pairs of spinal nerves are there? How may they be grouped? How many are there in each group?
3. Describe the phrenic nerve.
4. What forms the brachial plexus? List the nerves which arise from this plexus.
5. List the nerves arising from the lumbosacral plexus.
6. Describe the ulnar nerve.
7. Describe the sciatic nerve.
8. List the cranial nerves.
9. Describe the trigeminal nerve.
10. Describe the vagus nerve.
11. What are the two main subdivisions of the autonomic nervous system?
12. What are the anatomic characteristics of the thoracolumbar outflow?
13. What are the anatomic characteristics of the craniosacral outflow?
14. What is the cauda equina?
15. Name the subdivisions of the brain.
16. Name the four lobes of the cerebrum.
17. Where is the motor area of the cerebral cortex?
18. Where is the area of the cerebral cortex which governs speech?
19. Where are the areas of conscious perception for the following sensations: touch, vision, hearing, and smell?
20. What are association areas? Give two examples.
21. What is meant by cerebral dominance?
22. Where is cerebrospinal fluid formed? Where is it resorbed?
23. What is one important function of the cerebellum?
24. What are the main subdivisions of the brain stem?
25. What structures are found in the white matter of the cord?
26. Where is the gray matter of the cord located?
27. In an adult the spinal cord extends between what two vertebral levels?

CHAPTER 8

SPECIAL SENSE ORGANS

The special sense organs include the olfactory mucosa of the nose, the taste buds of the mouth, the eye, the ear, and the receptors in skin, muscle, and tendon.

OLFACTORY CELLS

The olfactory epithelium of the nose is limited to a small irregular area on the medial surface of the superior turbinate and the adjacent surface of the nasal septum. In living persons this area is more yellow in color than the surrounding pink respiratory mucosa. The olfactory nerve is described with the other cranial nerves in Chapter 7, The Nervous System.

In the olfactory mucosa there are two types of cells, the olfactory cells and the supporting cells. The supporting cells are columnar in shape. The olfactory cells are bipolar nerve cells (true neurons) whose axons pass through the cribriform plate of the ethmoid as the fibers of the olfactory nerve. The dendrites reach the surface of the mucosa by passing between the supporting cells, and each divides into many fine, hairlike processes. These processes receive the olfactory stimuli directly without any intervening sense organ. The cell bodies are analogous to the cells of the dorsal root ganglia of the spinal nerves, but there is no true ganglion associated with the first cranial nerve.

TASTE BUDS

Each taste bud is a small onion-shaped nest of cells in the mucosa of the mouth, and the free end of each bud opens on the surface as a gustatory pore. The supporting cells are spindle-shaped and are arranged about the outside to form the sheath of the bud and a few are within the bud. The taste cells themselves are long and slender and each ends as a fine hair at the surface level of the pore. The nerves carrying the sensory impulse from the taste buds to the central nervous system are discussed with the cranial nerves. (See facial and glossopharyngeal nerves.)

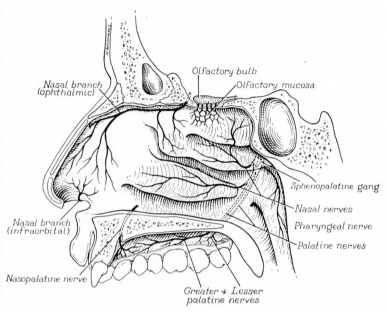

Fig. 194.—Lateral wall of the right nostril. The sphenopalatine ganglion is drawn in dotted lines to show its position.

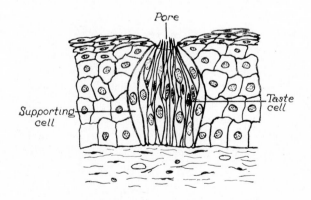

Fig. 195.—A taste bud.

The hair cells have no axons and are considered neuroepithelial cells. The first nerve cell bodies of the taste system are found in the ganglia of the seventh and ninth nerves. These cells send long dendrites to the taste buds where they end as fine branches about the bases of the hair cells. The taste cells receive the initial taste impulses, and transmit them to the nerve dendrites, which transform the stimuli into nerve impulses and conduct them to the ganglia and along the axons of the ganglion cells to the nuclear center of taste in the medulla.

THE EYE

The eyeball is almost spherical. It lies in the orbital cavity and is protected in front by the eyelids. With it must be considered the lacrimal glands and the nasolacrimal duct.

The space between the eyeball and the bony wall of the orbit is filled with fibrous tissue and fat. It lodges the extrinsic muscles of the eye, the blood vessels, and the optic nerve which passes from the eyeball through the optic foramen into the cranial cavity.

The outer fibrous covering of the eyeball is also called the capsule of Tenon. It covers the posterior two thirds of the eyeball and blends at the back with the sclera and sheath of the optic nerve. Anteriorly it is prolonged as a sheath for each of the extrinsic muscles of the eyeball. The sheaths for the medial and lateral rectus muscles are strong and form the medial and lateral check ligaments; they are thought to prevent overfunction of these muscles. Below the eyeball the fascia spreads out like a hammock to form the suspensory ligament of the eyeball.

Extrinsic Muscles of the Eye.—The four rectus muscles and the superior oblique muscle arise from a common round tendon of fibrous tissue surrounding the optic nerve at its emergence from the optic foramen. The four rectus muscles, called superior, inferior, lateral or external, and medial or internal because of their relation to the eyeball, pass forward to their insertions into the eyeball a short distance behind the margin of the cornea.

The superior oblique muscle arises from the round tendon in the angle between the superior and medial rectus muscles. It passes forward on the nasal side of the medial rectus over the eyeball to

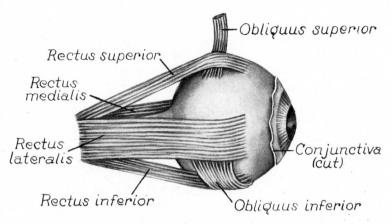

Fig. 196.—Extrinsic muscles of right eye, lateral view. The muscle belly of the superior oblique muscle has been removed, leaving only the distal portion of the tendon and its insertion into the eyeball. (W.R.U. museum specimen C248.)

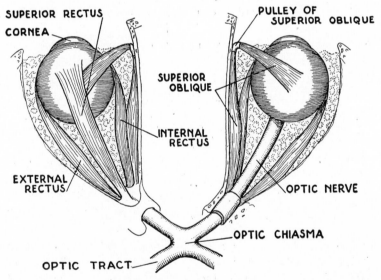

Fig. 197.—Diagram showing the eyeballs from above. On the right the superior rectus has been removed to show the insertion of the superior oblique behind the equator of the eyeball. (From Zoethout: Introduction to Human Physiology, St. Louis, 1948, The C. V. Mosby Co.)

the margin of the orbit where it becomes tendinous and passes through a fibrous pulley. The tendon then turns outward and backward to an insertion into the eyeball behind its equator and between the levels of insertion of the superior and lateral rectus muscles. Contraction of the superior oblique muscle rotates the eyeball downward and outward.

The inferior oblique muscle arises from the floor of the orbit on the medial side. The muscle passes outward beneath the eyeball to an insertion behind the equator and between the levels of insertion of the inferior and lateral rectus muscles. This muscle rotates the eye upward and outward. The need for the oblique muscles which direct the eyeball outward is clear when one remembers that, from their origin in the round tendon, the superior and inferior recti course forward and outward. Unopposed by the oblique muscles the superior rectus, on contraction, would direct the eyeball inward as well as upward, and the inferior rectus would turn the eyeball inward and downward. The inferior oblique and the superior rectus acting together rotate the eyeball directly upward; the superior oblique and inferior rectus turn it directly downward. The lateral rectus turns the eyeball directly outward (laterally), and the medial rectus turns the eyeball inward (medially).

Table 11
Action of Extrinsic Muscles of Eye

NAME	INNERVATION	FUNCTION*
Superior rectus	Oculomotor	Upward and inward
Medial rectus	Oculomotor	Inward
Inferior rectus	Oculomotor	Downward and inward
Lateral rectus	Abducent	Outward
Superior oblique	Trochlear	Outward and downward
Inferior oblique	Oculomotor	Outward and upward

*The function stated is that resulting if the muscle acts alone. The direction of movement refers to the portion of the eyeball containing the pupil.

The orbital muscle is a small mass of smooth muscle fibers found in the back of the orbit. It bridges across the inferior orbital fissure, the cleft in the lower lateral part of the back of the orbit.

Eyelids.—The eyelids are two fibromuscular curtains placed one in front of each eye. In addition to fibers of the orbicularis oculi muscle which are the chief muscle bundles of the lids, the upper lid is provided with a special muscle, the levator palpebrae superioris, which arises from the common round tendon surrounding the optic nerve and is innervated by the third cranial nerve. In each eyelid there is also a thin layer of smooth muscle.

In each lid there is a plate of fibrous tissue, the tarsus. The tarsus of the upper lid is the larger and is shaped like a half oval; that for the lower lid is smaller and rod-shaped.

The eyelashes are short hairs projecting from the free margins of the eyelids; the upper ones curve upward and the lower ones downward. There are numbers of small sebaceous and sweat glands in the lids which empty by minute openings along the free margin.

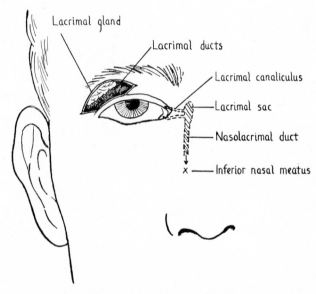

Fig. 198.—Lacrimal apparatus.

Eyebrows.—The eyebrows are a pair of arches of thickened skin placed one above each orbit and are closely studded with short coarse hairs. Fibers of the muscles of expression, particularly fibers of the frontalis and orbicularis oculi, are interlaced beneath this thickened area of skin.

Conjunctiva.—The conjunctiva is the layer of mucous membrane covering the inner surface of the eyelids and the surface of the eyeball. Its epithelium is stratified columnar on the eyelids; on the corneal surface the epithelium becomes stratified squamous.

Lacrimal Apparatus.—The lacrimal gland, a small organ the size and shape of an almond, lies in the upper, outer portion of the orbit. Its function is to secrete tears which are emptied by several small ducts onto the conjunctiva behind the outer half of the upper lid.

The small openings or puncta lacrimalia of the lacrimal canalicula are visible near the inner end of each eyelid. The lacrimal sac is formed by the union of the canaliculi of each eyelid; this sac drains by way of the nasolacrimal duct into the inferior meatus of the nose beneath the inferior turbinate. The canaliculi are limited by their small caliber to carry only a small amount of secretion, so that when the lacrimal gland is stimulated, excess tears overflow onto the cheek.

Wall of the Eyeball.—The wall of the eyeball is composed of three coats. The outer is called the sclera; it is thick and strong and opaque at the back, while in front it is transparent and is called the cornea. The sclera is continued backward as the outer sheath of the optic nerve and blends with the dura mater of the brain.

The middle coat is the choroid; it is heavily pigmented and vascular. In front the choroid is replaced by the iris, a colored disc behind the cornea. The color of the iris determines the color of the eye. In the center of the iris there is an opening, called the pupil, through which light is admitted into the interior of the eye. The iris is contractile and by varying the size of the pupil the eye adjusts itself to varying intensities of light. The iris contains many smooth muscle fibers. Part of these are arranged in a circular fashion about the pupil and form the sphincter of the pupil. The rest of the smooth muscle cells are arranged in a radial fashion, and their contraction causes dilatation of the pupil. The sphincter fibers are innervated by parasympathetic fibers of the third cranial nerve, while the dilator fibers are innervated by sympathetic fibers from the superior cervical ganglion. Attaching the iris to the choroid is the ciliary body which contains bundles of smooth muscle arranged in a radial manner and innervated by parasympathetic fibers from the third cranial nerve. The crystalline lens is suspended behind the pupil by a suspensory ligament which is attached at its periphery to the ciliary body. The lens focuses light rays on the retina.

The innermost layer of the eyeball is called the retina; it is a thin, delicate membrane composed of several layers of nerve cells which receive light rays and transmit impulses along the optic nerve to the brain. The retina is analogous to the dorsal root ganglion of a spinal nerve. That portion of the interior of the eyeball between the cornea and iris is known as the anterior chamber, and the small portion between the iris and lens is the posterior chamber. A thin, transparent fluid, called the aqueous humor, fills both the anterior and posterior chambers. The vitreous body is a transparent jellylike substance which fills the interior of the eyeball behind the lens.

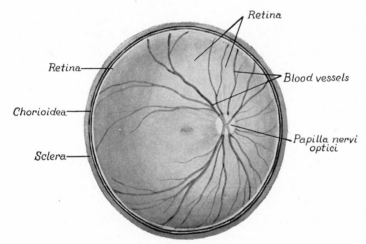

Fig. 199.—Fundus of right eye as seen with an ophthalmoscope. (From Anthony: Textbook of Anatomy and Physiology, St. Louis, 1946, The C. V. Mosby Co.)

By use of an instrument called an ophthalmoscope it is possible to look directly at the retina. This is an examination of the eye grounds or fundus of the eye. The physician directs a light through the pupil thus illuminating the interior of the eye. Fig. 199 is an illustration of what he sees. The retina is red because of the rich blood supply of the underlying choroid. Numerous small blood vessels are visible running over the inner surface of the retina. Toward the nasal side of the back of the eye there is a depressed white area called the optic disc or papilla of the optic nerve. Here the filaments of the optic nerve receive a myelin sheath as they leave the eyeball, thus producing the white color seen here. The optic disc is also known as the blind spot because light rays focused on the ensheathed nerve cannot be seen. The retinal artery enters the eyeball within the optic disc and the retinal veins leave. A few millimeters lateral to the disc and directly behind the pupil is a small yellow area called the macula lutea containing a central depression called the fovea centralis. The fovea is the area of most distinct vision.

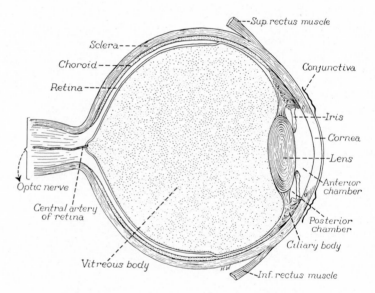

Fig. 200.—Vertical section of eyeball, diagrammatic.

The eye acts like a camera. Light rays pass through the transparent cornea at the front of the eyeball, through the pupil, and through the lens which focuses light rays upon the nerve cells of the retina. The light rays pass entirely through the transparent retina to the deepest layer, the rod and cone cells. These receive the stimulus and generate nerve impulses which are transmitted through the retinal layers to a layer of large ganglion cells. The axons from the ganglion cells pass out of the retina in the optic nerve and carry impulses to the visual centers of the brain.

The ophthalmic artery, a branch of the internal carotid, passes into the orbital cavity through the optic foramen beneath the optic nerve. The central artery of the retina, a branch of the ophthalmic, pierces the sheath of the optic nerve about one-half inch behind the eyeball and runs in the center of the optic nerve to supply the retina. Immediate and total blindness of that eye occurs if its retinal artery is obstructed. The veins of the orbit form two main trunks, the superior and inferior ophthalmic veins, which empty into the anterior end of the cavernous sinus. The superior vein communicates with the veins of the face and the inferior with the venous plexuses about the pterygoid muscles.

THE EAR

The organ of hearing has the following three subdivisions: (1) the external ear, (2) the middle ear, and (3) the inner ear.

External Ear.—The external ear has two parts—the auricle or pinna and the external auditory meatus or canal. The auricle is a shell-shaped organ attached to the side of the head. It is composed of an irregular plate of elastic cartilage covered with skin. It varies greatly in size and shape, and it is usually smaller in women than in men. The angle of its attachment to the head varies greatly. A number of vestigial muscles are associated with the auricle but rarely is any functional muscle found.

The external auditory meatus, a bent tube about one and one-half inches long and varying in diameter, is the connecting passageway between the auricle and the middle ear. The outer third of its wall is cartilaginous and the remainder is bony. The skin over the cartilaginous portion contains many fine hairs, sebaceous glands, and special glands for the secretion of ear wax. The external meatus receives sensory nerve fibers from the mandibular division of the trigeminal, the vagus, and great auricular nerves. The vagus is also sensory to the mucosa of the larynx, and for this reason stimulation of the auricular branch frequently causes a tickling sensation in the throat and a desire to cough.

Middle Ear.—The middle ear or the tympanic cavity, a small air chamber within the temporal bone, may be likened to a six-sided box. The lateral wall is the tympanic membrane or eardrum which separates the middle ear from the external ear. The

eardrum is a thin, translucent disc of fibrous tissue placed at the
inner end of the external canal, sealing it off from the cavity of the
middle ear.

The back wall of the middle ear has a small opening communicating with the mastoid air cells. It is this opening that transmits
the infections that travel from the middle ear to the air cells and
produce mastoiditis.

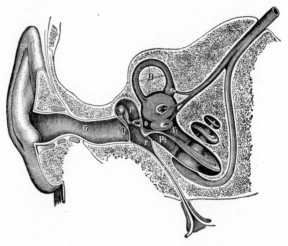

Fig. 201.—Section through the right ear (Czermak); *G,* external auditory meatus; *T,* tympanic membrane; *P,* tympanic cavity or middle ear with
the auditory ossicles stretching across it and the auditory tube entering
it from below; *O,* oval window; *r,* round window; *B,* semicircular canal;
S, cochlea; *Vt,* upper canal (scala vestibuli); *Pt,* lower canal of cochlea
(scala tympani). (From Howell: Textbook of Physiology, Philadelphia,
1913, W. B. Saunders Co.)

The front wall of the middle ear has the opening of the auditory
tube (Eustachian tube) which connects the middle ear with the
nasopharynx. By means of this tube the air pressure in the middle ear is equalized with atmospheric pressure. Infections may
pass from the nasopharynx to the middle ear along this tube.
The medial or pharyngeal end of the auditory tube is cartilaginous
and the outer end is bony. The cartilaginous part is about one
inch long, and the bony part about one-half inch long. The
inner orifice of the auditory tube is located in the lateral wall of
the nasopharynx about one-half inch directly behind the inferior
turbinate. From the inner end the tube is directed outward,
upward, and backward to the middle ear.

The floor of the middle ear is a thin sheet of bone that separates the ear cavity from the jugular fossa.

The roof of the middle ear, also a thin sheet of bone, separates the ear cavity from the middle cranial fossa.

The inner wall of the middle ear consists of dense bone in which are two openings, a round and an oval window, communicating with the inner ear. The foot piece of the stapes fits into the oval window. Beneath the oval window is the round window which is closed over by a small fibrous disc called the secondary drum membrane.

Extending across the middle ear cavity is a chain of three ossicles, the malleus (hammer), incus (anvil), and stapes (stirrup). It is by means of these bones that sound waves are transmitted from the outer to the inner ear.

The chorda tympani nerve crosses the cavity of the middle ear, passing between the malleus and the incus.

The tensor tympani muscle lies in a bony canal above the auditory tube. Its tendon is inserted on the long process of the malleus which in turn is firmly attached to the center of the inner surface of the tympanic membrane, thus regulating tension in the membrane. It is innervated from the motor part of the trigeminal nerve.

The stapedius muscle is inserted on the stapes. It is a tiny muscle arising within the temporal bone in the posterior wall of the middle ear and is innervated by the facial nerve. It assists in regulating pressure of the foot piece of the stapes in the oval window.

The middle ear cavity is lined with mucous membrane continuous with that of the auditory tube and nasopharynx and with that of the mastoid air cells. The ossicles and chorda tympani nerve are all covered with the same tissue. The mucous membrane of the middle ear receives its sensory innervation from the glossopharyngeal nerve.

Inner Ear.—The inner ear lies within the petrous portion of the temporal bone; it consists of complex bony passages within which are similar but much smaller membranous passages, called respectively the osseous labyrinth and the membranous labyrinth.

The osseous labyrinth consists of a central portion called the vestibule, which communicates with the three semicircular canals and with the cochlea. Each semicircular canal forms two thirds

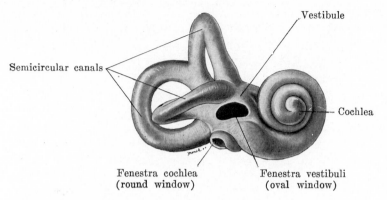

Fig. 202.—External view of right bony labyrinth, diagrammatic. (From Pitzman: Fundamentals of Human Anatomy, St. Louis, 1920, The C. V. Mosby Co.)

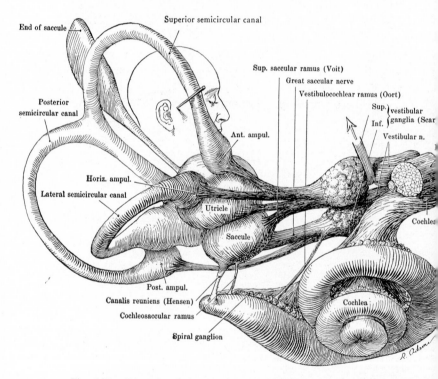

Fig. 203.—Diagram of the membranous labyrinth and the eighth cranial nerve (from a dissection by Max Brödel). The cochlea has been turned downward and outward and the superior branch of the vestibular nerve has been elevated. (From Mettler: Neuroanatomy, St. Louis, 1948, The C. V. Mosby Co.)

of a circle. The three canals on each side are placed at right angles to each other. A canal of each ear is parallel to a canal in the ear of the opposite side. The cochlea is a coiled tube which makes two and one-half turns around a central pillar called the modiolus. There is a thin shelf of bone winding around the modiolus that divides the tube of the cochlea into two portions, a scala tympani and scala vestibuli. These two portions communicate with each other through a small opening at the apex of the modiolus.

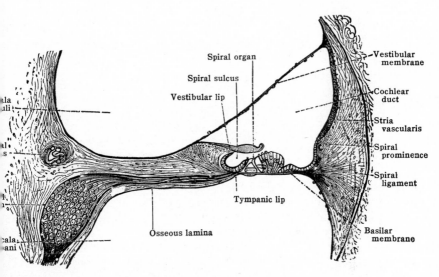

Fig. 204.—Radial section through one of the coils of the cochlea. (×50.) (From Toldt: Atlas of Human Anatomy, The Macmillan Co.)

The membranous labyrinth is a closed sac within, but not nearly filling, the bony labyrinth; it contains a clear fluid called endolymph. The clear fluid outside the membrane wall but within the bony labyrinth is called perilymph. The endolymph and perilymph do not mingle, each being in a closed compartment.

The utricle and saccule, two saclike portions of the membranous labyrinth, lie within the bony vestibule and communicate with each other. Three membranous semicircular canals, one for each bony canal, are connected with the utricle; each canal has a dilatation near one end called an ampulla. The cochlear duct or scala media is connected with the saccule by means of a tiny duct, the canalis reuniens. The cochlear duct coils up within the cochlea between the scala tympani and scala vestibuli. The end of the saccule is drawn out into a long diverticulum, the endolymphatic duct, which lies in a tiny canal, the aqueduct of the vestibule, extending from the vestibule through the temporal bone to the posterior fossa of the skull.

The acoustic nerve enters the cranial cavity on its emergence from the internal acoustic meatus of the temporal bone. Within this canal the trunk is composed of two parts, a cochlear and a vestibular portion.

The bipolar ganglion cells of the cochlear nerve are located in the spiral ganglion within the modiolus. The dendrites are distributed by many fine branches around the bases of the receptor cells, the hair cells of the organ of Corti (spiral organ). The axons form the cochlear nerve. The ganglion cells relay the sound impulses after changing them into nerve impulses to the auditory center of the brain stem, whence they are relayed to higher centers and finally to the auditory portion of the cortex where they give rise to sensations of hearing.

The vestibular nerve is distributed to the neuroepithelial hair cells of the sensory patches in the semicircular canals, the utricle, and saccule. The vestibular ganglion contains the bipolar cell bodies of the neurons which relay equilibratory impulses to centers in the brain stem and cerebellum.

SENSORY NERVE ENDINGS IN SKIN, MUSCLE, AND TENDON

The cutaneous nerves end in a variety of ways among the cells of the layers of the skin. Some terminate as free nerve endings, part of which serve as receptors for the sense of pain. Other nerve fibers terminate in specialized end organs which vary greatly in form. These are usually microscopic structures. Different nerve endings are specialized for the reception of special stimuli, such as heat, cold, pressure, vibration, and the size and shape of objects.

Fig. 205 is a drawing of the various kinds of sensory nerve endings. *A* in the drawing represents a Pacinian corpuscle. This type has many consecutive layers of fibrous tissue for a capsule, and the entire structure is just visible to the unaided eye. Pacinian

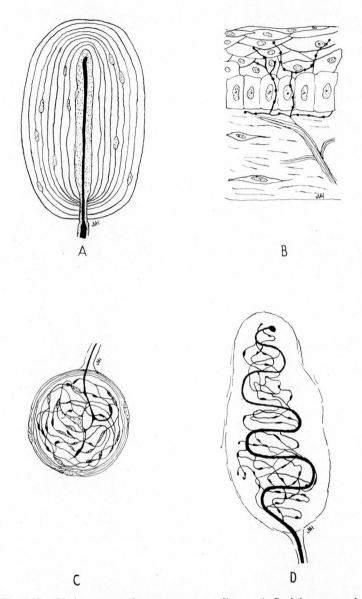

Fig. 205.—Various types of sensory nerve endings. *A*, Pacinian corpuscle;
B, free nerve endings; *C*, corpuscle of Krause; *D*, corpuscle of Meissner.

corpuscles are found in the deeper layers of the skin of the palms of the hands and the soles of the feet, in the areolar tissue of the posterior abdominal wall, and near joints. *B* in the drawing illustrates free nerve endings in stratified squamous epithelium. Free nerve endings are abundant in skin and mucous membranes, and a few are found about the roots of hair and in serous membranes. *C* illustrates a corpuscle of Krause, which is found in the conjunctiva, in the mucosa of the lips and tongue, and in the synovial membranes. Large corpuscles of this variety are found in the glans of the penis and clitoris. *D* in the drawing illustrates an oval corpuscle of Meissner. This type is found in the skin of the palms of the hands and the soles of the feet and in the tips of the fingers and toes.

There are spindle-shaped structures associated with voluntary muscles and tendons. These have a capsule of connective tissue and a core of fibers which is partly nervous and partly muscular.

The Pacinian corpuscles are probably the sensory receptors for pressure. The end organs of Krause, in some areas at least, may be stimulated by temperature changes, and Meissner's corpuscles are associated with touch. The neuromuscular spindle bundles associated with muscles and tendons are receptors for sense of position, balance, and muscle tension.

The paths of various types of sensory nerves within the cord and brain are discussed in Chapter 7, The Nervous System.

Review Questions

1. Where are the end organs for the sense of smell located?
2. Describe a taste bud.
3. What cranial nerves contain fibers carrying the sensation of taste?
4. List the extrinsic muscles of the eyeball and give the nerve supply of each.
5. What is the anterior chamber of the eye?
6. Describe the eyelids.
7. Describe the lacrimal apparatus.
8. Name the three coats of the eyeball.
9. What are the three subdivisions of the ear?
10. What is the sensory innervation of the external auditory meatus?
11. What is the sensory innervation of the mucosa of the middle ear?
12. What are the subdivisions of the osseous labyrinth?
13. Where is perilymph found? Where is endolymph found?
14. What two kinds of sensory fibers are found in the eighth cranial nerve?
15. Name three types of sensory end organs found in the skin.

CHAPTER 9

THE ENDOCRINE SYSTEM

The endocrine system includes the glands whose secretions are poured directly into the blood stream. They are known as the endocrine glands to distinguish them from the exocrine glands which pour their secretions through a duct on to a surface. Some glands are both exocrine and endocrine in function, and this explains why certain glands with obvious ducts are included in the endocrine group. The secretions of the endocrine group control the orderly functioning of the body; some are essential for life itself.

Functionally these glands may be studied from (1) the results of their removal, and (2) the result of the injection of extracts of the gland. Disturbances in the physiologic economy may result from (1) hypofunction, when the gland is not active enough to supply an adequate amount of its hormone for the body and (2) hyperfunction, when there is an overactivity of the gland.

Figs. 206 and 207 show the general position of ductless glands in the male.

HYPOPHYSIS

Anatomy.—The hypophysis or pituitary body is a small oval mass about the size of a pea lying in the sella turcica of the sphenoid bone and attached by a slender stalk to the under surface of the brain just behind the optic chiasm (Fig. 184). The sella is lined with dura mater. A sheet of the same tissue stretched over the fossa forms the diphragm of the sella. There is a small central hole in this diaphragm through which the stalk passes. The gland also has coverings derived from the arachnoid and the pia mater. It is supplied by small vessels which arise from the internal carotid arteries and from the arterial circle of the brain.

The pituitary is surrounded by a venous circle composed of the two cavernous sinuses laterally and the anterior and posterior intercavernous sinuses. The veins from the gland drain into these sinuses. Since the third, fourth, sixth, and part of the fifth cranial nerves pass through the cavernous sinus, it is obvious that many very important structures are in close relation to the pituitary. In

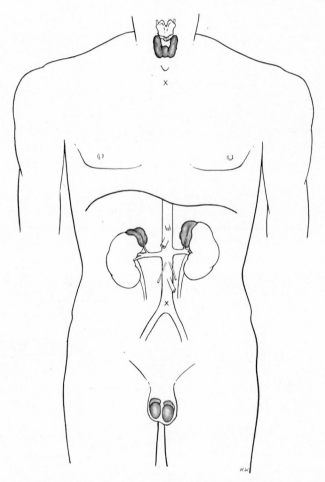

Fig. 206.—Diagram showing general position of certain ductless glands in the male: the thyroid, adrenals, and testes. The upper X marks the position in the infant of the thymus gland, and the lower X that of the aortic paraganglia.

tumors of this gland there are usually visual disturbances due to pressure on the optic chiasm, but there may be disturbances of the other nerves or of circulation.

Many nerve fibers enter the pituitary from the plexus on the internal carotid, and there are bundles of fibers connecting the pituitary with nuclei in the diencephalon.

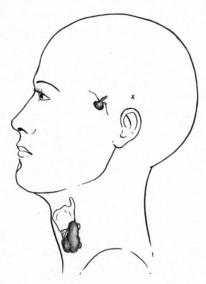

Fig. 207.—Diagram showing general position of ductless glands of head and neck. *X* marks the position of the pineal body.

The hypophysis is divided into a larger anterior lobe and a smaller posterior lobe by a thin sheet of tissue lying between the two lobes known as the intermediate part. In man the intermediate part is very thin, and the two lobes are not sharply separated. From the anterior lobe there is a thin, upward extension along the stalk called the tuberal part. Embryologically the posterior lobe is a derivative of the brain, and the remainder comes from the epithelial lining of the oral cavity. The posterior lobe and stalk are frequently referred to as the neurohypophysis, and the remainder of the gland as the adenohypophysis. In man the intermediate part has no known function.

Functions.—The adenohypophysis is known to secrete at least six different hormones. There is a somatotropic hormone which is essential for normal body growth. Underproduction of this substance during childhood results in a dwarf. Overproduction in childhood results in a giant, and in adult life produces acromegaly. There are other hormones which profoundly influence the thyroid gland, the adrenal cortex, and the gonads. These are known respectively as thyrotropic, adrenocorticotropic, and gonadotropic hormones. The follicle-stimulating hormone and the interstitial cell-stimulating hormone (luteinizing hormones) have exceedingly complex relationships with the ovaries or testes. They stimulate the production of mature ova or sperm cells, and in the female they aid in regulating the menstrual cycle. A hormone called prolactin is formed that stimulates the production of milk after childbirth. The two hormones influencing the gonads directly and prolactin are often grouped together as the three gonadotropic hormones of the adenohypophysis. Destruction of the adenohypophysis leads to atrophy and hypofunction of these glands of. internal secretion; excessive secretion of these hormones causes overactivity of these glands.

The neurohypophysis secretes a substance called the antidiuretic hormone which is needed for the kidneys to concentrate urine properly and thus conserve water in the body. If this hormone is deficient, diabetes insipidus results. Another secretion of the neurohypophysis stimulates the contraction of uterine musculature and also tends to raise blood pressure by causing increased constriction of arterioles.

Because of the large number of hormones produced by the hypophysis the gland is sometimes referred to as the "master" gland.

THYROID GLAND

Anatomy.—The thyroid gland, a horseshoe-shaped mass clasping the upper part of the trachea, lies in the lower part of the neck. It has a large lobe on each side and a median bar, the isthmus, which lies in front of the upper rings of the trachea (usually the second, third, and fourth).

The superior thyroid artery, a branch of the external carotid, enters the gland at the upper end of each lobe and the inferior thyroid artery, a branch of the subclavian, enters at the lower end of each lobe. Nerve fibers from the superior and middle cervical ganglia go to the blood vessels of the gland.

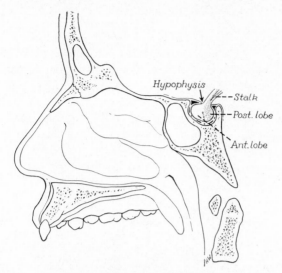

Fig. 208.—Diagram of sagittal section of skull to show the hypophysis in the sella turcica.

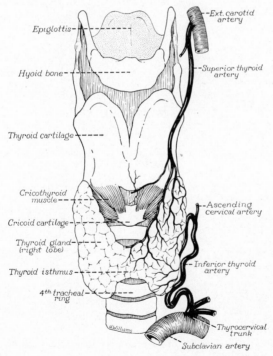

Fig. 209.—Anterior view of thyroid gland and larynx.

The gland is enclosed within a fibrous capsule which fuses on each side with the fascia surrounding the carotid artery and is intimately united to that of the trachea. In front of the thyroid are the sternohyoid and sternothyroid muscles, and these muscles must be pulled aside or cut in operations on the gland. Behind and lateral to each lobe is the carotid sheath, and a surgeon must avoid injury to the carotid artery, the vagus nerve, and particularly the recurrent laryngeal branch. Usually he does not disturb the posterior inferior portion of either lobe in order to avoid these structures as well as the parathyroid glands.

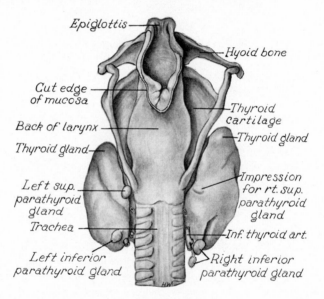

Fig. 210.—Thyroid and parathyroid glands, posterior view. The specimen is that of a child with an asymmetric larynx. The mucosa and perichondrium have been removed except around the aditus. The right inferior parathyroid gland is double in this case. (W.R.U. museum specimen N62.)

Goiter is an enlargement of the gland. This enlargement may involve part or all of the gland; it may be moderate or considerable. In hyperthyroidism the gland is softer, more vascular, and usually larger than it is in health. The size of the gland increases in adolescence, menstruation, and pregnancy.

Function.—The secretion of the thyroid gland is called thyroxin, a hormone which has a marked effect on the metabolism of all the cells of the body. Hypothyroidism results in a decrease in the basal metabolic rate and hyperthyroidism in an increase. Iodine is essential for the formation of thyroxin.

Hypothyroidism, if it occurs in infancy, leads to a condition known as cretinism. The child fails to grow and is imbecile and infantile. If treatment is not delayed too long, the feeding of thyroid gland or the injection of thyroxin will improve the condition. The disease is usually the result of an inadequate iodine intake by the mother and occurs most commonly in districts in which the soil contains little iodine.

Hypothyroidism in an adult produces myxedema. A person takes on a bloated appearance. The skin is sallow and dry and the senses are dulled. The victim is lethargic and mentally dull. Again, thyroxin will alleviate the symptoms.

In hyperthyroidism a person is nervous, restless, and irritable; the heart rate is increased, and the blood pressure is elevated. Despite a very good appetite the patient loses weight. The eyes frequently become protuberant. Removal of part of the gland and certain drugs alleviate the disease.

PARATHYROID GLANDS

Anatomy.—On the back of the thyroid gland and usually embedded within its capsule are several small, round, granular bodies called the parathyroid glands. (See Fig. 210.) There are usually two pairs, but there may be more or less. There is also a great variation in size, but commonly they resemble grains of wheat. Each gland is supplied by a single artery which may arise from any branch of the superior or inferior thyroid arteries.

Function.—The parathyroids are concerned with the regulation of the calcium content of the blood. Calcium is also important in the construction of bones and teeth, and the calcium level of the blood is important in determining this formation. Thus, the secretion of the parathyroids, Parathormone, plays a role along with vitamin D in the calcium balance of the body.

In hypoparathyroidism the most striking manifestation is tetany, an uncontrolled twitching of the muscles of the body. This is due to a lowering of the calcium ion concentration of the fluids of the body to the point where the nervous system becomes hyperirritable. Treatment to raise the blood calcium will correct the condition.

Hyperparathyroidism results in an increased blood calcium concentration and consequently lethargy and lassitude. As a result of the high blood calcium relatively huge quantities of calcium salts are excreted in the urine. A person cannot be kept in a positive calcium balance, and there is a progressive decalcification of the bones. Usually such a condition is associated with an adenoma of one of the parathyroid glands, the removal of which tends to relieve the condition.

ADRENAL GLANDS

Anatomy.—An adrenal or suprarenal gland fits like a cap over the upper end of each kidney. (See Fig. 292 and Plate 27.) There is a fibrous capsule, the tunica fibrosa, a cortex of glandular tissue, and an inner mass, the medulla, which is very vascular and composed of chromaffin tissue, so called because it stains yellow or brown when treated with dyes containing chromium salts. The cortex and medulla are functionally two endocrine glands and have different embryologic origins; the cortex is a derivative of the primitive body wall, whereas the chromaffin tissue develops in close relation to the sympathetic ganglia. Each adrenal gland has three arteries, one from the inferior phrenic, one from the aorta, and one from the renal artery.

Each gland is richly supplied with nerves forming an adrenal plexus in the capsule. There are nerve connections with the celiac plexus, the vagus nerve, and the phrenic nerve.

Functions.—The adrenal cortex is essential for life. A number of hormones are produced which collectively are called corticosteroids. At the present time they are being studied intensively. It is known that one of these corticosteroids stimulates the liver to produce glycogen and increases the amount of glucose in the blood. Another stimulates the kidneys to retain sodium. Animals deprived of the adrenal cortex show a rapid decline in body weight, profound weakness, low blood pressure, low blood volume, a decline in blood sodium, and an increase in blood potassium. In man, Addison's disease, which shows many of the signs just described, is relieved by the administration of properly prepared extracts of adrenal cortex or by the administration of the corticosteroids.

The adrenal cortex may also have an influence on the gonads. During childhood hypertrophy of the cortex leads to precocious sexual development and in an adult to excessive masculinization.

The adrenal medulla produces epinephrine, which has the same effects on the organism as does the stimulation of sympathetic nerves (thoracolumbar outflow) and may be looked upon as a mechanism to fortify the body for increased activity. It causes an increase in the heart rate, an increase in blood pressure, an increased blood flow, and decreased activity of the gastrointestinal tract. The adrenal medulla is not essential for life.

PANCREAS

The pancreas will be described as an exocrine gland with the discussion on the digestive system. Within its substance are the islets of Langerhans composed of irregular nests of polygonal cells which secrete insulin into the blood stream. (See Fig. 279.) This substance is necessary for normal metabolism. In the usual histologic preparation of pancreatic tissue the islet cells are pale and the cytoplasm is granular. The islets have a rich blood supply.

Insulin.—The hormone function of the pancreas is concerned with the carbohydrate metabolism of the body. The specific secretion is known as insulin.

In hypofunction the blood sugar rises to abnormally high levels (hyperglycemia), and as a result glucose is excreted in the urine (glycosuria). These are the outstanding characteristics of diabetes mellitus. There seems to be an impaired ability in both the storage and the oxidation of glucose.

In hyperinsulinism the blood sugar is low (hypoglycemia), and the glycogen stores of the body are scanty as a result of an increased sugar utilization. When the blood sugar level falls low enough (20 mg. per 100 cc.), a person becomes anxious, perspires, and, if not supplied with sugar, will become unconscious.

GONADS

The testes and ovaries, in addition to forming the male or female reproductive cells, also secrete into the blood stream certain substances which control the appearance of the secondary sex characters, among which are the contours of the body, the distribution of hair, and pitch of the voice. The testes and the ovaries will be described in the chapters on male and female genitalia.

PLACENTA

The placenta is an organ developed within the uterus during pregnancy in order that the growing fetus may secure nourishment from the maternal blood stream and may excrete its waste material into the maternal blood. Certain cells of the placenta are known to be a source of sex hormones, and they may secrete other hormones. Therefore the placenta must be listed as a temporary gland of the endocrine system.

The glands described in the foregoing sections of this chapter are known to have endocrine functions. In the remaining sections certain structures of the body are grouped which, at the present time, have not been proved to have any endocrine function. It is, however, convenient to describe them here.

PINEAL BODY

The pineal body is a small cone-shaped mass of tissue, about one quarter of an inch in length, attached by means of a hollow stalk to the roof of the third ventricle of the brain and lying on the superior colliculi (Fig. 185). The cavity of the stalk is a recess of the third ventricle.

The pineal body is covered by pia mater, and fibrous septa formed from the pia subdivide the gland into small lobules. The most distinctive cells within the lobules are large and round, with granular cytoplasm and deeply staining nuclei.

PARAGANGLIA

Associated with the plexuses of the sympathetic system and with its ganglia are tiny masses of chromaffin tissue known as paraganglia. In development, chemical reactions, and structure each of these tiny structures resembles the medulla of the adrenal gland. They vary greatly in number and as many as seventy have been found; usually there are not nearly this many.

The most prominent are the aortic paraganglia. In the newborn child these are a pair of elongated masses of tissue nearly half an inch in length lying in front of the abdominal aorta near the origin of the inferior mesenteric artery. They regress during childhood and in the adult are scarcely visible.

Review Questions

1. Where is the hypophysis located?
2. List the hormones produced by the adenohypophysis.
3. What hormones are produced by the neurohypophysis?
4. Describe the thyroid gland. What is its function?
5. What is the result of hypothyroidism in infancy? In adult life?
6. Where are the parathyroid glands located? What is their function?
7. Where are the adrenal glands located?
8. What are the symptoms of a deficiency in adrenal cortical activity?
9. What portion of the pancreas has an endocrine function?
10. Name three secondary sex characteristics.

unit 4   **MAINTENANCE OF THE BODY TISSUES**

CHAPTER 10

THE CIRCULATORY SYSTEM

The circulatory system consists of:

1. A muscular pump, the heart
2. A system of distributing vessels—arteries, capillaries, and veins
3. A circulating fluid, the blood
4. An auxiliary system for returning fluid from the tissue spaces, the lymphatic system

The blood is discussed in Chapter 3 and the lymphatic system is discussed in Chapter 11.

The blood is pumped from the heart through the arteries, which subdivide into smaller and smaller vessels, ending in capillaries which form networks in all the tissues of the body except cartilage, the cornea, and outer layers of the skin. From these capillaries arise venules which unite to form small veins, these in turn are tributaries of larger vessels which give place to the great veins emptying into the heart.

This entire system has one continuous smooth lining, endothelium, which, together with a small amount of connective tissue, forms the tunica intima. Capillaries have only this one coat, but veins and arteries have two other coats, the tunica media composed of smooth muscle and the tunica adventitia composed of connective tissue. The smooth muscle fibers of the tunica media have a circular arrangement, and in a few of the largest arteries a small number of longitudinal muscle fibers are found in the tunica adventitia. The amount of fibrous and elastic tissue varies, the arteries having more elastic tissue than the veins; in the first portions of the aorta and pulmonary arteries there is a great deal of elastic tissue and almost no smooth muscle. In a cross section of any artery and its accompanying veins, the arterial wall is thicker and stronger and the lumen remains round; the veins collapse when empty and the lumen almost disappears. There are semilunar folds of the tunica intima of veins forming valves which are arranged in pairs and have the free border directed toward

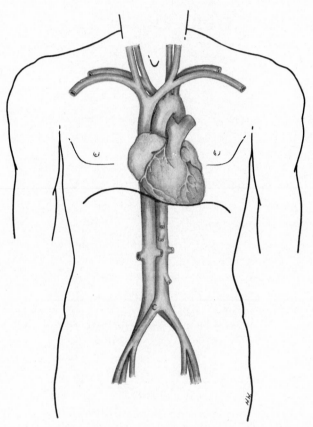

Fig. 211.—The general position of the heart and great vessels.

the heart, thus preventing a backflow of blood. Valves are more common in the deeper veins than in the superficial and in the lower extremity than in the upper.

Arteries with their accompanying veins usually run along the flexor side of a limb where they are well protected from injury and where there is little stretch on the vessels during movement. An artery is usually more deeply placed than its accompanying veins and lymphatic channels.

Arteries are well supplied with fine nerve fibers which are received from nearby nerve trunks.   These fibers form extensive

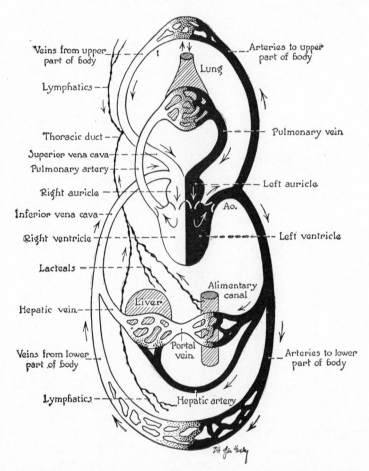

Fig. 212.—Diagram of the circulation of the blood.   The arterial, or oxygenated blood is shown in black; the venous blood in white; the lymphatics by beaded black lines.   The arrows indicate the direction of flow. The two arrows above lung indicate the interchange of air.   The auricle is sometimes used as a synonym for atrium as in the illustration.   (From McClendon: Physiological Chemistry, St. Louis, 1946, The C. V. Mosby Co.)

plexuses about the arteries and contain sensory fibers as well as vasomotor fibers. The larger blood vessels have within their walls smaller vessels to nourish the tunics, and these are known as vasa vasorum (vessels of vessels).

The blood carries oxygen and dissolved food material to the tissues of the body and carries waste material from the tissues to

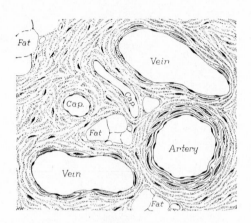

Fig. 213.—Cross section of small artery, accompanying veins, and capillaries.

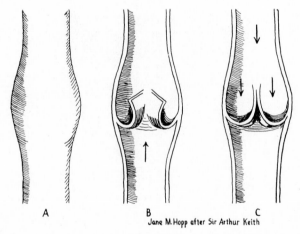

Jane M. Hopp after Sir Arthur Keith

Fig. 214.—Vein valves. *A,* External view showing dilatation at site of valve; *B,* vein opened and valves opened; *C,* valves closed to prevent backflow of blood.

the excretory organs of the body, namely, to the lungs, the kidneys, and the skin.

Blood vessels are subdivided into the following three groups:

1. The pulmonary system, which carries blood to and from the lungs
2. The portal system, which carries blood from the spleen, stomach, and intestines to the liver
3. The general or systemic system, which carries blood to and from the heart for the rest of the body

HEART

The heart is a four-chambered muscular organ completely divided into right and left portions by a septum. In each half there is an upper chamber, the atrium, which receives blood from the veins and a lower chamber, the ventricle, which pumps blood out into the arteries. There is an opening leading from the atrium to the ventricle supplied with valves which prevent blood from flowing back into the atrium when the ventricle contracts. There are valves performing a similar function at the outlet of each ventricle into the artery.

The heart, enclosed by pericardium, lies in the lower part of the mediastinum behind the sternum, between the lungs, above the middle portion of the diaphragm, and in front of the esophagus and the thoracic portion of the aorta.

The base of the heart is formed largely by the left atrium. The left pulmonary veins enter the left atrium on its left border. On the right border the superior and inferior venae cavae enter the right atrium while the right pulmonary veins pass transversely behind the right atrium to enter the left atrium.

The right border of the heart, formed by the right atrium, lies closely parallel to the right margin of the sternum from the level of the third to the sixth costal cartilage.

The inferior border of the heart extends from the level of the junction of the sixth right costal cartilage with the sternum to the fifth left intercostal space, about three inches from the sternum. This border is formed mostly by the right ventricle, but on the extreme left, the left ventricle enters into its composition at the apex of the heart.

The left border extends from the apex obliquely upward to the junction of the left third costal cartilage and the sternum. It

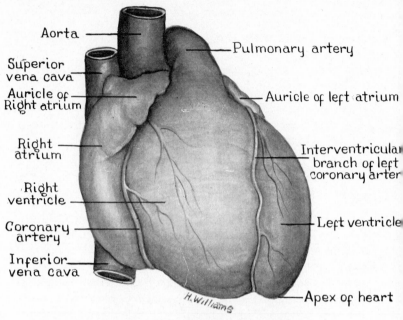

Fig. 215.—Heart, front view. (W.R.U. museum specimen.)

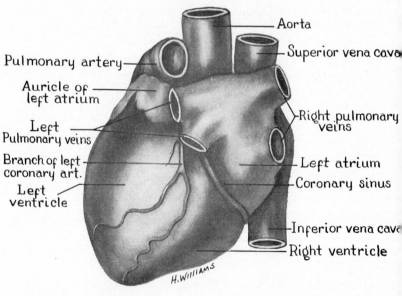

Fig. 216.—Heart, posterior view. (W.R.U. museum specimen.)

is formed mainly by the left ventricle but at its upper end by a small part of the left atrium also.

In short, thickset persons the heart lies more horizontally on the diaphragm, and its apex is a little higher and more to the left than in slender, tall persons.

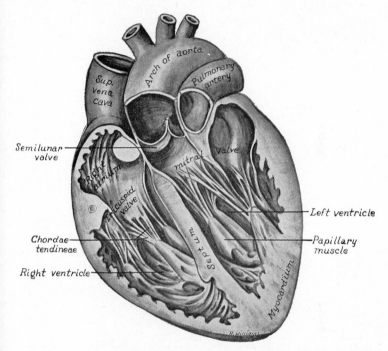

Fig. 217.—Anterior view of the interior of the heart. (From Anthony: Textbook of Anatomy and Physiology, St. Louis, 1946, The C. V. Mosby Co.)

Chambers of Heart.—The right atrium receives venous blood (blood, poor in oxygen and rich in carbon dioxide, returning from all parts of the body) from the venae cavae and from the walls of the heart itself by way of the coronary sinus. The opening from the right atrium into the right ventricle is called the tricuspid orifice because the valve has three cusps. The walls of the right atrium are relatively thin and smooth except in front where the muscles are arranged in columns to form pectinate bundles. The outer side of the atrium has an outpouching called the auricle because of its earlike shape.

The left atrium receives oxygenated blood from the lungs by way of the four pulmonary veins. The left atrioventricular valve is called the mitral valve and has only two cusps. There are pectinate muscles in the wall, and there is an auricular appendage on the outer side.

In the wall separating the two atria is a small oval depression, the fossa ovalis, marking the site of an opening between the two atria which closed at birth.

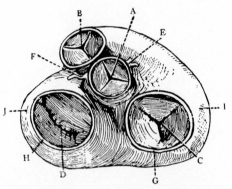

Fig. 218.—Valves of heart. The valves are viewed from above, the atria having been partially removed. *A*, Aorta with semilunar valve; *B*, pulmonary artery and valve; *C*, tricuspid valve; *D*, mitral valve; *E*, right coronary artery; *F*, left coronary artery; *G*, wall of right atrium; *H*, wall of left atrium; *I*, wall of right ventricle; *J*, wall of left ventricle. (From Stewart: Manual of Physiology, New York, 1914, William Wood & Co.)

The right ventricle has much thicker walls than the atria. It receives venous blood from the right atrium and pumps it through the pulmonary artery into the lungs. The opening into the artery is guarded by a valve having three cusps. The musculature of the ventricle is arranged in projecting muscle columns, called trabeculae carneae. Other muscle bundles form cone-shaped masses, called papillary muscles. From the apex of each papillary muscle a strong, white band, chorda tendinea, extends to the edge of the tricuspid valve. One of the trabeculae carneae stretches across the lower part of the cavity of the right ventricle and is known as the moderator band.

The left ventricle has even thicker walls than the right ventricle. It receives oxygenated blood from the left atrium and sends it through the aorta to all parts of the body. The aortic opening has a valve of three cusps similar to the one for the pulmonary artery. The ventricular wall is provided with trabeculae (columnae) carneae. The papillary muscles of the left ventricle are larger than those of the right and connect with the edges of the mitral valve by means of chordae tendineae.

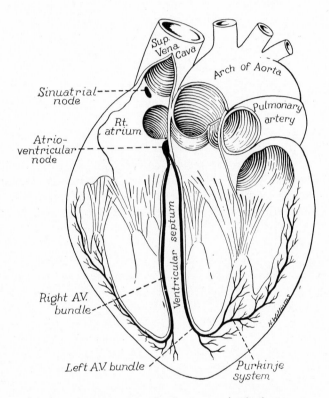

Fig. 219.—Nerve conducting system in the heart.

The valves between the right ventricle and the pulmonary artery and between the left ventricle and the aorta are three simple semilunar flaps attached at their outer border to the wall of the vessel. They are composed of endothelium, with some strengthening bands of fibrous tissue. Each ventricular valve is a fold of endothelium, but the free margin is irregular and attached to the chordae tendineae. In contractions of the ventricle the chordae tendineae keep the valves from turning inside out. The action is very similar to that of the cords of a parachute. The right atrioventricular orifice will admit three fingers and the left two.

In the septum between the two halves of the heart is a bundle of pale muscle fibers which partakes somewhat of the nature of nervous tissue and is the conducting system of the heart. It begins as a small node in the lower part of the posterior wall of the right atrium near the opening of the superior vena cava; this node is known as the sinoatrial, or sinuatrial, node (SA node or node of Keith and Flack). The atrioventricular node (AV node or node of Tawara) is located in the interatrial wall of the right atrium just above the opening of the coronary sinus. From the AV node arises the atrioventricular bundle (bundle of Kent or bundle of His) which runs forward in the atrial septum and then into the ventricular septum where it divides into right and left branches which break up into many fine strands beneath the endocardium and pass to the muscle bundles of the ventricles. This final network is also called the Purkinje system. In summary, the conducting system of the heart consists of the sinoatrial node, the atrioventricular node, the atrioventricular bundle with two branches, and the final network beneath the endocardium of the ventricles.

Nerve fibers pass to the heart from the vagus nerves (cranial autonomic outflow) and from the upper thoracic nerves (thoracolumbar autonomic outflow). Sensory nerve fibers accompany the thoracic branches, and since the first and second thoracic nerves also receive sensory fibers from the inner side of the arm, patients with heart disease (angina pectoris or coronary thrombosis) often complain of severe pain in the inner side of the left arm when the actual source of the pain is in the heart.

The postnatal circulation of blood through the heart may be summarized in the following manner. Venous blood received from the venae cavae into the right atrium passes through the tricuspid orifice into the right ventricle, which in turn pumps the blood through the pulmonary orifice into the pulmonary artery and thus to the lungs. Oxygenated blood is received from the lungs into the left atrium through the pulmonary veins and passes through the mitral orifice into the left ventricle, which pumps it into the aorta and so to all parts of the body.

In the fetus the placenta acts as an organ of nourishment, excretion, and respiration. Fetal blood passes to the placenta by way of the umbilical arteries which are branches of the internal

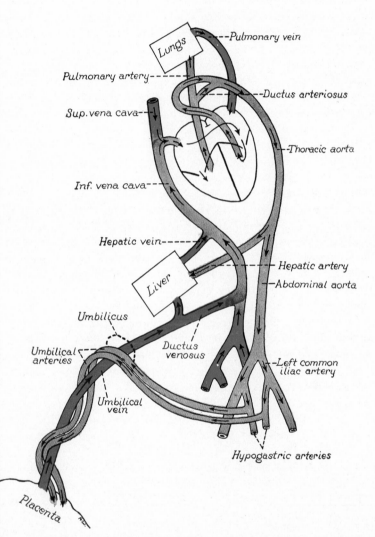

Pulmonary vein

Lungs

Pulmonary artery

Ductus arteriosus

Sup. vena cava

Thoracic aorta

Inf. vena cava

Hepatic vein

Hepatic artery

Abdominal aorta

Liver

Umbilicus

Umbilical arteries

Ductus venosus

Left common iliac artery

Umbilical vein

Hypogastric arteries

Placenta

PLATE 9.—Diagram of fetal circulation. (From Anthony: Textbook of Anatomy and Physiology, The C. V. Mosby Co.)

iliac (hypogastric) arteries. Oxygenated blood returns to the fetus by way of the umbilical vein. When the arterial blood reaches the liver, most of it is shunted around this organ by means of the ductus venosus and empties into the inferior vena cava and on into the right atrium. From there some blood passes into the right ventricle and some through an opening in the atrial septum, the foramen ovale, into the left atrium. The blood which passes into the right ventricle is pumped into the pulmonary artery, but very little goes to the lungs because most of it is shunted by means of the ductus arteriosus into the aorta. The blood in the left atrium goes to the left ventricle and thence into the aorta. At birth the placenta ceases to function, and the lungs become the organ of respiration. The umbilical arteries eventually become the lateral umbilical ligaments, two fibrous bands lying beneath the anterior parietal peritoneum and passing from the umbilicus into the true pelvis. The umbilical vein becomes the ligamentum teres hepatis, or round ligament of the liver, passing as a cord from the umbilicus within the falciform ligament of the liver to the porta hepatis. The ductus venosus and the ductus arteriosus become fibrous cords. The foramen ovale is closed by valves and eventually becomes the fossa ovalis, a thin, oval area of the atrial septum.

In health the heart is roughly proportionate to the size of a person and is often said to be as large as the clenched fist. Average measurements for the adult heart are five inches in length, three and one-half in breath, and two and one-half in thickness.

Pericardium.—The pericardium is the sac which surrounds the heart. It lies in the middle mediastinum behind the sternum. The pericardium has a serous lining like that of the pleura; the parietal layer lines the pericardial sac; the visceral layer covers the heart itself.

The visceral layer continues over the beginnings of the great vessels to merge into the parietal layer at the base of the heart.

Enveloping the parietal serous membrane is a tough, fibrous coat called the fibrous pericardium.

ARTERIES

Pulmonary Artery.—The pulmonary artery arises from the upper left portion of the right ventricle on the front of the heart, curves up and then back, passing to the left of the ascending aorta to divide about two inches from its origin into right and left

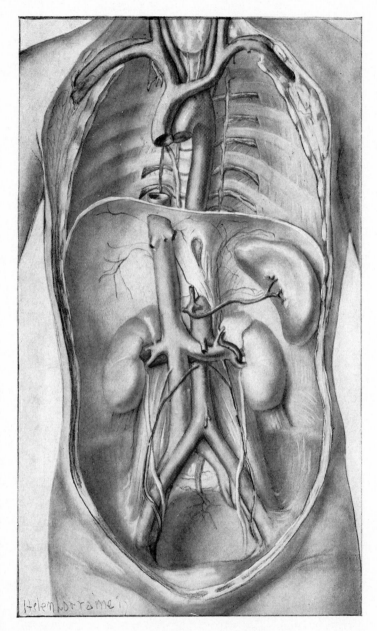

PLATE 10.—The aorta and its branches. (From Christian: Anatomy for Nurses, The C. V. Mosby Co.)

branches. The right branch passes behind the ascending aorta and the superior vena cava, enters the hilus of the right lung, and subdivides into branches for the lobes. The left branch of the pulmonary artery passes into the hilus of the left lung.

Thoracic Aorta and Branches.—The aorta arises from the base of the left ventricle. At its origin it lies to the right and behind the pulmonary artery. The ascending part of the aorta passes upward in front of the right branch of the pulmonary artery. The aortic arch curves over this vessel to occupy a position to the left of the vertebral column. The aorta then descends through the posterior part of the mediastinum and passes behind the diaphragm into the abdomen.

At its origin the ascending aorta has a dilated portion, and the three semilunar valves which guard the orifice form three secondary sinuses (the sinuses of Valsalva). The two coronary arteries which supply the heart arise from two of these sinuses. The right coronary arises from the anterior sinus and has several branches: the interventricular, right atrial, right marginal, and anterior ventricular branches. The left coronary arises from the left posterior aortic sinus and has circumflex, interventricular, and left atrial branches. The two interventricular branches anastomose with each other at the apex of the heart, and the circumflex branch of the left coronary anastomoses with the terminal part of the right coronary to form an arterial ring around the base of the ventricles.

Three branches originate from the arch of the aorta:

1. Innominate (brachiocephalic)
2. Left common carotid
3. Left subclavian

The innominate artery subdivides to form the right subclavian and right common carotid arteries. The subclavian artery supplies the upper extremity and gives one important branch, the vertebral artery, to the brain.

Each common carotid artery passes up into the neck beside the trachea and divides into the external and internal carotid arteries. The carotid sinus is a dilatation of the terminal portion of the common carotid and of the beginning of the internal carotid. Its walls are quite elastic, and the sensory nerve endings from this region passing to the glossopharyngeal nerve are part of the blood pressure and respiratory regulating mechanisms.

The external carotid supplies the structures in the neck, face, mouth, jaws, and scalp.   Its branches are the superior thyroid, lingual, external maxillary (facial), occipital, posterior auricular, ascending pharyngeal, superficial temporal, and internal maxillary (maxillary) arteries.   The middle meningeal artery is a branch

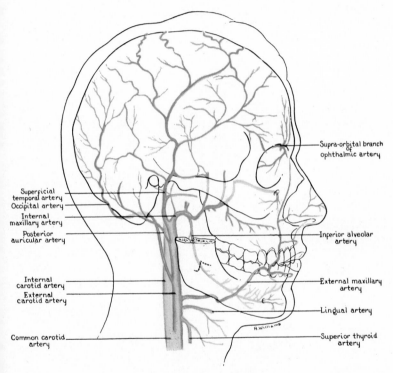

Labels on image:
Supra-orbital branch of ophthalmic artery
Superficial temporal artery
Occipital artery
Internal maxillary artery
Posterior auricular artery
Inferior alveolar artery
Internal carotid artery
External carotid artery
External maxillary artery
Lingual artery
Common carotid artery
Superior thyroid artery
H. Williams

PLATE 11.—Arteries of the face.   Deeper vessels are shown in paler color than superficial vessels.

of the internal maxillary artery which plays an important role in the blood supply of the meninges of the brain.   Other branches of the internal maxillary artery supply the nasal cavity and palate.

The internal carotid enters the middle cranial fossa through the carotid canal where it helps to form the arterial circle at the base of the brain.   The vertebral arteries pass up through the lateral foramina of the cervical vertebrae and through the foramen magnum into the cranial cavity. On the under surface of the brain stem the two vertebral arteries unite to form the basilar artery which continues into the middle cranial fossa. By means of anastomotic branches the two internal carotids and the basilar artery form an arterial circle at the base of the brain (circle of Willis). From these vessels arise the arteries supplying the brain. The anterior and middle cerebral arteries are branches of the internal carotid; the posterior cerebral artery is a branch of the basilar. The ophthalmic artery supplying the eyeball and forehead also comes from the internal carotid.

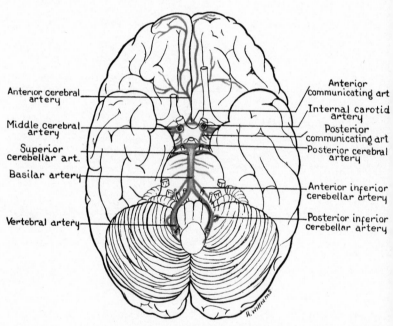

PLATE 12.—Arteries of base of brain.   (W.R.U. 540, male, Negro, aged 45 years, and museum specimen C182.)

The subclavian artery, having given origin to the vertebral artery, supplies branches to the shoulder, chest wall, and neck. These branches are the thyrocervical trunk, the transverse cervical artery, the internal mammary artery, and the costocervical trunk. The continuation of the subclavian artery into the armpit is called the axillary artery, which in turn continues into the upper arm as the brachial artery. The axillary artery has six branches which supply the region of the shoulder joint, the supreme thoracic, thoracoacromial, lateral thoracic, subscapular, and anterior and posterior humeral circumflex arteries. The brachial artery has

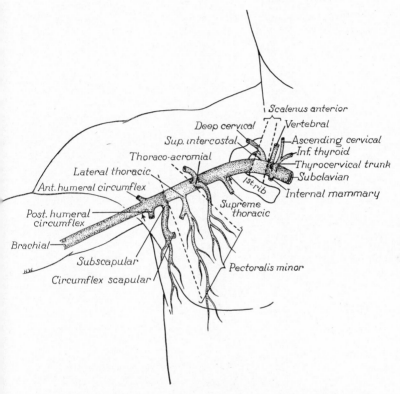

Fig. 220.—Branches of subclavian and axillary arteries. The anterior scalene and pectoralis minor muscles are shown in dotted outline. The arrows mark the anatomical limits of the axillary artery.

muscular branches and also gives off the profunda artery of the arm and the superior and inferior ulnar collateral arteries. At the elbow the brachial artery divides into the radial and ulnar arteries which pass down, one on each side of the forearm, giving off muscular and interosseous branches. In the palm the ulnar

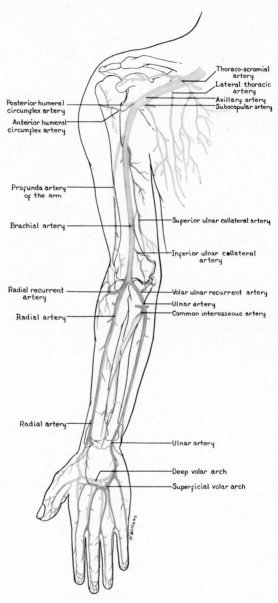

Thoraco-acromial artery
Lateral thoracic artery
Axillary artery
Subscapular artery
Posterior humeral circumflex artery
Anterior humeral circumflex artery
Profunda artery of the arm
Brachial artery
Superior ulnar collateral artery
Inferior ulnar collateral artery
Radial recurrent artery
Volar ulnar recurrent artery
Ulnar artery
Common interosseous artery
Radial artery
Radial artery
Ulnar artery
Deep volar arch
Superficial volar arch

PLATE 13.—Arteries of front of upper extremity. Deeper vessels shown in paler color than superficial vessels.

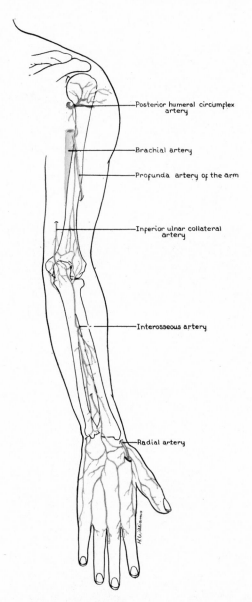

Posterior humeral circumflex artery

Brachial artery

Profunda artery of the arm

Inferior ulnar collateral artery

Interosseous artery

Radial artery

PLATE 14.—Arteries of back of upper extremity. Deeper vessels are shown in paler color than superficial vessels.

and radial arteries form two palmar arches, a superficial and a deep, which give off numerous branches to the hand and fingers. The rich anastomosis of the palmar arteries makes it difficult to control arterial hemorrhage of the hand, and often each end of a cut vessel must be tied. The pulse is usually palpated in the lower end of the radial artery where it lies just under the skin on the front of the radius.

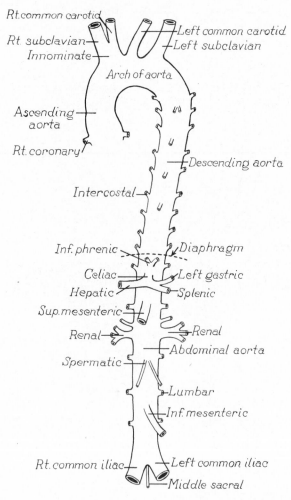

Fig. 221.—The branches of the aorta.

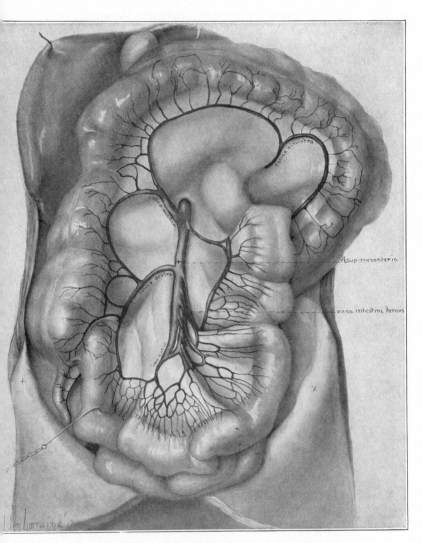

PLATE 15.—Superior mesenteric artery. (From Christian: Anatomy for Nurses.)

The descending portion of the thoracic aorta supplies branches to the chest wall, the esophagus, the bronchi, and the mediastinum. There are usually nine pairs of intercostal arteries for the nine lower intercostal spaces. There are also intercostal branches from the internal mammary artery, and the first and second intercostal spaces are supplied from the costocervical trunk.

Abdominal Aorta and Branches.—The abdominal aorta supplies both visceral and parietal branches. The visceral branches are:

1. One adrenal artery to each adrenal gland
2. One renal artery to each kidney
3. One spermatic artery to each ovary (or testis)
4. A single median celiac artery dividing into three main branches, namely, hepatic, splenic, and left gastric (See Plate 24.)

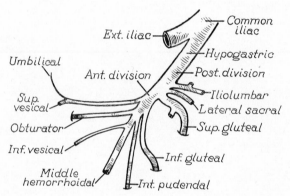

Fig. 222.—The branches of the right internal iliac (hypogastric) artery.

5. A single median superior mesenteric artery which supplies many branches to the small intestine and the proximal half of the large intestine. (See Plate 15.)
6. A single median inferior mesenteric artery which supplies branches to the distal half of the large intestine (See Plate 25.)

The parietal branches go to the diaphragm (phrenic artery) and to the dorsal abdominal wall (lumbar arteries).

There are anastomoses in the region of the pancreas between branches of the celiac and superior mesenteric arteries, and branches from superior and inferior mesenteric arteries going to the colon anastomose with each other in the mesocolon.

The abdominal aorta divides into the common iliac arteries in front of the fourth lumbar vertebra. Each common iliac artery in turn divides into the internal iliac (hypogastric) and external iliac arteries.

The internal iliac artery supplies the structures lying within the walls of the pelvis, the buttocks, and the external genitalia. It has an anterior and a posterior division, and its branches are quite variable. Usually from the posterior division arise the iliolumbar, lateral sacral, and superior gluteal arteries. From the posterior division arise the obturator, inferior gluteal, internal pudendal, inferior vesical, middle hemorrhoidal (rectal), and superior vesical (remains of the umbilical artery of the fetus) arteries. In the female the uterine and vaginal arteries also arise from the anterior division.

A more detailed description of the arterial supply is given with the discussion of the individual visceral organs.

The main blood supply of the lower extremity is the external iliac artery which becomes the femoral in the thigh and the popliteal behind the knee, beyond which it subdivides into the anterior and posterior tibial arteries which pass down the front and back of the leg. The posterior tibial passes around the medial malleolus into the sole of the foot where it subdivides into medial and lateral plantar branches. The posterior tibial artery can be palpated just below and behind the medial malleolus. The anterior tibial artery passes down the front of the leg on the outer side of the tibia to the dorsum of the foot where it is called the dorsalis pedis. The terminal branches of the anterior and posterior tibial arteries anastomose to form arterial arches in the sole of the foot from which vessels pass to the toes.

The external iliac artery has the following branches: inferior epigastric and deep circumflex iliac. The femoral artery, in addition to numerous muscular branches, has the superficial circumflex iliac, superficial epigastric, superficial and deep external pudendal arteries, the profunda artery of the thigh, and the highest artery of the knee. The popliteal gives off five genicular branches which enter into an anastomosis at about the knee joint.

Within each extremity there are numerous anastomosing branches about each joint. If the main blood channel is blocked off, the distal portion of the limb is able to receive nourishment

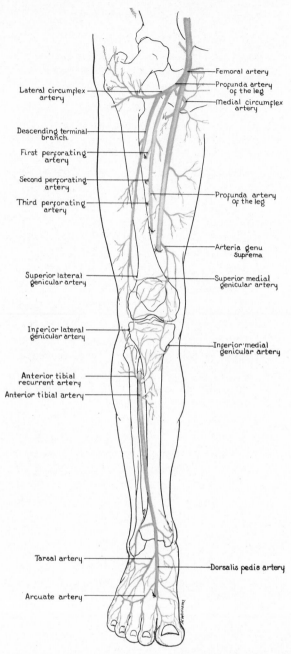

Lateral circumflex artery

Descending terminal branch.

First perforating artery

Second perforating artery

Third perforating artery

Superior lateral genicular artery

Inferior lateral genicular artery

Anterior tibial recurrent artery

Anterior tibial artery

Tarsal artery

Arcuate artery

Femoral artery

Profunda artery of the leg

Medial circumflex artery

Profunda artery of the leg

Arteria genu Suprema

Superior medial genicular artery

Inferior medial genicular artery

Dorsalis pedis artery

PLATE 16.—Arteries of front of lower extremity. Deeper vessels are shown in paler color than superficial vessels.

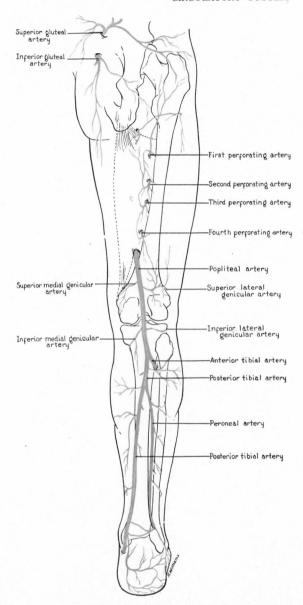

Superior gluteal artery

Inferior gluteal artery

First perforating artery

Second perforating artery

Third perforating artery

Fourth perforating artery

Popliteal artery

Superior medial genicular artery

Superior lateral genicular artery

Inferior lateral genicular artery

Inferior medial genicular artery

Anterior tibial artery

Posterior tibial artery

Peroneal artery

Posterior tibial artery

PLATE 17.—Arteries of back of lower extremity.   Deeper vessels shown in paler color than superficial vessels.   The adductor magnus muscle is dotted in to show relation to perforating arteries.

by blood flowing through these communicating channels which in time become large enough to permit normal functioning of the part. The main anastomoses about the hip, knee, ankle, shoulder, elbow, and wrist joints are shown in the colored drawings of the arteries.

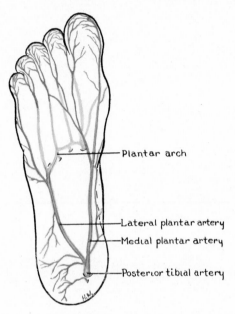

PLATE 18.—Arteries of sole of foot. Deeper vessels are shown in paler color than superficial vessels.

In the foregoing description of the arteries reference has been made to counting the pulse by palpating various peripheral vessels. For convenience this information will be summarized here. It is customary to take the pulse by palpating the radial artery at the wrist, but if this is impractical, the pulse may be obtained by palpating the superficial temporal artery in front of the ear, the common carotid artery along the anterior border of the sternocleidomastoid muscle, the external maxillary artery along the lower border of the mandible about halfway between the angle and symphysis, the brachial artery along the medial edge of the biceps brachii muscle, the femoral artery in the groin, the posterior tibial artery behind the medial malleolus, and the dorsalis pedis artery on the dorsum of the foot.

Table 12
Main Arteries

NAME	CHIEF BRANCHES	AREA SUPPLIED
Ascending aorta	Coronary	Heart
Aortic arch	Innominate Left subclavian Left common carotid	
Innominate	Right subclavian Right common carotid	
Common carotid	Internal carotid External carotid	Brain Neck and face
Subclavian	Vertebral Internal mammary Thyrocervical trunk Axillary	Brain **Chest** Neck Upper extremity
Axillary	Thoracoacromial trunk Subscapular Brachial	
Brachial	Profunda humeri Radial Ulnar	
Abdominal aorta	Celiac Superior mesenteric Inferior mesenteric Renal Spermatic Common iliac	Small intestine Large intestine Kidney Testis or ovary
Celiac	Hepatic Left gastric Splenic	Liver Stomach Spleen
Common iliac	Internal iliac External iliac	Pelvic region
External iliac	Inferior epigastric Femoral	Lower abdominal wall Lower extremity
Femoral	Profunda femoris Popliteal	
Popliteal	Anterior tibial Posterior tibial	

VEINS

The very large arteries and those for the viscera usually have but one accompanying vein, but the remaining arteries usually have two companion veins which have the same name as the artery they accompany. The veins from the inferior extremities and abdomen empty into the inferior vena cava; those of the head, neck, upper extremity, and chest wall empty into the superior vena cava. The coronary sinus returns blood from the heart. From each lung there are two pulmonary veins which empty into the left atrium.

Certain veins and venous sinuses and systems require special mention. These are the superficial veins of the head and extremities, the azygos vein, the venous sinuses of the cranium, the portal vein, and the vertebral venous system.

The pattern of superficial veins is extremely variable from person to person and indeed there are marked differences on the right and left sides of the same person. The following descriptions define the usual formation.

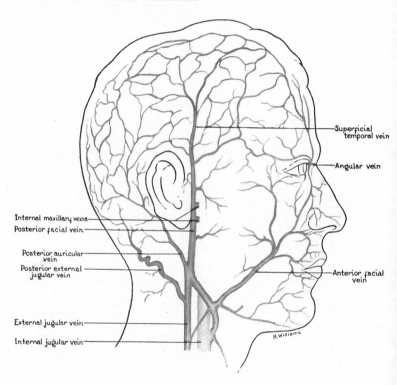

PLATE 19.—Superficial veins of the face and neck.

Superficial Veins.—The superficial veins of the face and scalp are abundant and anastomose freely. They tend to converge at a common meeting point below the ear by three main channels: the posterior auricular, the posterior facial, and the anterior facial channels. These form the external jugular vein which passes downward over the sternocleidomastoid muscle to the base of

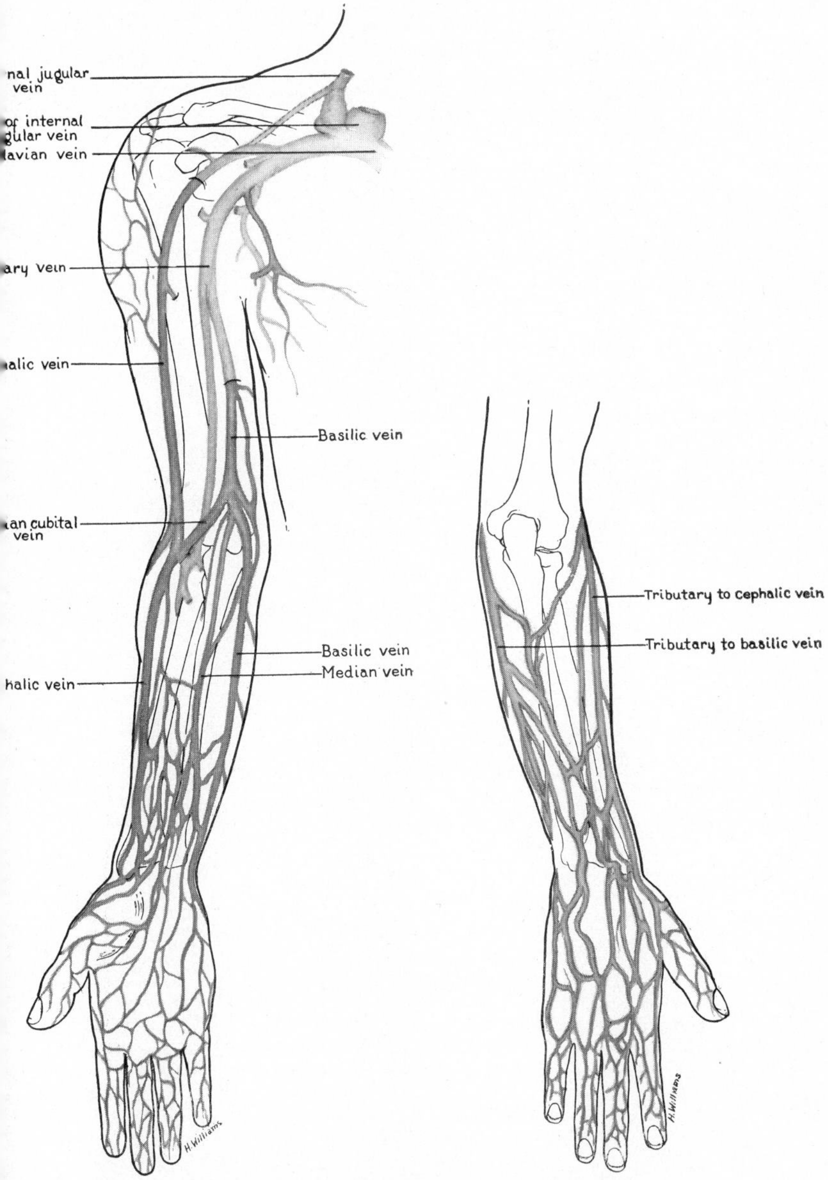
nal jugular vein
of internal
gular vein
lavian vein
ary vein
alic vein
Basilic vein
an cubital vein
Basilic vein
Median vein
halic vein
Tributary to cephalic vein
Tributary to basilic vein
H. Williams
H. Williams

PLATE 20.—*Left,* Superficial veins of front of upper extremity. An occasional connection between cephalic vein and external jugular vein is shown in dotted lines. *Right,* Superficial veins of back of forearm.

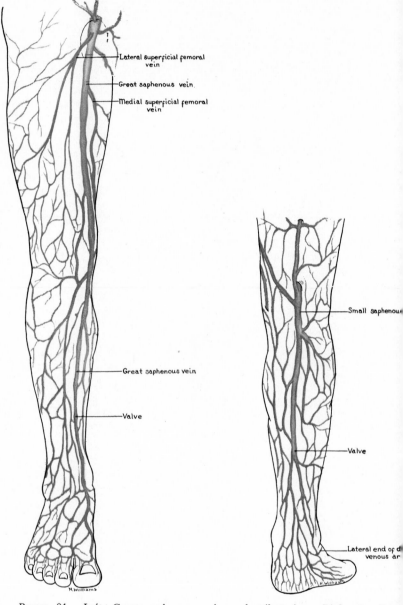

Lateral superficial femoral vein

Great saphenous vein

Medial superficial femoral vein

Great saphenous vein

Valve

Small saphenou

Valve

Lateral end of d venous ar

H.Williams

H.Williams

PLATE 21.—*Left,* Great saphenous vein and tributaries. *Right,* Small saphenous vein and tributaries.

the neck where it empties into the junction of the internal jugular and the subclavian veins.

The superficial veins of the upper extremity begin in the dorsal and volar venous arches of the hand. These arches at the wrist tend to form two main channels, a cephalic vein and a basilic vein.

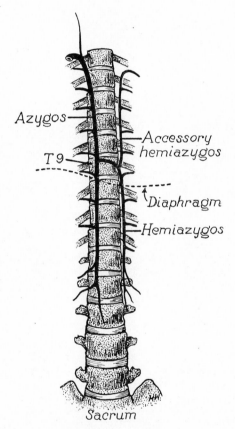

Fig. 223.—Azygos veins.

The cephalic vein passes up the outer side of the forearm and upper arm, emptying into the axillary vein just below the clavicle. Occasionally it passes over the clavicle to empty into the external jugular vein.

The basilic vein passes up the inner side of the forearm and upper arm, ultimately joining the axillary vein. There are several connecting veins in the forearm. In front of the elbow there is usually a prominent vessel, called the median cubital vein, which connects the basilic and cephalic veins. This is the vessel of choice for venepuncture and blood transfusions.

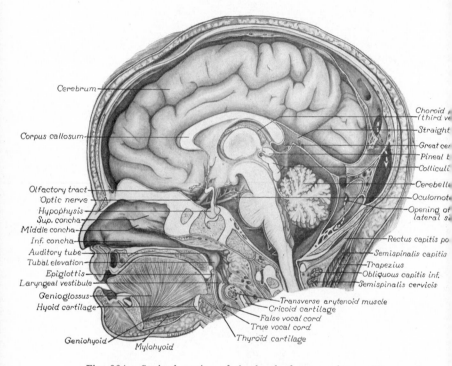

Cerebrum

Corpus callosum

Olfactory tract
Optic nerve
Hypophysis
Sup. concha
Middle concha
Inf. concha
Auditory tube
Tubal elevation
Epiglottis
Laryngeal vestibule
Genioglossus
Hyoid cartilage

Geniohyoid
Mylohyoid

Choroid (third ve
Straight
Great cer
Pineal b
Colliculi
Cerebelle
Oculomot
Opening of lateral si
Rectus capitis po
Semispinalis capitis
Trapezius
Obliquous capitis inf.
Semispinalis cervicis

Transverse arytenoid muscle
Cricoid cartilage
False vocal cord
True vocal cord
Thyroid cartilage

Fig. 224.—Sagittal section of the head of a term fetus. Because there was a subdural hemorrhage, the brain has been compressed and the blood sinuses and subdural spaces are dilated. (W.R.U. C202.)

The superficial veins of the lower extremity begin at the ends of the dorsal venous arch on the foot. The great saphenous vein (long saphenous) springs from the arch at the front on the inner side of the ankle. It passes up the inner side of the leg and thigh and empties into the femoral vein just below the inguinal ligament. The small saphenous (short saphenous) vein begins on the outer side of the ankle, passes up the back of the leg, and empties into the popliteal vein behind the knee. Venous valves which break up the column of blood into segments are common in the saphenous veins, forming small expansions in the course of the vessel. Valves are also found in other veins but are less numerous.

Azygos Veins.—The azygos vein arises from the back of the inferior vena cava at the level of the first or second lumbar vertebra and passes upward on the right side of the vertebral column through the aortic opening of the diaphragm and empties into the terminal part of the superior vena cava. On the left the hemiazygos passes upward through the left crus of the diaphragm, crosses in front of the vertebral column, and empties into the azygos vein. The accessory hemiazygos drains blood from the upper intercostal spaces on the left into the azygos or the hemiazygos vein. The azygos veins drain blood from the lumbar area, from the chest wall, from the bronchial veins, and from the mediastinum and serve as an intermediate blood channel between the superior and inferior venae cavae.

Venous Sinuses Within the Cranium.—These sinuses are found between the layers of the dura mater and receive blood from the brain. The superior sagittal sinus begins near the crista galli in the anterior cranial fossa and passes backward in the superior margin of the falx cerebri. When the sinus reaches the level of the internal occipital protuberance, it usually turns to the right, forming the right transverse sinus which passes around the wall of the posterior cranial fossa and becomes the right internal jugular vein in the jugular foramen.

The inferior sagittal sinus begins near the crista galli but passes back in the free inferior margin of the falx cerebri. Immediately behind the corpus callosum it is joined by the great cerebral vein (the vein of Galen) from the cerebral hemispheres. In this manner the straight sinus is formed. The straight sinus passes back in the line of union of the falx cerebri with the tentorium cerebelli, as far as the internal occipital protuberance. At this point it becomes the left transverse sinus which is continued into the left internal jugular vein. At the internal occipital protuberance there is frequently a communication between the right and left transverse sinuses.

There are several other smaller venous sinuses in the base of the skull. The cavernous sinuses together with the anterior and posterior intercavernous sinuses form a circular sinus about the sella turcica. The superior and inferior petrosal sinuses are lodged along the petrous portion of the temporal bone. The spheno-parietal sinuses are found along the edge of the small wings of the sphenoid. The occipital sinus is found behind the foramen magnum and the basilar sinus in front of the foramen magnum. These sinuses all drain eventually into the internal jugular veins. Through the emissary foramina the blood sinuses within the cra-

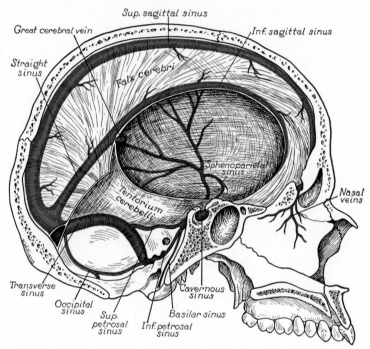

PLATE 22.—Venous sinuses of dura mater. The anterior and posterior in-tercavernous sinuses are not labeled but their cut edges are shown on the anterior and posterior walls of the sella turcica. The connection between the nasal veins and the beginning of the superior sagittal sinus is not al-ways demonstrable.

nium communicate with the veins of scalp and face and with the diploic veins; these communications form one possible pathway for the passage of infections into the cranial cavity.

In addition to the great cerebral veins, a number of superficial cerebral veins empty directly into the superior longitudinal sinus; veins from the cerebellum, pons, and medulla drain into the various venous sinuses in the base of the skull.

Portal Vein.—The portal vein is formed by the union of the inferior mesenteric vein, the superior mesenteric vein, and the splenic vein. The portal vein receives blood from the large and small intestines, stomach, spleen, and pancreas and conveys it to the liver. The portal blood is distributed within the liver by a

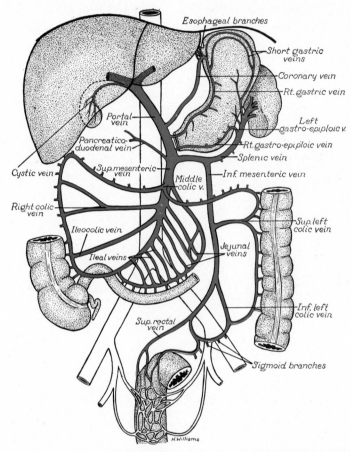

PLATE 23.—Portal vein and tributaries. Note the anastomosis with inferior esophageal veins and with inferior hemorrhoidal veins of the systemic circulation.

set of venous capillaries which empty into the hepatic veins, and they, in turn, are tributaries to the inferior vena cava. The portal blood conveys absorbed food material from the intestine to the liver.

Vertebral Venous System.—Within the spinal canal is a rich plexus of thin-walled veins without valves. These veins form anterior and posterior venous sinuses extending the entire length of the canal. They communicate freely with each other about the spinal cord; they have connections above with the blood sinuses within the cranium; they receive branches from the veins of the trunk by way of connecting channels which pass through the intervertebral foramina; they have connections with the veins which drain the pelvic viscera.

When the pressure within the thorax and abdomen is increased, less blood flows toward the heart in the venae cavae, and there is a tendency for a retrograde flow of blood into the vertebral venous plexuses. This is a path by which infections and metastatic tumors may find their way into the brain and bones without going through the portal, systemic, or pulmonary circuits.

Review Questions

1. What are the differences between an artery, a vein, and a capillary?
2. Name the four main chambers of the human heart.
3. What structures form the borders of the heart?
4. Name the main parts of the conducting system of the heart.
5. Trace a drop of blood through the pulmonary blood system starting at the right atrium.
6. Trace a drop of blood from the inferior vena cava to the aorta.
7. The portal vein carries blood from what organs?
8. List five places in the body where the pulse may be taken.
9. Describe the great saphenous vein.
10. List the venous sinuses of the dura mater.
11. Describe briefly the arterial supply of each of the following: the upper extremity, the lower extremity, and the brain.
12. What is the function of the heart?
13. Describe the coronary circulation.

CHAPTER 11

THE LYMPHATIC SYSTEM

The lymphatic system begins in meshes of connective tissues as closed capillaries which anastomose to form rich plexuses or networks. These capillaries unite to form the first collecting trunks or afferent vessels which go to regional lymph nodes. A node is an encapsulated mass of lymphocytes. Within the node the collecting trunks break up into capillaries and are reunited into efferent trunks. The terminal collecting trunks empty lymph into the subclavian veins. The entire lymphatic system acts as a secondary system for the return of fluid from the periphery to the superior vena cava.

A lymph nodule or follicle is a small, nonencapsulated mass of lymphocytes in a mesh of reticular tissue. Each lymph node contains several nodules. Also, lymph nodules occurring singly or in groups are found beneath the epithelium of mucous membranes, particularly of the respiratory and digestive tracts. The tonsils are aggregates of lymph nodules and are described in the discussion on the pharynx. The lymph nodules of the small intestine are described in the discussion on that organ.

The capillary walls of the lymphatic system have only an endothelial layer, but the collecting trunks have, in addition, a covering of connective tissue containing scattered smooth muscle and elastic fibers. The wall of a collecting trunk is similar to that of a vein. The shape of lymphatic vessels varies with the structures through which they pass. In muscles, such as the diaphragm, the lumen in cross section looks like a mere slit, but in loose connective tissue the lumen is widely dilated. Lymphatics course almost exclusively through the structures of connective-tissue type; they are found on the surface of an organ and deep within it. There is very little anastomosis between the superficial and deep lymphatics of any structure. Collecting trunks tend to be grouped in the vicinity of blood vessels and lie superficial to and not deeper than those vessels, a fact of much significance in surgery.

A lymph node has a capsule of white fibrous connective tissue, with trabeculae extending inward and partially subdividing the substance of the node into lobules and forming the structural framework. Dense masses of lymphocytes in reticular tissue form the follicles of the cortex beneath the capsule. The central portion or medulla contains cords of lymphocytes in reticular tissue. At

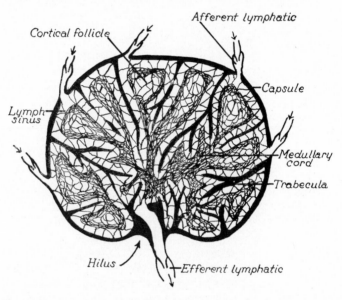

Fig. 225.—A lymph node. This is a diagram showing the connective tissue framework of a node; the fine mesh represents reticular tissue; the lymphocytes have been omitted.

the hilus where the blood vessels of the node enter and leave and where the efferent lymphatic trunk arises, the medulla reaches the surface and there is no cortex. The afferent lymphatic vessels, of which there are usually several for each node, pierce the capsule separately. The lymph sinuses are spaces beneath the capsule and around the trabeculae, extending inward along the follicles and cords of cells. The lymph enters the node from the afferent vessels, filters through the sinuses, and leaves at the hilus through the efferent vessel.

Lymph nodes vary markedly in shape, color, size, consistency, and number. Though lymph nodes are present throughout life, they are characteristically frequent, large, and obvious in childhood. They increase in size and regress according to the subjection to, or freedom of tissues from, bacterial invasion or tumor growth. The lymph nodes which drain the air passages become black because they receive and deposit particles of dust brought to them by way of the lymphatics of the lungs. Other lymph nodes, such as those of the abdomen, remain pink throughout life. In persons suffering from long-continued illness, such as chronic tuberculosis, the lymph nodes are large, firm, and apparently more numerous. In acute infections they are swollen and tender and may break down into abscesses.

Lymphatics not only drain lymph back into the blood stream from the tissue spaces, but also the lacteals or the lymph capillaries in the villi of the small intestine absorb the products of fat digestion and empty them into the blood stream by way of the thoracic duct.

LYMPHATICS OF HEAD AND NECK

There are no lymph nodes or lymphatics within the cranium. The superficial nodes are arranged in a ring which lies along the lower border of the mandible, about the ear, and at the junction of neck and head. The deep nodes lie along the deeper blood vessels of the neck. There are numerous lymphatics connecting the nodes of the superficial ring and others passing from superficial to deep nodes. There are also many channels draining lymph from the tonsillar masses of the pharynx. The lymphatic masses of the air passages together with the various lymph nodes constitute very important barriers to infections of the mouth and upper air passages. (See section on Tonsils.)

1. Superficial nodes:

   a. Suboccipital group at the back of the head

   b. Mastoid (posterior auricular) group over the mastoid process behind the ear

   c. Parotid group (anterior auricular) in and about the parotid gland

d. Submandibular (submaxillary) group below and parallel to the mandible

e. Submental group beneath the chin

2. Deep nodes:

a. Retropharyngeal nodes between the pharynx and the vertebral column

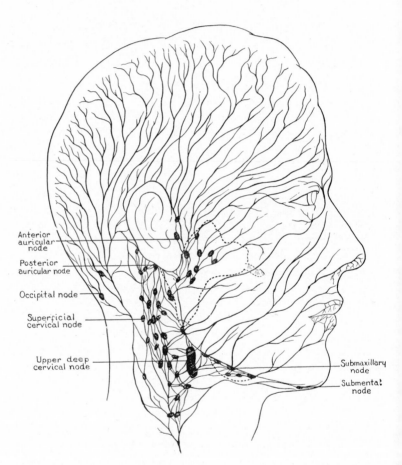

Fig. 226.—Superficial lymphatics of the face (after Sappey). Lymphatic vessels represented by black lines. In life they are actually moniliform. Parotid and submandibular salivary glands are indicated by dotted lines to show their relation to lymph nodes.

b. Deep cervical chain along the internal jugular vein

c. Supraclavicular group along the subclavian artery

The lymphatics of the scalp form a rich plexus and unite into three sets of collecting trunks on each side: a frontal group ending in the anterior auricular nodes, a parietal group draining into the posterior auricular nodes, and an occipital group going to the suboccipital nodes. Lymphatic channels pass from these nodes into deep cervical nodes.

The lymphatics of the lips, eyelids, cheeks, gums, and skin of the nose drain to nearby nodes and thence into cervical nodes.

Lymphatics of the nasal cavity, air sinuses, and pharynx drain into cervical and retropharyngeal nodes. At the angle of the jaw is a submandibular node which becomes enlarged and tender in infections of the tonsillar region. This must not be mistaken for the tonsil itself. The retropharyngeal nodes are likely to become very large in infections of the nose and throat. In young children they may become so large as to push the posterior wall of the pharynx far forward. If pus forms, a retropharyngeal abscess results.

The lymphatics of the tongue drain from the tip to the submental nodes, from the sides to the submandibular nodes, and from the back and deeper portions to the deep cervical nodes.

LYMPHATICS OF UPPER EXTREMITY

In the axillary nodes nearly all the superficial and deep lymphatics of the upper limb meet. There are, however, a few scattered nodes in other parts of the arm which lie on the course of collecting trunks.

The epitrochlear node, usually single, lies on the deep fascia about one and one-half inches proximal to the medial epicondyle of the humerus. Into this node drain some of the superficial collecting trunks on the medial (ulnar) side of the hand and the fourth and fifth fingers. The efferent vessels accompany the basilic vein and pierce the deep fascia in the middle part of the upper arm to empty into the deep lymphatics which accompany the axillary vessels.

Axillary Nodes.—The axillary nodes drain not only the upper extremity, but also the thoracic wall down to the level of the umbilicus. The axillary nodes are embedded in the axilla and are subdivided in the following manner:

1. The humeral, or lateral chain, in close relation to the axillary vein, receives nearly all the lymphatics of the upper limb.

2. The thoracic, pectoral, or medial chain, lying along the lateral thoracic artery, drains particularly the anterior chest wall and breast.

3. The subscapular, or posterior chain, lying along the subscapular vessels, drains the scapular region and the lower part of the neck.

4. An infraclavicular, subpectoral, or anterior group, lying along the upper border of the pectoralis minor, receives mainly efferent vessels from the other axillary groups.

5. A central group in the apex of the axilla receives efferent vessels from the other groups.

The superficial lymphatic network reaches its maximum development on the palmar surface of the fingers and is much less rich on the dorsum. These networks give rise to collecting trunklets which converge toward the sides of the fingers and run over the dorsum of the hand in the interdigital spaces, forming numerous anastomoses.

The trunklets from the medial and lateral sides and from the distal portion of the palm drain into the network on the dorsum of the hand; those from the central portion of the palm drain by a single trunk, formed beneath the superficial palmar fascia, and pass laterally around the side of the hand to the dorsum. The trunklets from the central proximal part of the palm drain into collecting trunks on the volar aspect of the forearm.

From the course of the lymphatics it is easy to understand why spreading infections from fingers and from most of the palm cause early swelling and redness of the dorsum of the hand even though the source of the infection is on the palmar aspect.

As the collecting trunks pass up the forearm, they merge with each other, thus diminishing their total number. In the forearm there are about thirty but in the upper arm fifteen to eighteen (Sappey).

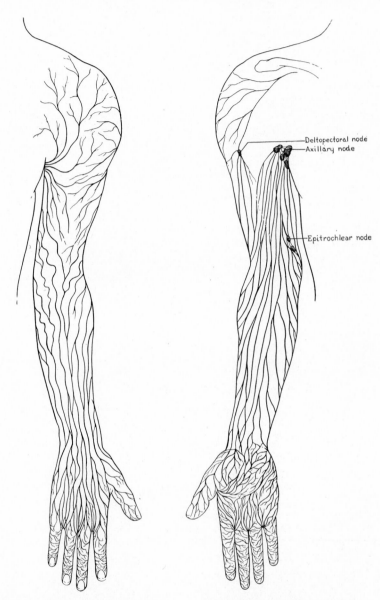

Fig. 227.—Superficial lymphatics of back of upper extremity. (After Sappey.)

Fig. 228.—Superficial lymphatics of front of upper extremity. (After Sappey.)

On the ventral (anterior) aspect of the forearm are three groups of collecting trunks: the medial and lateral groups coursing along the respective borders and the middle group accompanying the median vein. The trunks on the dorsum are more tortuous, especially near the elbow. In the upper arm the three anterior

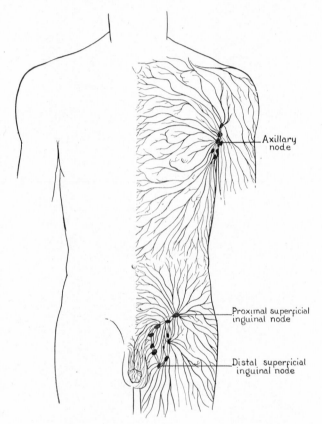

Fig. 229.—Superficial lymphatics of front of trunk. (After Sappey.)

groups course in parallel lines, with frequent intercommunications, to empty into the humeral chain of nodes. The innermost trunks may be interrupted by the epitrochlear node and follow the deep lymphatics of the arm; the outermost trunk may drain to nodes in the deltopectoral triangle.

The deep lymphatics accompany the brachial artery and its branches.   There are radial, ulnar, and interosseous trunks arising in the neighborhood of the peripheral distribution of these vessels which they accompany.   They terminate in the humeral trunk along the brachial artery.

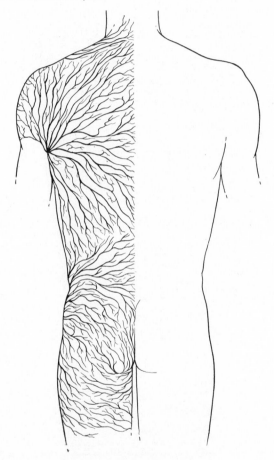

Fig. 230.—Superficial lymphatics of back of trunk.   (After Sappey.)

LYMPHATICS OF LOWER EXTREMITY

The lymphatics of the lower extremity terminate in the inguinal lymph nodes which are subdivided into a superficial and a deep group.

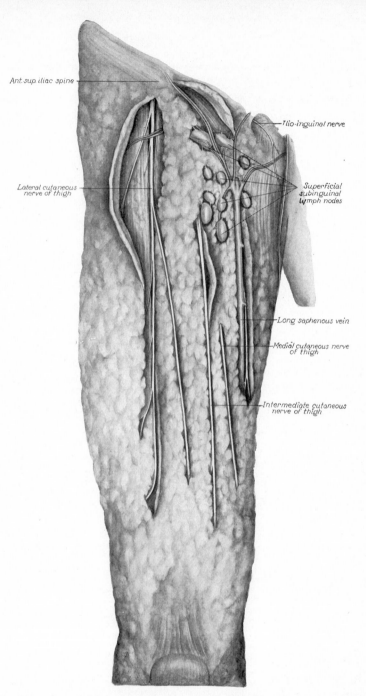

Fig. 231.—Superficial inguinal lymph nodes. (W.R.U. 3333, male, white, aged 62 years.)

1. The superficial inguinal nodes are found in the subcutaneous tissue about the inner end of the inguinal ligament. There is a proximal group which lies parallel to the ligament and a distal group lying parallel to the great saphenous vein. The nodes vary greatly in number and size. Their afferent vessels originate in the leg, perineum, scrotum or labia, skin of penis or clitoris, anus, and wall of the trunk up to level of umbilicus. The efferent vessels end in deep inguinal nodes and their continuation, the nodes along the external and common iliac arteries.

2. Deep inguinal nodes are few in number and lie around the femoral artery as it enters the thigh.

Behind the knee and lying close to the popliteal vein are several small nodes to which afferent vessels come from the outer side of the calf of the leg above the small saphenous vein, from the collecting trunks accompanying posterior tibial and peroneal arteries, from the knee joint, and from the anterior tibial lymph node. Most of the efferent lymphatics drain into the deep inguinal nodes.

The superficial lymphatic network gives rise to three groups of collecting trunks. Those accompanying the great saphenous vein drain the region of the first, second, and third toes and the medial portion of the foot. They ascend in parallel lines to the inguinal nodes. The collecting trunks of the lateral aspect of the foot pass upward and forward to empty into collecting channels accompanying the great saphenous vein. Some collecting trunks from the lateral aspect of the foot and from the heel accompany the small saphenous vein to the knee and empty into the most superficial popliteal node. Collecting trunks from the lateral gluteal region pass around the outer side of the thigh to reach the superior lateral superficial inguinal nodes. From the inner third of the buttock and anal region the collecting trunks pass medially around the thigh to the lower superficial inguinal nodes.

The deep lymphatics accompany the main blood vessels, namely the pedal and anterior tibial vessels and the plantar and posterior tibial vessels. They communicate with the popliteal nodes and then course along the femoral vessels. Accessory lymphatics from the obturator and gluteal vessels join the femoral collecting trunks and terminate in the deep inguinal or internal iliac (hypogastric) nodes. Deep and superficial lymphatics are independent, though generally they do communicate with each other through popliteal and superficial inguinal nodes.

The superficial lymphatics of the scrotum, skin, and prepuce of the penis, and labia majora, and the coverings of the clitoris and skin of anal region and buttocks, together with those of the abdominal wall up to the umbilicus, drain to the superficial inguinal lymph nodes.

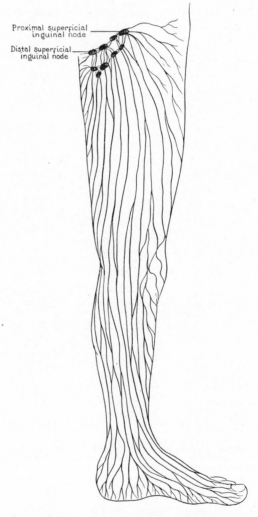

Fig. 232.—Superficial lymphatics of medial aspect of lower extremity. (After Sappey.)

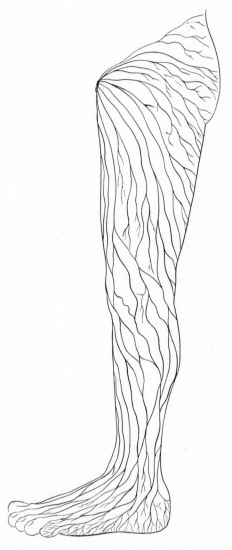

Fig. 233.—Superficial lymphatics of lateral aspect of lower extremity.
(After Sappey.)

Afferent vessels of the deep inguinal lymph nodes are those from the superficial nodes, lymphatics accompanying the femoral vessels, and lymphatics from the glans of the penis or clitoris.

The lymphatic drainage of the skin and subcutaneous tissue has been given in considerable detail because of its importance in the spread of infections. It explains the apprehension of a surgeon when he sees red streaks of inflammation on a forearm and upper arm produced by infections spreading along the collecting trunks. The disappearance of these red streaks under treatment means that the infection is being localized to the original site.

LYMPHATICS OF PELVIS

The lymph nodes lying within the cavity of the pelvis are more or less artificially grouped in accordance with their location along the blood vessels.

1. External iliac lymph nodes are scattered along the course of the vessels and receive lymph from the inguinal nodes and some from the anterior abdominal wall.

2. Internal iliac (hypogastric) lymph nodes lie in relation to the internal iliac artery and its branches and receive lymph from the pelvic viscera and some also from the perineum and buttocks.

3. The common iliac lymph nodes are in reality an upward extension of the internal and external iliac chains and above are continued as the aortic nodes of the abdominal cavity.

It is simpler to look upon the internal iliac group as the nodes of the cavity of the pelvis and upon the external and common iliac groups as the nodes of the brim.

In general the lymphatics of a viscus are distributed in a superficial network beneath the capsule and in a series of deep channels within the substance. These channels drain toward the hilus or site where the chief blood vessels enter and leave.

The lymphatics of the pelvic organs usually drain along the accompanying blood vessels. The nodes of the brim (external and common iliac nodes) receive the efferent vessels of the nodes of the cavity (internal iliac) and, in addition, numerous direct efferents from the pelvic organs. Also efferent vessels from the upper part of the rectum, the upper part of the uterus, and the uterine tube and ovary (in the male, the testis) pass directly into aortic nodes of the abdominal cavity.

LYMPHATICS OF ABDOMEN

The nodes situated within the upper abdominal cavity may, for purposes of description, be subdivided into numerous groups, but the subdivision is artificial and there are many intercommunications.

1. Aortic lymph nodes are most numerous on the left side of the aorta between the origin of the left renal artery and the beginning of the left common iliac artery. This group becomes continuous with the nodes lying above the inferior mesenteric artery. Above the level of the renal arteries the aortic group is difficult to distinguish from the celiac and superior mesenteric groups. There are some small nodes, the lateral lumbar lymph nodes, scattered along the parietal branches of the aorta to the dorsal abdominal wall.

2. Inferior mesenteric lymph nodes are subdivided into groups lying along the branches of the artery.

3. Superior mesenteric lymph nodes have a less regular distribution than those of the inferior mesenteric group but are very numerous. The nodes scattered within the mesentery are said to number between one and two hundred.

4. Celiac lymph nodes are arranged about the celiac artery and its branches. Most of the celiac nodes are situated along the upper edge of the pancreas but some are located within the lesser and greater omenta.

The lymphatics of the stomach pass by means of three streams to the celiac nodes: from the fundus and upper part of the gastric tube to nodes on the left side, from the lower portion of the gastric tube to nodes just above the pancreas, and from the pyloric canal to the lower celiac nodes on the right side. These streams intermingle and boundaries of drainage are not clear cut.

The lymphatics of the small intestine drain into nodes lying in the mesentery. The lymph is usually relayed through several nodes before reaching the main nodes of the superior mesenteric group.

The lymphatics from the proximal portion of the large intestine drain to the superior mesenteric group of nodes and from the distal portion to the inferior mesenteric group.

The lymphatics of the pancreas drain to adjacent nodes.

The lymphatics of the gallbladder and of most of the liver drain to the celiac group, but the collecting vessels from the surface next

to the diaphragm and the anterior abdominal wall drain upward
to nodes in the thoracic cavity.

The lymphatics of the spleen drain lymph to nodes in the left
portion of the celiac group.

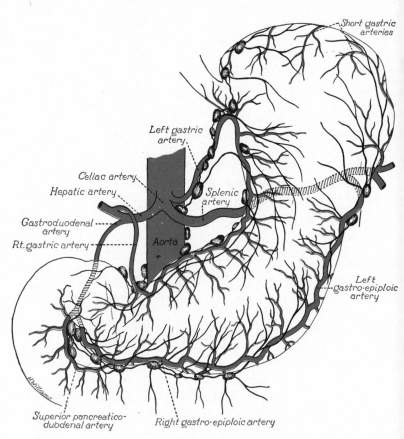

PLATE 24.—Arterial supply and lymphatic drainage of the stomach.   (After
Cutler and Zollinger.)

Lymphatics of the kidneys are not numerous and drain to nearby
aortic nodes.

Lymphatics of the adrenal glands go mainly to aortic and celiac
nodes but some pass upward to thoracic nodes.

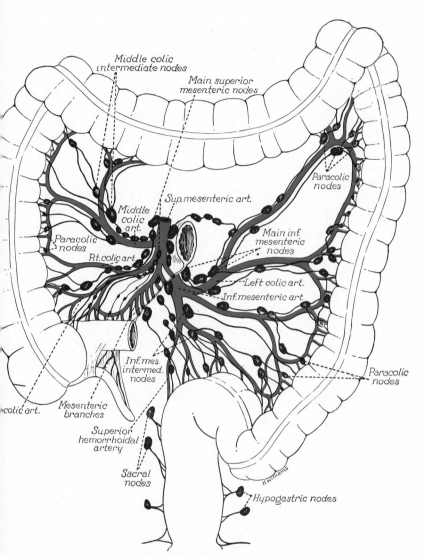

PLATE 25.—Arterial supply and lymphatic drainage of the colon.   (After Cutler and Zollinger.)

LYMPHATICS OF THORAX

The lymph nodes of the thorax are divided into several small superficial groups and a large bronchial group. The superficial group includes the following:

1. Sternal nodes lying just behind the sternum and receiving afferents from the thoracic wall and diaphragm

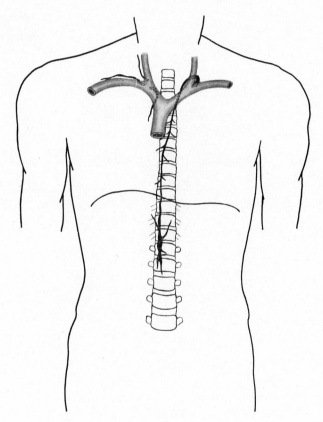

Fig. 234.—The position of the thoracic duct.

2. Intercostal nodes found in the intercostal spaces and draining lymph from the chest wall
3. Anterior mediastinal nodes which receive afferent vessels from the liver, diaphragm, and mediastinum

4. Posterior mediastinal nodes which receive afferents from the diaphragm, mediastinum, and esophagus

The bronchial group includes all the nodes associated with the distal portion of the trachea and bronchi and is subdivided into the following groups:

1. Tracheobronchial nodes situated in the angle between trachea and bronchus on either side
2. Intertracheobronchial nodes placed below the trachea in the angle between the bronchi

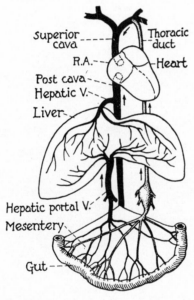

Fig. 235.—Diagram of thoracic duct and portal system. (After Wieman, from Jackson: Experimental Pharmacology and Materia Medica, St. Louis, 1939, The C. V. Mosby Co.)

3. Bronchopulmonary nodes located in the hilus of each lung
4. Pulmonary nodes lying within the substance of the lung, usually in the angle between two bronchial branches

The lymphatics of the lungs and visceral pleura drain through the pulmonary and bronchopulmonary nodes to the nodes about the trachea.

The lymphatics of the heart drain to the tracheobronchial nodes.

Terminal Collecting Trunks.—The lymphatics of the abdomen and legs unite to form a single channel, the thoracic duct, which commences as the cisterna chyli at the upper border of the second lumbar vertebra and terminates at the junction of the left internal jugular and subclavian veins. The left jugular, subclavian, and bronchomediastinal collecting trunks usually empty into the terminal part of the thoracic duct but may empty separately into the vein. On the right side these three collecting trunks usually empty singly into the junction of the right internal jugular and subclavian veins, and there is no common right lymphatic duct.

The thoracic duct runs upward in front of the bodies of the vertebrae, through the aortic orifice of the diaphragm and behind the esophagus, crossing from the right side to the left of the vertebral column at the lower border of the body of the sixth thoracic vertebra. It curves upward to the left above the subclavian artery to its termination. It may, and frequently does, empty by several openings.

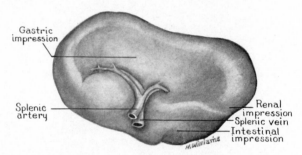

Gastric impression

Splenic artery

Renal impression
Splenic vein
Intestinal impression

Fig. 236.—Medial aspect of the spleen.   (W.R.U. museum specimen.)

SPLEEN

The spleen is a lymphatic organ lying beneath the left dome of the diaphragm. It lies lateral to the left kidney and above and behind the cardiac portion of the stomach and the splenic flexure of the colon.

In formalin-embalmed bodies the spleen has definite borders and impressions upon its surface produced by the molding contact with adjacent viscera. The diaphragmatic surface is convex, but the under surface has three concave areas due to contact with the stomach, kidney, and splenic flexure.

The spleen is much like a large lymph node, but the capsule is thicker and the trabeculae are larger. The supporting tissue contains more elastic fibers and a few smooth muscle cells. Therefore, the spleen, in contrast with a lymph node, may be distended and contracted. During life it is soft and elastic and varies in size with the blood flow. It becomes larger and softer in acute infections, and in certain diseases such as malaria and leukemia, it becomes permanently enlarged and firmer than normal.

Fig. 237.—The arteries of the spleen. (Injection by A. Cherney and K. Wolfe. Photograph by Dr. D. R. L. Duncan.) (W.R.U. term fetus.)

The splenic artery, a branch of the celiac, enters the organ at the hilus. The splenic vein drains into the portal circulation. Nerves pass to the spleen from the celiac ganglion.

The spleen has a peritoneal covering, the tunica serosa. Beneath this is the tunica propria, a strong fibroelastic covering containing some smooth muscle. Trabeculae pass inward from the tunica propria to divide the central portion of the organ into lobules. The lobules contain masses of lymphatic cells arranged about a central arteriole. Each of these masses is a splenic nodule. The larger nodules are visible to the naked eye as small dots. The splenic nodules compose the white pulp of the spleen. The diffuse masses about the nodules form the red pulp. The red pulp contains lymphocytes, reticuloendothelial cells, and all the cells found in circulating blood. There is a fine mesh of reticular tissue in both the red and the white pulp.

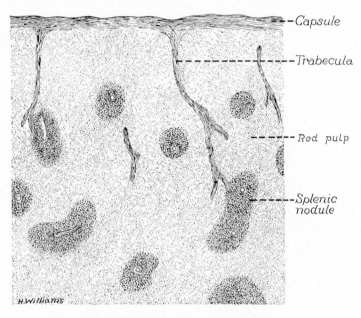

Fig. 238.—Section of human spleen.

The spleen has various functions. It produces lymphocytes. It acts as a storehouse for red cells and aids in altering the relation between the amount of blood plasma and cells with varying needs of the body. The reticuloendothelial cells destroy worn-out red cells.

THYMUS

The thymus is a two-lobed structure lying just behind the upper part of the sternum in front of the beginning of the aorta and pulmonary artery. It is relatively large at birth but begins to shrink at about the age of puberty, and in an adult is usually represented by a small mass of connective tissue and fat. At any given age there may be great variation in size. The gland is pink in early life and becomes yellowish-pink with age. It has a fibrous capsule from which septa pass into the substance of the organ, separating it into primary and secondary lobules. The lobules contain lymphatic nodules.

Branches of the internal mammary artery supply the thymus, and nerve filaments come from the vagus and upper thoracic segments of the cord.

REVIEW QUESTIONS

1. What is the general function of the lymphatic system?
2. Give a brief description of a lymph node.
3. Describe briefly the lymphatic drainage of the scalp.
4. The axillary lymph nodes drain lymph from what areas of the body?
5. The inguinal lymph nodes drain lymph from what areas of the body?
6. Where does the thoracic duct begin? Where does it terminate?
7. Where is the spleen located?
8. Give three functions of the spleen.

CHAPTER 12

THE RESPIRATORY SYSTEM

The organs of breathing consist of a series of air passages including the nasal chambers, pharynx, larynx, trachea, and bronchi and the lungs to which these passages lead. The mouth serves as a secondary respiratory passage if the nasal passages are blocked. In man the pharynx is a pathway used by both the digestive and respiratory systems. The nose possesses an area specialized to register the sense of smell.

NOSE

The external nose is roughly triangular in shape. The upper angle is called the root, and the portion containing the external openings or nostrils is called the base. The lateral wall of each external opening is called the ala of the nose. The tip of the nose is the apex, and the bridge of the nose is that bony portion between the root and the apex. The root, dorsum, and upper portion of the sides of the nose are bony, but the lower and more prominent part is formed by several cartilages. The nasal cavity is subdivided into two portions by the nasal septum, the hinder part of which is formed from the vomer and vertical plate of the ethmoid; the forward part is composed of cartilage.

Attached to the lateral wall of the nasal cavity are three scroll-like processes of bone, the nasal conchae or turbinates. The inferior concha is a separate bone articulating with the maxilla, but the superior and middle conchae are portions of the ethmoid.

Each turbinate is covered by mucous membrane; that covering the inferior turbinate is thick and soft, giving a rounded, bulbous appearance to the posterior end, that covering the middle turbinate is less thick, and that covering the superior turbinate is thin and firm.

The lining of the nose just within the nostrils is stratified squamous epithelium, but this soon changes to pseudostratified, ciliated, columnar epithelium lying upon a dense layer of connective tissue, the tunica propria. Within the tunica propria are branched tubulo-alveolar glands. A small portion of the mucosa covering the medial surface of the superior concha and the nearby surface of the septum contains the cells specialized for the registration of odors. This area is known as the olfactory area and is further described in Chapter 8, The Special Sense Organs.

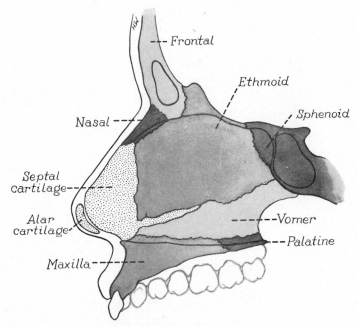

Fig. 239.—Nasal septum.

The nasal mucosa is richly supplied with blood vessels, particularly that over the inferior concha. Most of the blood vessels are terminal branches of the internal maxillary artery, but the external portion of the nose receives small arterial branches from the external maxillary artery, and the upper portion of each nasal cavity receives branches from the ophthalmic artery. The veins drain into the anterior facial veins, into a plexus of veins about the pterygoid muscles, and also into the blood sinuses of the dura mater of the brain.

The turbinates, especially the inferior, act as radiators for warming and moistening the inhaled air. Just inside the nostrils are many hairs which act as a sieve to remove dust particles from the air, thus protecting the air passages leading to the lungs.

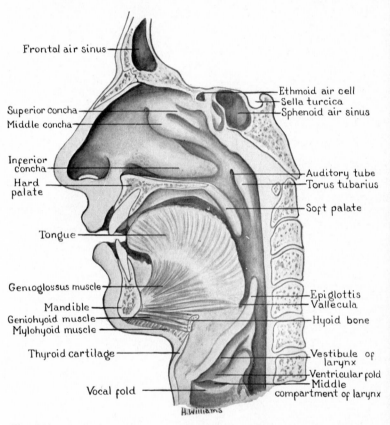

Fig. 240.—Sagittal section of face and neck. (W.R.U. museum specimen C228.)

The conchae subdivide the nasal cavity into several parts. The inferior meatus lies below the inferior concha and is the chief air passage; the middle meatus, which is closed in front, lies between the middle and inferior conchae; the superior meatus lies between the superior and middle conchae; the sphenoethmoid recess lies above and behind the superior concha. The superior meatus serves as an air trap to hold the air relatively motionless, thus facilitating the sense of smell. Air sinuses, discussed in detail below, open into it, as into the middle meatus. The nasolacrimal duct empties into the inferior meatus.

The hard palate, which also serves as the floor of the nasal cavity, is formed by the palatine process of the maxilla and the horizontal palatal process of the palatine bone.

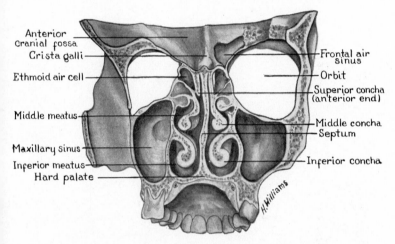

Fig. 241.—Vertical section through the nose. Plane of the section passes slightly obliquely through the left first molar tooth and behind the second right premolar tooth. Posterior wall of right frontal sinus removed. (W.R.U. museum specimen.)

The roof of the nasal cavity is formed mainly by the cribriform plate of the ethmoid.

The nasal cavity communicates with the upper portion of the pharynx through two posterior openings called the choanae or posterior nares.

AIR SINUSES OF THE SKULL

The air sinuses connected with the nose are the frontal, ethmoid, sphenoid, maxillary, and, indirectly, the mastoid sinuses. Each is lined with mucous membrane continuous with that of the nose.

The frontal air sinuses located in the frontal bone above and between the orbits are generally two in number, varying greatly in size and shape; they may be partially subdivided by extra septa and are usually not symmetrical. The frontal air sinus empties into the middle meatus.

The ethmoid air sinuses form a labyrinth of small irregular spaces within the ethmoid bone. These vary greatly in size and number, but are usually divided into three groups: a posterior group which empties into the superior meatus, and anterior and middle groups both of which usually empty into the middle meatus.

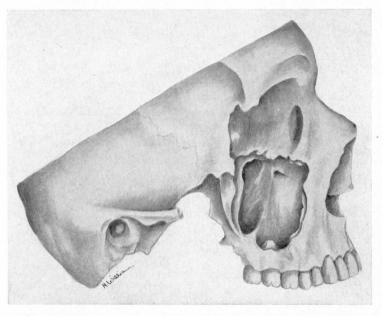

Fig. 242.—Right maxillary sinus. Outer wall of the sinus removed. Note partial septum in floor of sinus, and upward bulge produced by the roots of second molar tooth. (W.R.U. museum specimen.)

The sphenoid air sinuses are located in the body of the sphenoid bone. They are usually two in number, separated by a septum. The sphenoid sinus empties into the sphenoethmoid recess. Occasionally the sphenoid sinuses are completely absent.

The maxillary sinuses are found one on each side beneath the orbit within the body of the maxilla. Each empties into the middle meatus behind the opening of the frontal sinus.

The mastoid air cells open into the middle ear which is connected with the nasopharynx by way of the auditory tube. All the air sinuses therefore open into the nose or nasopharynx.

The ophthalmic division of the trigeminal nerve carries sensory fibers from the frontal, ethmoid, and sphenoid sinuses, the maxillary division from the maxillary sinus, and the glossopharyngeal nerve from the mastoid air cells.

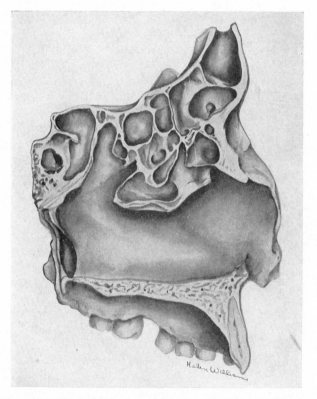

Fig. 243.—Vertical section of left ethmoid labyrinth. (W.R.U. museum specimen.)

Since the opening of an air sinus usually lies above the level of its floor, drainage is impeded if excess fluid is secreted. Furthermore, the openings during life are quite small and, in an acute cold, frequently become obstructed by the swelling of the mucous membrane. Infection within a sinus is known as sinusitis.

PHARYNX

During respiration the pharynx serves as a passageway for air from the nose to the larynx. The pharynx is discussed in Chapter 13, The Digestive System.

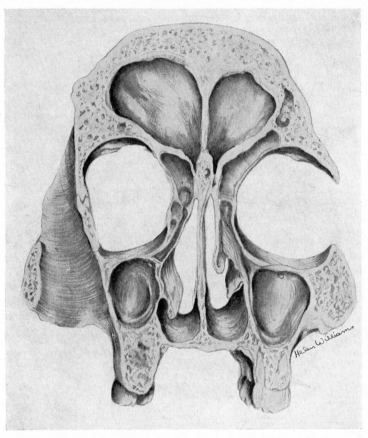

Fig. 244.—Vertical section (coronal plane) through frontal sinuses. (W.R.U. museum specimen.)

LARYNX

The larynx or voice box lies in the midline of the neck in front of the fourth, fifth, and sixth cervical vertebrae. Behind it lies the lower part of the pharynx leading to the esophagus. The great vessels of the neck and vagus nerve lie on each side. In front two layers of muscles arise on the sternum and are inserted into the front of the laryngeal wall (sternohyoid and sternothyroid muscles). The sternocleidomastoid muscle is the prominent muscular mass on each side of the larynx. The larynx is a hollow box lined with mucous membrane. Its walls are formed by several cartilages bound together by elastic membranes.

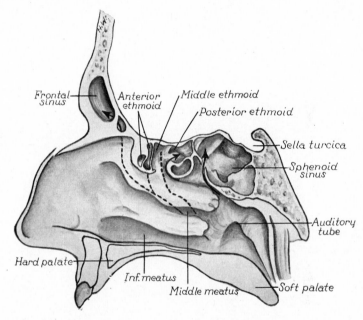

Fig 245.—Openings of air sinuses. Arrows indicate the openings from the nasal passages into the sinuses. (W.R.U. 3192, male, white, aged 57 years.)

Cartilages of Larynx.—There are three single cartilages (thyroid, cricoid, and epiglottis) and three paired cartilages (arytenoid, corniculate, and cuneiform).

The thyroid is the largest of these cartilages. It forms the front of the voice box and is shaped somewhat like the covers of an open book, with the back of the book forming the prominent projection in the neck (Adam's apple). The cricoid cartilage is shaped like a signet ring, with the signet part behind and the band in front. The epiglottis is a leaflike cartilage. Its stem is directed

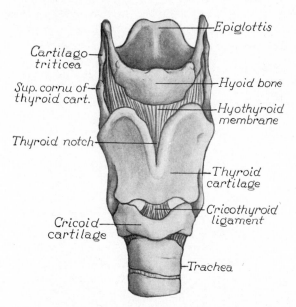

Epiglottis

Cartilago triticea

Sup. cornu of thyroid cart.

Hyoid bone

Hyothyroid membrane

Thyroid notch

Thyroid cartilage

Cricothyroid ligament

Cricoid cartilage

Trachea

Fig. 246.—Front of larynx. (W.R.U. 2707, male, white, aged 64 years.)

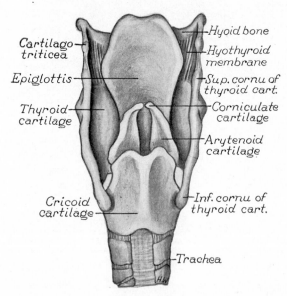

Hyoid bone

Cartilago triticea

Hyothyroid membrane

Epiglottis

Sup. cornu of thyroid cart.

Thyroid cartilage

Corniculate cartilage

Arytenoid cartilage

Cricoid cartilage

Inf. cornu of thyroid cart.

Trachea

Fig. 247.—Back of larynx. (W.R.U. 2707, male, white, aged 64 years.)

downward to attach to the thyroid cartilage in the midline between the two leaves. Its upper broad portion projects upward behind the base of the tongue.

The arytenoid cartilages are two small pyramid-shaped masses crowning the signet part of the cricoid at the back of the larynx. The corniculate cartilages are two tiny cones placed one on the apex of each arytenoid cartilage. The cuneiform cartilages, not always present, are two tiny rods placed in the mucous membrane fold joining the epiglottis to the arytenoids.

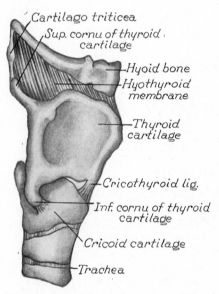

Fig. 248.—Right lateral view of larynx. (W.R.U. 2707, male, white, aged 64 years.)

The thyrohyoid membrane fills the interval between the hyoid bone and upper margin of the thyroid cartilage. The triticeous cartilage is an inconstant bit of cartilage within the lateral edges of this membrane.

The elastic cone or cricothyroid membrane is attached to the lower border of the thyroid and arytenoid cartilages above and to the cricoid cartilage below, completing the wall of the larynx in front and on each side. The thickened central portion of the membrane is known as the cricothyroid ligament. The upper portion of this membrane, attached to the arytenoid behind and to the thyroid in front, forms the vocal ligament underlying the vocal fold.

Cavity of Larynx.—The laryngeal cavity is subdivided into three parts by two pairs of mucous membrane folds in the lateral wall, the upper pair being the ventricular folds or false cords and the lower pair the vocal folds or true cords. The portion of the larynx above the ventricular folds is called the vestibule of the larynx. The aryepiglottic folds of mucous membrane, extending from the epiglottis in front to the arytenoid cartilages behind, separate the vestibule from the piriform recess (food gutter) of the pharynx on each side. The epiglottis separates the vestibule from the vallecula, which is the space between the base of the tongue and the epiglottis. The middle compartment (ventricle) of the larynx is quite small and lies between the ventricular and vocal folds. The lowest compartment of the larynx lies below the vocal folds and is continuous with the trachea.

The mucous membrane of the larynx is closely adherent to the epiglottis and to the vocal folds. Over the upper surface of the epiglottis and the vocal folds is stratified squamous epithelium; elsewhere the mucous membrane is loosely attached, has pseudostratified ciliated columnar epithelium, and may become enormously swollen, preventing the passage of air. A surgeon must then insert a tube through the larynx to open up a passageway (intubation) or make an external opening into the trachea (tracheotomy) in order to preserve life.

Muscles of Larynx.—The numerous muscles associated with the larynx are divided into an extrinsic group and an intrinsic group. The extrinsic group includes all muscles attached to the larynx and to the hyoid bone which is functionally a portion of the larynx.

In front of the larynx are placed the sternohyoid, sternothyroid, and thyrohyoid muscles. The sternohyoid is a thin, straplike muscle which originates from the upper edge of the manubrium of the sternum and passes upward to be inserted into the front of the hyoid bone. The sternothyroid is also a thin, flat muscle which arises from the upper edge of the sternum. It lies beneath (deeper than) the sternohyoid muscle and is inserted into the anterior surface of the thyroid cartilage. The thyrohyoid muscle arises just above the insertion of the sternothyroid muscle and is inserted into the lower edge of the hyoid bone.

Above the larynx are the digastric, stylohyoid, mylohyoid, and geniohyoid muscles. The digastric has two muscular bellies and a middle tendinous portion. The posterior belly arises from the mastoid bone and passes downward and forward toward the hyoid bone. The intermediate tendon has a fibrous attachment to the body of the hyoid, and then the anterior belly of the muscle continues upward and forward to be inserted into the lower edge of the

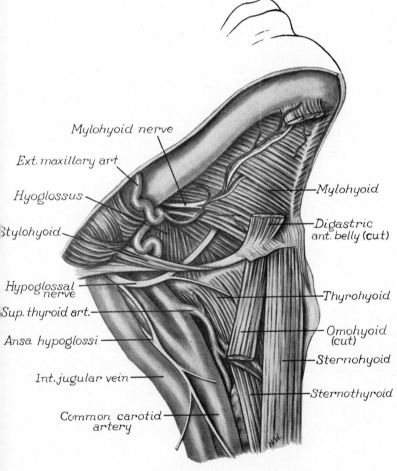

Fig. 249.—Extrinsic muscles of larynx.

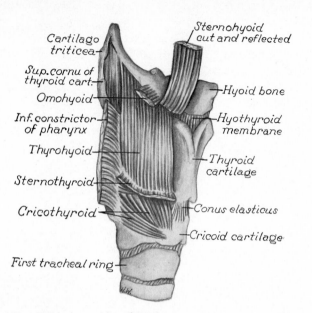

Fig. 250.—Extrinsic muscles of the larynx. This is a right oblique view of the structures. (Dissection by Dr. L. D. Chapin.) (W.R.U. 2686, male, white, aged 65 years.)

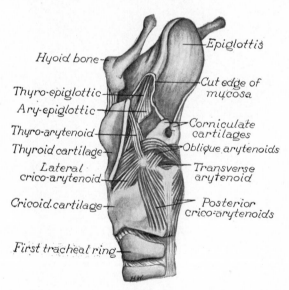

Fig. 251.—Intrinsic muscles of the larynx, left oblique view. (Dissection by Dr. L. D. Chapin.) (W.R.U. 2686, male, white, aged 65 years.)

mandible near the midline. The stylohyoid arises from the styloid
process of the temporal bone and passes downward beside the posterior belly of the digastric muscle to be inserted into the body of
the hyoid bone. The mylohyoid arises from the mylohyoid line of
the mandible and is inserted partly into the body of the hyoid bone
and partly into a fibrous band extending from the middle of the
hyoid to the symphysis of the mandible. This muscle helps to form
the floor of the mouth and is further described on page 397. The
geniohyoid is associated with the mylohyoid in forming the floor
of the mouth.

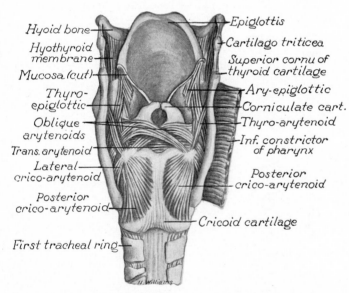

Fig. 252.—Intrinsic muscles of the larynx, viewed from behind. (Dissection by Dr. L. D. Chapin.)   (W.R.U. 2686, male, white, aged 65
years.)

The muscles just described have a varied nerve supply. The
posterior belly of the digastric and the stylohyoid are supplied
from the facial nerve, the anterior belly of the digastric and the
mylohyoid from the motor portion of the trigeminal, and the remaining muscles are innervated from branches of first, second, and
third cervical nerves.

The intrinsic muscles of the larynx alter the shape of the various portions of the larynx itself. It is not necessary to learn the attachments of this very complex group, but the more important functions should be known.

The aryepiglottic muscles lying within the aryepiglottic folds and the transverse and oblique arytenoids placed between the arytenoid cartilages act as a sphincter of the laryngeal inlet. In swallowing, these muscles close the vestibule and thus prevent food from entering the larynx. The epiglottis does not fold back as a lid to the laryngeal opening, but it does tend to divert liquids to either side. The ventricular muscle lying within the ventricular fold acts as an accessory sphincter closing the middle compartment of the larynx. The cricothyroids are said to tense the vocal cords, while the vocal muscles and thyroarytenoids relax them. The lateral and posterior cricoarytenoids alter the position of the vocal cords, the former drawing them together and the latter separating them.

The ability to alter the position of the vocal cords is of great physiologic importance. The interval between the vocal cords is never more than a few millimeters and is the narrowest part of the air passages. In speaking we vary this width and thus regulate the rate of air flow from the lungs. When a person holds his breath, he does it mainly by contraction of the lateral cricoarytenoid muscles which pull the vocal cords together and close the opening completely. The posterior cricoarytenoid muscles are the only muscles which have the opposite action; in persons in whom these muscles are paralyzed, the opening between the vocal cords becomes permanently and dangerously narrowed. The action of separation of the vocal cords, or abduction, is so vital that it has led some anatomists to regard the posterior cricoarytenoid muscles as the most important striate muscles in the body.

All the intrinsic muscles of the larynx are supplied by the recurrent laryngeal nerve except the cricothyroid which is supplied by the external laryngeal branch of the superior laryngeal nerve. The internal laryngeal branch of the superior laryngeal nerve carries the sensory fibers for the mucosa of the larynx above the vocal folds. The mucosa of the inferior compartment of the larynx receives sensory innervation through the recurrent laryngeal nerve.

The larynx is larger in the male than in the female, the difference becoming particularly noticeable at puberty. It is associated with the "change of voice" characteristic of boys at that time.

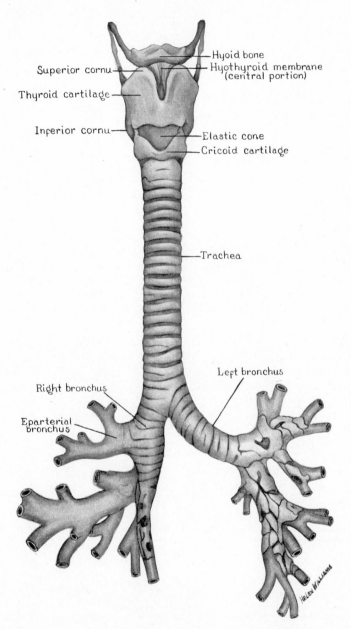

Fig. 253.—Larynx and trachea, front view. Cartilage plaques omitted from branches of right bronchus. (W.R.U. museum specimen 245.)

TRACHEA

The trachea or windpipe extends from the level of the lower border of the sixth cervical vertebra to the upper border of the fifth thoracic vertebra where it divides into two bronchi. In the neck the isthmus of the thyroid gland lies in front, and the lobes of the thyroid gland lie on each side of the trachea. Within the

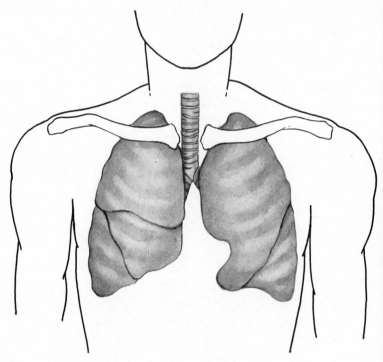

Fig. 254.—The position of the lungs and trachea.

thorax the trachea lies in the posterior part of the mediastinum behind the heart and great vessels. Behind the trachea is the esophagus, and behind that again are the bodies of the vertebrae. In the groove between the trachea and esophagus the recurrent laryngeal nerve passes upward to the larynx.

In the lower part of the neck below the isthmus of the thyroid gland, the anterior surface of the trachea is covered only by fascia and skin.

The trachea is kept permanently patent by a series of cartilaginous bands. These bands only partially encircle the trachea, for the back part is missing. The back of the trachea is therefore flat and composed of fibromuscular tissue. The walls between the cartilaginous rings are quite elastic, enabling the trachea to adjust itself to various positions of the body. The mucous membrane lining the trachea is continuous with that of the larynx above it and is continued below into the bronchi. It has ciliated pseudostratified columnar epithelium.

In infancy and early childhood the tracheal cartilages are soft; they stiffen in the later years of childhood.

BRONCHI

The bronchi which connect the trachea with the lungs have incomplete rings and plaques of cartilage in their walls to keep them open. The left bronchus is smaller than the right and passes more directly laterally, while the right continues almost vertically. For this reason foreign bodies which get into the trachea almost always lodge in the right bronchus or in one of its branches. All the branches of the left bronchus are given off below the left pulmonary artery, but the right bronchus just below its origin gives off a branch above the right pulmonary artery. This branch is called the eparterial bronchus.

There are usually two left bronchial arteries arising from the aorta and one right bronchial artery which may arise from the aorta or from an intercostal branch or from a left bronchial artery. The bronchial arteries accompany the bronchi and carry oxygenated blood to the bronchi, the pleura, and some mediastinal structures.

THORACIC CAVITY

Before discussing the lungs it is best to discuss the thoracic cavity and its subdivisions. Around the trachea, esophagus, and blood vessels the thoracic cavity is closed above in the root of the neck by a sheet of fascia (Sibson's fascia). Below, it is separated from the abdominal cavity by a sheet of muscle called the diaphragm.

The thoracic cavity lodges the two pleural cavities, each containing a lung. The pleural cavities are completely separated from each other by the mediastinum or connective tissue in which the heart lies. In addition to the heart the mediastinum contains the pericardium surrounding the heart, the pulmonary artery, the thoracic aorta and its branches, the trachea and part of the bronchi, the esophagus, the vagus nerves, the phrenic nerves, the thoracic duct, many lymph nodes and lymph vessels, and the thymus or its fibrous remainder.

Each pleural cavity has a lining of serous membrane, the pleura, which completely covers its inner surface. This serous membrane is reflected at the root of the lung. The layer lining the chest wall is called the parietal pleura and the layer over the lung the visceral pleura.

The parietal pleura is well supplied with sensory nerve endings. These give rise to the sensations of pain in pleurisy. In empyema pus collects between the two layers of pleura and occasionally between lobes of a lung. In pleural effusions fluid collects between the visceral and parietal pleurae. In operating to withdraw fluid a surgeon passes a hollow needle through the chest wall and through the parietal pleura.

At the back, the parietal pleura is reflected from the inner surface of the ribs to the sides of the mediastinum in a straight line parallel and close to the vertebral column from the first to the twelfth thoracic vertebrae.

In front, on the right, the pleura is reflected from the costal surface to the mediastinal surface along a line extending from the root of the neck down the middle of the sternum to the level of the junction of the sixth costal cartilage. On the left the line is like that of the right, down to the level of the fourth costal cartilage where it deviates from the midline, being pushed aside by the heart. In this roughly triangular space behind the left half of the sternum the parietal pericardium is in contact with the anterior chest wall. The extent of this triangular area is extremely variable. If the pericardial sac is distended, it pushes the pleural sac still farther to the left and then, if great care is used, fluid may be aspirated from the pericardial cavity.

At the line of attachment of the diaphragm to the body wall the pleura is reflected from the inner surface of the thorax onto the upper surface of the diaphragm. Since this line of reflection marks the lowest limit to which the fully distended lung can descend, its position should be kept in mind. On the left the line starts in front at the junction of the sixth costal cartilage with the sternum; it passes almost horizontally around the chest, crossing, successively, the obliquely directed seventh rib at the junction with its costal cartilage, the eighth rib in the midclavicular line, the tenth rib in the midaxillary line, and the junction of the twelfth rib with the last thoracic vertebra. On the right the line of reflection follows the cartilage of the seventh rib, crosses the eighth rib at the midclavicular line, and from there on pursues a course identical with that of the left.

LUNGS

A healthy adult lung is spongy in consistency throughout and completely fills its pleural cavity. It is attached to the mediastinum on its medial aspect by the reflection of pleura and by the pulmonary vessels and bronchi which enter the substance of the lung. Normally the parietal pleura is nowhere adherent to the visceral pleura. The color of the lung of a baby is pink, owing to contained blood, but in an adult this color is masked by a mottled blue-gray color produced by particles of dust and soot permanently incorporated in its tissue. The lung of a baby who has not breathed is solid and sinks in water. After birth, respiration causes the lung to become spongy and filled with air, so that it no longer sinks in water. Complete opening of the air spaces of the lung is not attained until two or three weeks after birth.

The apex of the lung is the blunt, rounded, upper end which projects up into the base of the neck above the first rib. The base of the lung is concave and rests on the diaphragm. The hilus is a wedge-shaped area on the medial surface where the great vessels and bronchi enter the lung substance. These structures grouped together are called the root of the lung, each composed of one pulmonary artery, two pulmonary veins, nerves, lymphatics, bronchial vessels, and a bronchus. The parietal pleura is reflected over these vessels onto the surface of the lung where it becomes the visceral pleura. The reflection extends downward for some distance below the hilus to form the pulmonary ligament.

The left lung has two lobes, an upper and a lower lobe. The right lung has three lobes, an upper, middle, and lower lobe. The right upper and middle lobes correspond to the left upper lobe.

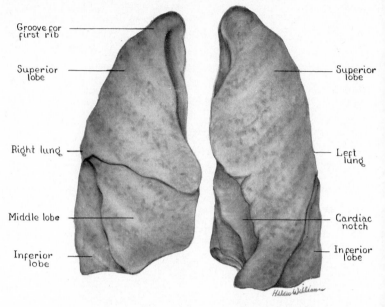

Groove for
first rib

Superior
lobe

Superior
lobe

Right lung

Left
lung

Middle lobe

Cardiac
notch

Inferior
lobe

Inferior
lobe

Fig. 255.—Anterior surface of lungs. (W.R.U. museum specimen.)

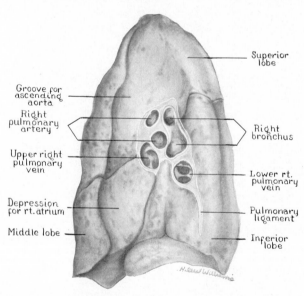

Superior
lobe

Groove for
ascending
aorta

Right
pulmonary
artery

Right
bronchus

Upper right
pulmonary
vein

Lower rt.
pulmonary
vein

Depression
for rt. atrium

Pulmonary
ligament

Middle lobe

Inferior
lobe

Fig. 256.—Medial surface of the right lung. Same lung as seen in Fig.
255.

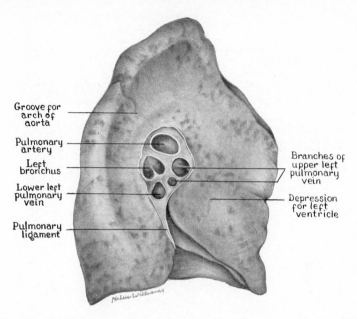

Groove for arch of aorta

Pulmonary artery

Left bronchus

Lower left pulmonary vein

Pulmonary ligament

Branches of upper left pulmonary vein

Depression for left ventricle

Fig. 257.—Medial surface of the left lung. Same lung as seen in Fig. 255.

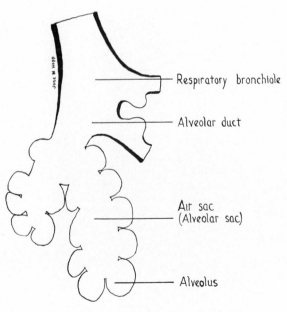

Respiratory bronchiole

Alveolar duct

Air sac (Alveolar sac)

Alveolus

Fig. 258.—Pulmonary lobule.

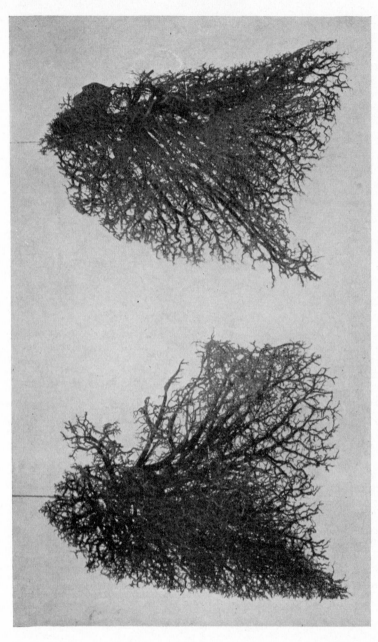

Fig. 259.—The arterial system of the lungs. (Injection by A. Cherney and K. Wolfe. Photograph by Dr. D. R. L. Duncan.) (W.R.U. term fetus.)

The right lung is shorter, wider, and slightly larger than the left. The lower medial portion of the left lung presents a hollowed area occupied by the heart.

Table 13

RIGHT LUNG	LEFT LUNG
Shorter	Longer
Wider	Narrower
Larger	Smaller
3 lobes	2 lobes
No cardiac notch	Cardiac notch
An eparterial bronchus	No eparterial bronchus

As the bronchi pass into the substance of the lung, they subdivide into smaller and smaller tubes known as bronchioles. These in turn end in small ducts having many outpocketings or alveoli. The larger subdivisions of the primary bronchi have an inner lining of pseudostratified columnar epithelium. Beneath this is a layer of smooth muscle and a layer of connective tissue and cartilage plaques. As the air passages become smaller, the epithelium gradually changes, the cilia are lost, and the cells become flatter until finally they become squamous in the alveolar ducts. The cartilage plaques entirely disappear in the smaller bronchi, and the smooth muscle fibers cease in the alveolar ducts.

There is a very rich capillary network about the alveoli. Respiration occurs by an interchange of gases through the walls of alveolus and capillary.

A pulmonary lobule is considered to be the primary unit of the lung. It consists of the final bronchiole (respiratory bronchiole), the associated alveolar ducts and alveoli, capillaries, and nerve fibers.

The nerves to the lung come from the vagus (cranial autonomic outflow) and the upper thoracic segments of the cord (thoracolumbar autonomic outflow).

In certain parts of the air passages the surface epithelium possesses cilia. These cilia beat in such a manner as to cause the mucus on the surface to flow toward the pharynx. In the nasal cavity this is a backward flow, and in the lower respiratory passages it is an upward flow. Small particles of dust and carbon (smoke) are carried by the mucus into the pharynx. Here, the mucus may be swallowed or expectorated.

MUSCLES OF RESPIRATION

The muscles used in breathing include the diaphragm, a large number of small muscles between the ribs, and certain accessory muscles which are attached above to the upper ribs and others which are attached below to the xiphoid and lower ribs.

The diaphragm is a muscular septum placed between the thoracic and abdominal cavities. It arises by a series of muscular bands from the back of the xiphoid, from the inner surface of the lower six costal cartilages, from the front of the lumbar vertebrae, and from the fascia covering the deep muscles of the back. The central portion is tendinous and the various muscle bundles are inserted into the central tendon.

The diaphragm presents domes which are concave below and convex above, the dome on the right rising to a higher level than the one on the left. The liver lies under the right dome and the stomach under the left. The heart rests on the upper surface of the diaphragm between the two domes.

The upper surface is covered on each side by parietal pleura and in the central portion by parietal pericardium. Most of the lower surface is covered by parietal peritoneum.

Numerous structures pass through the diaphragm—namely, the inferior vena cava, the esophagus, the vagal trunks, and several small arteries. The aorta and thoracic duct pass through an arch at the back of the muscle and not through its substance, and the azygos vein passes behind the diaphragm just to the right of the aorta.

The small muscles attached to the ribs include the following:

1. Eleven pairs of intercostal muscles are present on each side (an external and an internal intercostal muscle in each intercostal space). An external intercostal muscle arises from the lower border of a rib, and its fibers pass downward and forward to be inserted into the upper edge of the rib below. An internal intercostal arises from the lower border of a rib, and its fibers pass downward and backward to be inserted into the rib below.

2. Twelve pairs of levatores costarum muscles arise from the transverse processes of the last cervical and upper eleven thoracic vertebrae and attach to the rib below.

3. The subcostal muscles are similar to the internal intercostals, but are found only in the lower chest. They are not attached to adjacent ribs but pass over several ribs between origin and insertion.

4. The transverse thoracic muscle arises from the deep surface of the sternum and fans out to an insertion into the costal cartilages.

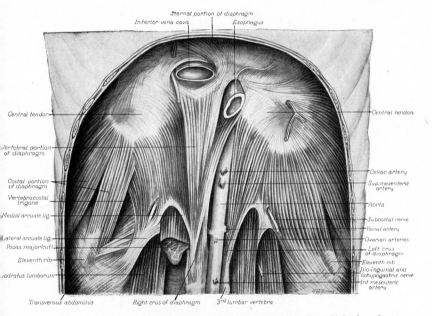

Fig. 260.—Abdominal surface of the diaphragm. (W.R.U. 2975, female, Negro, aged 31 years.)

In the neck are three scalene muscles which arise from the tubercles of the transverse processes of cervical vertebrae. The anterior scalene is inserted into the first rib in front of the subclavian artery. The middle scalene is inserted into the first rib behind the subclavian artery. The posterior scalene is inserted into the outer side of the second rib.

In inhalation of air the size of the pleural cavity is increased in three directions. Expansion of the chest wall lowers the intrathoracic pressure, and air enters from the outside through the air passages into the lungs.

The vertical length of the pleural cavity is increased by contraction of the diaphragm. The muscular bands pull on the central tendon from every side, flattening out the diaphragm and pushing the abdominal viscera downward and forward. The muscles of the abdominal wall control and limit this visceral movement.

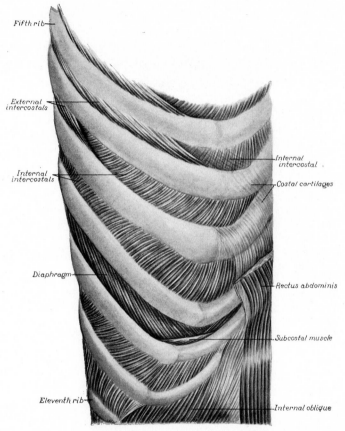

Fig. 261.—Intercostal muscles of the right chest wall.   (W.R.U. 3700, male, Negro, aged 57 years.)

The ribs are so articulated with the vertebral column that they tend to rotate out and up with inhalation. Thus the size of the chest is increased from side to side and from front to back. The first rib is raised and fixed by contraction of the scalene muscles.

The small muscles attached to the ribs likewise contract in series from above downward.

The abdominal muscles, particularly the rectus abdominis, anchor the sternum so that raising of the ribs must result in a more horizontal position of the obliquely placed costal cartilages. This increases the expansibility of the chest.

In exhalation the respiratory muscles relax. The weight of the thoracic cage, the elasticity of the costal cartilages, the inherent elasticity of the lungs, and the tone of the abdominal muscles which push the abdominal viscera and diaphragm upward all cause air to be forced out of the lungs.

The diaphragm is innervated by the phrenic nerves, the intercostal muscles by branches of the thoracic nerves.

REVIEW QUESTIONS

1. What organs are included in the respiratory system?
2. Describe the inferior turbinate.
3. Name the air sinuses of the skull. Where is each located? Where does each empty?
4. Name the cartilages of the larynx. Which are paired and which are unpaired?
5. What is the nerve supply of the intrinsic muscles of the larynx?
6. Give a brief description of the trachea.
7. What structures form the walls of the thoracic cavity?
8. How do the lungs of an adult differ from those of a newborn child?
9. List the muscles of respiration.
10. Describe the diaphragm.
11. Describe the mechanical processes involved in inspiration and expiration.

CHAPTER 13

THE DIGESTIVE SYSTEM

The digestive system receives food which it breaks up into simple substances for absorption through its walls into the body fluids (blood and lymph). The residue of food which is not digested or which cannot be digested is excreted. The system is a muscular tube with associated glands. The tube extends from the mouth, through the neck, thorax, and abdomen, to end in the perineum at the anus. The alimentary canal has the following subdivisions: mouth, pharynx, esophagus, stomach, small intestine, and large intestine.

MOUTH

The mouth is bounded on each side by the cheeks, above by the hard and soft palates, and below by a muscular sheet attached to the mandible. In front the mouth is closed by the lips and behind it opens into the pharynx. The mouth contains the teeth and tongue. The ducts of the salivary glands empty into the mouth.

The vestibule of the mouth is the space between the teeth and the mucous membrane of the cheeks and lips. The main cavity of the mouth lies within the dental arches and below the palate.

The lips have a layer of skin on the outer side which is continuous with the mucous membrane covering the lip margins and extending into the mouth. Beneath this outer layer are bands of muscle and connective tissue. These are the various muscles of expression which are discussed in Chapter 6, Muscles. The lips are richly supplied with blood vessels, lymphatics, and sensory nerves.

Like the lips, the cheeks have skin on the outer surface, mucous membrane on the inner surface, and muscles and connective tissue between the two surfaces. The buccinator, the most important muscle of the cheek, helps to keep the cheeks pressed firmly against the teeth, thereby acting as an accessory muscle of mastication.

The hard palate, formed from portions of the maxillary and palatine bones, separates the mouth from the nasal cavity. The under surface is covered by a thick layer of mucoperiosteum, so called because the mucous membrane is firmly adherent to the periosteum covering the bone.

Mucous glands are found throughout the mouth but are particularly abundant in certain areas. Beneath the mucous membrane of the lips is an almost continuous layer of small compound alveolar glands (racemose) that empty into the vestibule of the mouth. On the back of the hard palate and on the oral surface of the soft palate there are also very numerous glands.

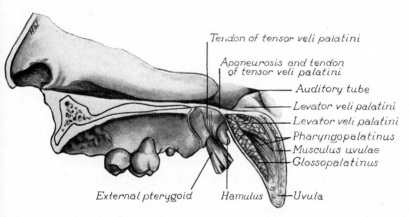

Fig. 262.—Sagittal section of the soft palate. (W.R.U. 3161, female, Negro, aged 44 years.)

The soft palate is attached to the back of the hard palate and to the sides of the mouth. It is a muscular fold covered above and below by mucous membrane. In mastication it hugs the back of the tongue, shutting off the mouth from the pharynx and allowing air to flow freely into the larynx. In swallowing, the soft palate is raised, closing off the nasopharynx and permitting food to pass downward into the esophagus. In speaking and singing also the soft palate is raised, shutting off the nasopharynx and thus directing the passage of air through the mouth. The soft palate ends behind in a median free projection called the uvula.

Laterally the soft palate is continuous with a fold of the side wall in front of the palatine tonsil. This is known as the glosso-palatine arch (anterior pillar of the fauces). Behind the palatine tonsil there is another fold in the side wall of the pharynx called the pharyngopalatine arch (posterior pillar of the fauces). There are muscles within these folds attached at the upper end to the soft palate and at the lower end to the side of the tongue and pharynx respectively. The glossopalatinus is the muscle of the anterior fold, and the pharyngopalatinus is the muscle of the posterior fold. The glossopalatinus may be said to arise from the dense fascia forming the midline of the soft palate. Here the fibers are continuous with those of the muscle of the other side of the palate. The pharyngopalatinus is a similar muscle arising in the midline of the soft palate where its fibers are continuous with those of the other side. These muscles aid the soft palate in closing off the mouth from the pharynx during mastication. They also make a narrow opening through which the tongue must push food during swallowing.

The levator veli palatini muscle arises from the lower surface of the petrous portion of the temporal bone and passes downward and forward into the soft palate and some of its fibers are continuous with those of the same muscle of the other side. In this way a sling for the soft palate is formed, and in contraction of the muscles the soft palate is pulled upward from the back of the tongue.

The tensor veli palatini arises from the under surface of the sphenoid bone. As it passes downward in the side wall of the pharynx, it becomes tendinous and is inserted into the soft palate. Its function is somewhat uncertain, but it is thought to open the inner end of the auditory tube during swallowing.

The tongue is a muscular organ covered by mucous membrane continuous with the lining of the mouth. Muscle bundles pass through the substance of the tongue longitudinally, vertically, and laterally, thus making it a very mobile organ. Its function in chewing is to mix the food with saliva and to keep the mass of food pressed between the grinding surfaces of the teeth. It acts in swallowing by forcing the food back into the pharynx. It is also an organ of speech, aiding particularly in the production of con-sonantal sounds. Taste buds distributed over the mucous membrane of the tongue are the end organs for the reception of taste. The fibers carrying sensory impulses of taste for the anterior two thirds of the tongue pass through the chorda tympani branch of the seventh cranial nerve, and those for the posterior third through the ninth cranial nerve.

Other types of sensory impulses for the anterior portion of the tongue are transmitted through the fibers of the fifth nerve and for the posterior portion through the ninth nerve. The motor nerve of the tongue is the twelfth cranial or hypoglossal nerve.

The mucous membrane of the tongue has a layer of stratified squamous epithelium. On the upper surface are many projections or papillae which make the surface rough. Most of the papillae are filiform or slender and threadlike, some are fungiform or knoblike, and a few are vallate or knoblike with a circular depression around each one.

The extrinsic muscles of the tongue include the hyoglossus, genioglossus, styloglossus, and glossopalatinus. The last has already been described in the discussion on the soft palate. The hyoglossus arises from the upper border of the hyoid bone and passes directly upward and forward to be inserted into the side of the tongue. The genioglossus arises from the back of the symphysis of the mandible. Its fibers pass out in a fan-shaped manner and are inserted into the entire length of the tongue near the midline. The styloglossus arises from the styloid process of the temporal bone and passes downward and forward in the side wall of the pharynx to be inserted into the side of the tongue. Its fibers are intermingled with those of the hyoglossus and genioglossus muscles. The styloglossus pulls the tongue back and up, the hyoglossus pulls the tongue down and back, and the genioglossus protrudes the tongue. The latter also keeps the base of the tongue from falling back into the oral pharynx which would obstruct the airway from nose to larynx. The glossopalatinus muscles receive motor fibers from the pharyngeal plexus. The other extrinsic muscles of the tongue receive their motor innervation from the hypoglossal nerve.

The floor of the mouth, composed of a muscular diaphragm, is covered by mucous membrane. The most important muscle of the diaphragm is the mylohyoid, which arises on each side from the mylohyoid line on the inner surface of the mandible. The two muscles meet in the midline beneath the tongue. They fill in the space between the two halves of the mandible and are attached below to the hyoid bone. The geniohyoid muscle arises from the back of the symphysis of the mandible and is inserted into the central portion of the hyoid. It lies in the midline deeper than the mylohyoid. The genioglossus muscle which lies deeper than the geniohyoid is one of the extrinsic muscles of the tongue. The anterior belly of the digastric muscle which lies superficial to the mylohyoid is described in the discussion on the extrinsic muscles of the larynx.

SALIVARY GLANDS

The salivary glands secrete saliva, a clear fluid which moistens the food and also contains an enzyme which digests cooked starch. The salivary glands are arranged in pairs: the parotid, the submandibular (submaxillary), and the sublingual glands.

The parotid gland lies in the side of the face just below and in front of the ear and on the masseter muscle. The facial nerve passes forward beneath the gland and there breaks up into a number of branches. The posterior facial vein, the external carotid artery and its terminal branches, the great auricular nerve, and the auriculotemporal nerve are all in intimate relation with the deep surface of the gland. The parotid or Stensen's duct passes forward around the edge of the masseter muscle, pierces the buccinator muscle, and empties into the vestibule of the mouth at the level of the upper second molar tooth. In mumps this gland becomes swollen. Since the gland has a tonguelike process projecting between the temporomandibular joint and the mastoid process, opening the mouth compresses the swollen glandular process and causes pain. In mumps the other salivary glands may also be swollen.

The submandibular salivary gland is smaller than the parotid and lies beneath the body of the mandible about halfway between the angle and the point of the lower jaw. It rests on the under (superficial) surface of the mylohyoid muscle. The submandibular or Wharton's duct passes through this muscle and opens into the floor of the mouth near the midline, under the anterior end of the tongue.

The sublingual salivary glands lie in the floor of the mouth on either side of the tongue, on the upper (deep) surface of the mylohyoid muscle. Each gland possesses several small ducts opening into the floor of the mouth behind the opening of the submandibular duct.

Secretory nerve fibers for the parotid gland come from the otic ganglion (cranial autonomic outflow from the ninth cranial nerve) and from the superior cervical ganglion (thoracolumbar outflow along the blood vessels). The secretory nerve fibers for the submandibular and sublingual glands come from the submandibular ganglion (cranial autonomic outflow from the chorda tympani branch of the seventh cranial nerve) and the superior cervical ganglion (thoracolumbar outflow along the blood vessels). The sensory nerves for all the salivary glands are branches of the trigeminal nerve.

Table 14
Salivary Glands

NAME	LOCATION	SITE OF OPENING OF DUCT	INNERVATION*
Parotid	Below and in front of the ear	Vestibule of mouth opposite upper second molar	Glossopharyngeal
Submandibular	Below mylohyoid muscle	Floor of mouth near anterior end of tongue	Facial
Sublingual	In floor of mouth above mylohyoid muscle	Several openings in floor of mouth near midline	Facial

*Source of parasympathetic fibers. Thoracolumbar fibers from superior cervical ganglion go to blood vessels of each gland.

TEETH

Each tooth has a crown, the portion projecting above the gum, a neck, the constricted part at the gum line, and a root embedded in the jawbone. At the apex of the root there is an opening through which nerves and blood vessels enter the pulp cavity within the tooth.

The surface coating for the crown of the tooth is a very dense, smooth, white, translucent layer called enamel. This layer ends at the gum line where it is slightly overlapped by the outer layer covering the root of the tooth. The latter, called cementum, is a layer of modified bone forming a sheath for the root. The bulk of the tooth lying beneath these two outer layers is called dentine. This is a dense, yellow-white, hard material having a striated appearance in thin sections. The tooth cavity within the dentine contains the dental pulp which is composed of connective tissue surrounding the nerve endings and small blood vessels.

The alveolar periosteum or periodontal membrane is a layer of fibrous connective tissue containing many blood vessels and sensory nerves, which fixes the root of the tooth in the alveolar process. This membrane is firmly attached to the cement of the tooth and to the bone of the alveolar process.

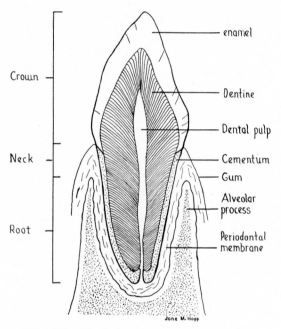

Fig. 263.—Vertical section of an incisor tooth.

Enamel and dentine are very rich in mineral, particularly calcium phosphate and calcium carbonate, rendering them hard and resistant to wear.

The teeth are divided into four groups:

1. *Incisors:* These are the cutting teeth which have crowns shaped like a chisel.

2. *Canines:* These are the cuspids in which each crown terminates in a sharp point.

3. *Premolars:* These are the bicuspids in which each crown has a grinding surface with two small projections called cusps.

4. *Molars:* These are larger teeth than the premolars and have a broad grinding surface with four cusps.

Each incisor and canine has one root; the premolars usually have but one root; the molars two or three roots.

There are two successional sets of teeth—a deciduous and a permanent.

The deciduous or milk dentition consists of twenty teeth, ten in each jaw.   There are eight incisors, four canines, and eight molars.   There are no premolars in the milk teeth.   The permanent dentition consists of thirty-two teeth, sixteen in each jaw. There are eight incisors, four canines, eight premolars, and twelve molars.   The upper lateral incisors may be small or occasionally absent.   Some or all of the third molars may be absent or may be present in the jaws though they do not erupt.   There is also an occasional extra incisor or a fourth molar.   Table 15 gives the average time for the eruption of teeth, but there are great individual variations from this general order, and the teeth tend to erupt earlier in girls than in boys.

Table 15
Time of Eruption of Teeth

DECIDUOUS TEETH	MONTHS
Lower central incisors	6-8
Upper central incisors	9-12
Upper lateral incisors	12-14
Lower lateral incisors	14-15
First molars	15-16
Canines	20-24
Second molars	30-32
PERMANENT TEETH	YEARS
First molars	6
Central incisors	7
Lateral incisors	8
First premolars	9-10
Second premolars	10
Canines	11
Second molars	12
Third molars	17-18

Roentgenograms of the jaws show that a tooth begins to calcify, that is, to form enamel and dentine, long before it erupts.   The cusps of all the milk teeth are well formed at birth.   The first permanent molar or the "six-year" molar begins to form cusps at three months, the second or "twelve-year" molar at three years, and the third molar or "wisdom tooth" at nine years. If the teeth are to be healthy and strong, children must have ample mineral in their diet when the cusps are calcifying.

Healthy deciduous teeth are more nearly white in color than the permanent teeth, but all should be translucent. The deciduous incisors and canines are much smaller than their permanent successors. The deciduous molars are larger than their successors, the permanent premolars.

The sensory nerve supply of the upper teeth comes from branches of the maxillary division of the trigeminal nerve, and that of the teeth in the lower jaw from the mandibular division of the same nerve.

Inasmuch as the teeth are the organs of mastication, the muscles used in chewing are discussed here.

MUSCLES OF MASTICATION

There are four muscles of mastication—the masseter, temporal, external pterygoid, and internal pterygoid muscles. They are aided by certain accessory muscles of which the most important is the buccinator.

The masseter rises from the lower border and deep surface of the zygomatic arch and is inserted into the outer side of the ramus above the angle of the mandible. The temporal muscle arises from the temporal fossa on the lateral surface of the skull. It is a fan-shaped muscle. The converging fibers pass beneath the zygomatic arch to be inserted into the coronoid process of the mandible. The external (lateral) pterygoid arises from the outer side of the lateral pterygoid lamina of the sphenoid bone and the nearby under surface of the great wing of the sphenoid. It is inserted into the neck of the mandible. The internal (medial) pterygoid arises from the inner side of the lateral pterygoid lamina and from the nearby surface of the palatine and maxillary bones and is inserted into the inner surface of the ramus of the mandible.

All four are supplied from the motor part of the mandibular division of the trigeminal nerve (the masticator nerve).

The masseter, temporal, and internal pterygoid muscles close the mouth and clench the teeth. The external pterygoids working together pull the lower jaw forward. The pterygoids on one side, working alternately with those on the other, produce lateral movements of the mandible. The posterior fibers of the temporal muscle retract or pull the jaw backward, and the anterior fibers of the temporal aid in protracting or pulling the jaw forward.

When the masticator muscles relax, the mandible drops in response to the action of gravity. When the mouth is opened widely, gravity is aided by certain muscles running from the hyoid to the mandible, namely, the anterior belly of the digastric, the geniohyoid, the mylohyoid, and the platysma muscles.

The functions of the tongue, buccinator, and orbicularis oris in mastication have already been discussed.

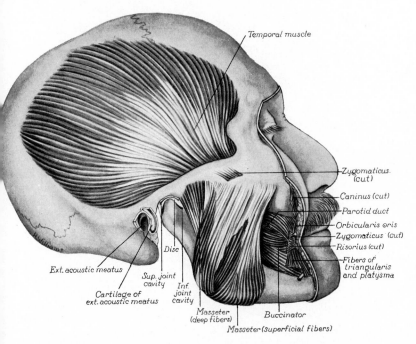

Fig. 264.—Right temporal and masseter muscles. (W.R.U. museum specimen. Dissection by Dr. C. A. Hamann.)

PHARYNX

The pharynx may be divided functionally into three parts. The upper part or nasopharynx lies behind the nose and is an air passage only. The middle part or oropharynx lies behind the mouth and serves both the respiratory and digestive tracts as a common passageway. The lower part or laryngopharynx lies behind the larynx and is a pathway for food passing into the esophagus.

The pharynx is a funnel-shaped cavity with fibromuscular walls. It is widest above, beneath the skull, and gradually narrows toward its lower end where it becomes the esophagus. It is about five

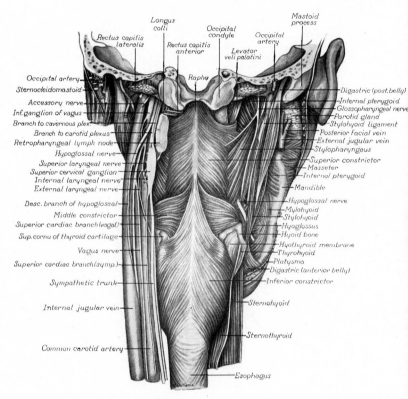

Fig. 265.—Posterior view of the pharynx. (Dissection by Dr. J. R. Nickerson.) (W.R.U. 3168, male, Negro, aged 53 years.)

inches long and lies in front of the cervical portion of the vertebral column. It is lined with mucous membrane which is covered with respiratory epithelium in its upper part and with stratified squamous epithelium below. A number of important muscles form the essential structure of the wall.

There are three constrictors of the pharynx arranged like three cones, each fitting within the next below. The superior constrictor arises from the posterior portion of the medial pterygoid lamina, the fascia between that bone and the mandible, the mylohyoid line of the mandible, and the side of the tongue. The fibers pass around the side of the pharynx, spreading out like a fan to be attached to a fibrous band or median raphe in the midline behind. This raphe extends from the base of the occiput downward.

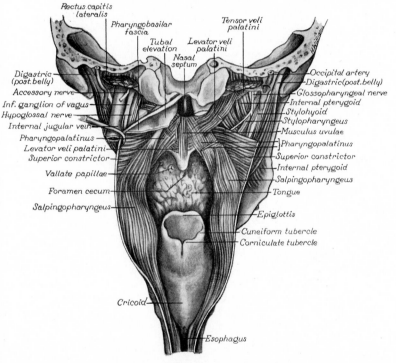

Fig. 266.—Interior of the pharynx from behind. The posterior wall has been split and each half has been reflected laterally. (W.R.U. 3168, male, Negro, aged 53 years.) (Dissection by Dr. J. R. Nickerson.)

The middle constrictor arises from the cornua of the hyoid bone and passes back to overlap the lower portion of the superior constrictor and to be inserted into the median raphe.

The inferior constrictor arises from the side of the thyroid and cricoid cartilages. It passes back on each side like the others to be inserted into the median raphe overlapping the lower portion of the middle constrictor.

The stylopharyngeus arises from the back of the styloid process. It passes downward to be inserted into the lateral wall of the pharynx between the superior and middle constrictors.

The pharyngopalatinus arises in the soft palate and passes downward in the pharyngopalatine arch to an insertion into the side

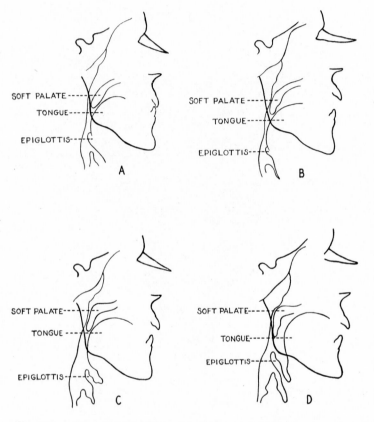

Fig. 267.—Alterations of position of pharynx and larynx in phonation of vowels.

A, Position in quiet respiration, W.R.U. X 2976.

B, Position when phonating *a* as in *father,* W.R.U. X 2976 (2)a.

C, Position when phonating *oo* as in *stool,* W.R.U. X 2976 (2)b.

D, Position when phonating *ee* as in *feet,* W.R.U. X 2976 (2)c. (Tracings made from x-rays of adult male, white.)

wall of the pharynx between the middle and inferior constrictors. A bundle of muscle fibers which arises from the cartilage of the auditory tube and blends with the rest of the pharyngopalatinus is called the salpingopharyngeus.

In the act of swallowing, the constrictor muscles direct the passage of food downward into the esophagus. The stylopharyngeus and pharyngopalatinus also take part in this action by assisting the geniohyoid, the mylohyoid, and anterior belly of the digastric to draw the larynx upward and forward out of the direct line of passage of food.

Vowel sounds are produced in the pharynx, which is capable of considerable change in form by the action of its constituent muscles. Roentgenoscopic observation shows that in the enunciation of the letter "a," as in father, the pharyngeal cavity is narrowed from front to back, and the soft palate is partly raised. In saying "oo" as in stool, the larynx is drawn moderately forward, and the soft palate is strongly arched. In saying "e" as in feet, the pharynx is widely dilated, the larynx is pulled forward, and the soft palate is pulled sharply up and back into the nasopharynx. The increasing pull of the mylohyoid and geniohyoid muscles may be felt by pressing the finger beneath the chin and saying the vowels in order.

The constrictors and pharyngopalatinus muscles are supplied through the pharyngeal plexus; the stylopharyngeus muscle is supplied by the glossopharyngeal, which is also the main sensory nerve for the mucosa of the pharynx.

It is well to summarize the seven openings into the pharynx. In front, above, are the openings of the two choanae into the nose, below is the single opening into the mouth, still farther down is the opening into the larynx, and behind that is the opening into the esophagus. In the lateral wall high up on each side is the opening into the auditory tube.

TONSILS

Lying in the walls of the pharynx are masses of lymphatic tissue forming a ring about the openings into the mouth and nose. The aggregation of lymphatic tissue between the pillars of the fauces is called the tonsil. The tonsils vary greatly in size with age and with health. In a newborn infant they are quite small, but during infancy they increase in size, reaching a maximum at about the third year of age. After this they gradually diminish and should be quite small in adult life.

Like other lymphatic structures the tonsils aid in combating disease by releasing phagocytes or scavenging leukocytes to cope with bacteria on the mucosa. They therefore become enlarged in infections and irritations of the nose and throat. If the bacteria gain the upper hand, the tonsils become inflamed. If they are chronically diseased, the surgeon removes them. In nasal allergy they tend to become enlarged by accumulation of fluid (edematous swelling). The connections of the lymphatic masses of the throat with the deep and superficial lymph nodes of the neck have been discussed in Chapter 11, The Lymphatic System.

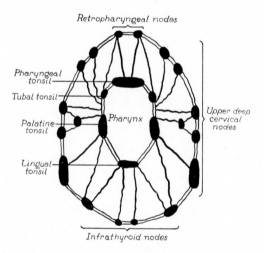

Fig. 268.—Lymphatic drainage of tonsils.

Each tonsil is a mass of lymph nodules with a fine reticular tissue framework and a covering of mucous membrane. The surface is irregular because of the openings of many small pits on it. Sometimes the word *tonsil* is used widely to designate any of the lymphatic masses of the throat. By this nomenclature there are the following "tonsils":

1. The palatine tonsil is a mass lying on each side in the lateral wall of the pharynx between the glossopalatine arch and the

pharyngopalatine arch.   The internal maxillary artery and several of its branches lie just lateral to the fibrous capsule which covers the lateral surface of the tonsil.   Injury to these vessels during a tonsillectomy may lead to severe hemorrhage.   Quinsy is an abscess outside the fibrous capsule and is usually above the tonsil itself.

2. The pharyngeal tonsil is a mass lying in the upper back wall of the pharynx behind the choanae.   This is also known as the "adenoid" and, when enlarged, it produces a lobulated mass which may block the nasopharyngeal passage and the medial opening of the auditory tube.

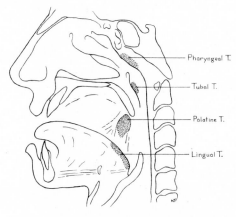

Fig. 269.—Diagram to show the location of the various tonsillar masses.

3. The tubal tonsil is a small mass lying just behind the auditory tube.

4. The lingual tonsil is a lymphatic mass covering the posterior third of the tongue.

ESOPHAGUS

The esophagus or gullet is a muscular tube extending from the pharynx at the level of the sixth cervical vertebra, through the posterior mediastinum and diaphragm, to the cardiac orifice of the stomach.   It is ten to twelve inches long.

The esophagus has four coverings: (1) an inner lining of mucous membrane, (2) a tela submucosa of connective tissue, (3) a muscular coat composed of an inner layer of circular muscle fibers and an outer layer of longitudinally arranged muscle bands, and (4) an outer layer of connective tissue blending with that in the neck and mediastinum.

The muscular coat in the upper portion is composed of striate muscle innervated through the pharyngeal plexus. Lower down, smooth muscle replaces the striate muscle, and this is innervated by the vagus and thoracic sympathetic nerves.

The lumen of the esophagus is stellate in outline owing to the tonic contraction of its musculature. It is distended by the passage of food, but it has three relatively constricted portions, one at the upper end, a second where the esophagus passes behind the left bronchus, and a third where it passes through the diaphragm.

ABDOMINAL CAVITY

The abdominal cavity is that portion of the general body cavity lying below the diaphragm. In front it is bounded by the muscles of the anterior abdominal wall, below by the bones of the pelvic girdle and by the pelvic diaphragm formed by the levator ani muscles, and behind by the vertebral column and by the psoas muscles and the muscles of the flanks. It is lined by a serous membrane called the peritoneum. As in other body cavities this serous lining is reflected over the organs within the cavity. The layer lining the walls is called the parietal peritoneum and the continuation over the organs the visceral peritoneum. During life the organs lie closely touching each other so that there is only a potential cavity within the parietal peritoneum.

Certain organs lying between the peritoneum and the walls of the abdominal cavity are covered only on one surface by peritoneum. These are the kidneys, ureters, urinary bladder, uterus, inferior vena cava, and abdominal aorta. Such organs are called retroperitoneal organs. The pancreas and portions of the duodenum, the ascending colon, and the descending colon become retroperitoneal secondarily; that is, they had mesenteries in the embryo but lost them later. Most of the abdominal digestive tract is completely clothed by peritoneum. The folds of peritoneum which are reflected from the walls over the viscera are called mesenteries. Certain of these have special names. The mesentery of the small intestine is known as "the mesentery." The transverse mesocolon is the mesentery of the transverse colon.

The mesoappendix is the mesentery of the appendix, and the mesovarium the mesentery of the ovary. The mesentery of the greater curvature of the stomach is prolonged as a great fat-containing fold, the greater omentum, which hangs like an apron over the front of the small intestine. Between the lesser curvature of the stomach and the hilus of the liver the peritoneum continues as the lesser omentum or gastrohepatic ligament. Other folds of

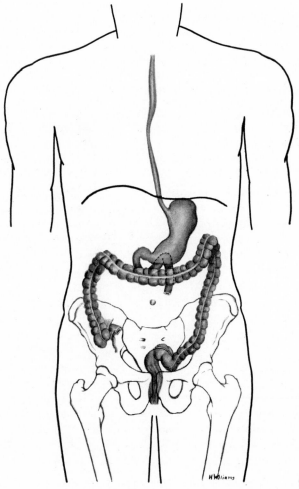

Fig. 270.—Position of digestive organs.

the peritoneum are called ligaments; these are the gastrosplenic ligament from the stomach to spleen, the hepatoduodenal ligament from liver to duodenum, and the phrenocolic ligament from the diaphragm to the splenic flexure of the colon. In addition to acting as supporting structures, the various mesenteries serve as passageways for the arteries, veins, lymphatics, and nerves supplying the viscera to which they are attached.

STOMACH

The stomach is a thick-walled tube into which the esophagus empties. A healthy, empty stomach has a thick wall and a small cavity. It is capable of great distention and may assume a great variety of shapes, depending upon its contents, the amount of tone of the muscles in its walls, and the position of a person.

Fig. 271 is a tracing of a stomach of a young adult made from an x-ray picture taken while the person was standing. The stomach was visualized by means of a "barium meal." On the right is the lesser curvature extending from the cardia or esophageal opening to the pylorus or outlet. The lesser curvature is the upper or concave margin of the stomach near the liver. The lesser omentum is attached to this margin and extends toward the right to the porta hepatis of the liver. The greater curvature is the left or convex margin of the stomach. It is much longer than the lesser, and attached to it is the greater omentum. The fundus of the stomach is the dome-shaped portion above the cardia, lying directly beneath the left dome of the diaphragm. The body of the stomach is the midportion of the tube; its lower end is called the pyloric portion.

The wall of the stomach has the following four coats:

1. An inner layer, called the tunica mucosa, is soft and velvety in appearance. This layer is thrown into numerous folds or rugae which, when the organ is contracted, run in a general longitudinal direction. As the stomach distends, the rugae lose their longitudinal disposition and ultimately disappear. The epithelium of this layer has columnar epithelial cells and numerous small glands which secrete mucus, enzymes, and hydrochloric acid.

2. The tela submucosa lies beneath the first layer and is composed of connective tissue.

3. The tunica muscularis has three layers of smooth muscle—an outer longitudinal layer, a middle circular layer, and an inner oblique layer.

4. The tunica serosa is composed of visceral peritoneum continuous at the greater and lesser curvatures with the peritoneum of the greater and lesser omenta.

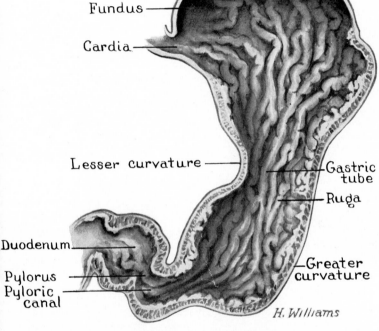

Fundus

Cardia

Lesser curvature

Gastric tube

Ruga

Duodenum

Pylorus

Pyloric canal

Greater curvature

H. Williams

Fig. 271.—Vertical section of the stomach. Traced from x-ray of adult white female who had been given water containing enough barium sulfate to outline gastric walls. (W.R.U. X 3892A.)

The blood vessels from the stomach lie between the layers of the omenta along each curvature and send long branches onto the anterior and posterior surfaces. Along the lesser curvature are the left gastric artery (a branch of the celiac artery) and the right gastric branch of the hepatic artery; along the greater curvature are the left gastroepiploic branch of the splenic artery and the right gastroepiploic branch of the gastroduodenal artery of the hepatic artery. The upper portion of the greater curvature receives a few arterial branches (short gastric) directly from the splenic artery.

The stomach receives motor nerves from two sources, the vagus nerves and the thoracolumbar autonomic outflow. The vagal trunks which pierce the diaphragm together with the esophagus subdivide into many fine branches on the anterior and posterior surfaces of the stomach. The sympathetic fibers are derived from the celiac ganglion and pass to the stomach along the branches of the celiac artery. There is an intrinsic nerve plexus containing some ganglion cells in the tela submucosa, and a similar nerve plexus in the tunica muscularis between the layers of smooth muscle.

There are sensory nerve fibers from the stomach and the conscious impressions arising from stimulation of these nerves are a good example of the indefiniteness of visceral sensation. We are well aware of the great discomfort of nausea, but we cannot localize the site of the sensation nor describe it accurately. The "gnawing" sensation of a gastric ulcer is another example.

LIVER

The liver is the largest gland in the body. It secretes bile and also receives digested carbohydrates and protein from the intestine by way of the portal vein. It fills the right upper portion of the abdominal cavity from the under surface of the diaphragm to below the costal margin. There is an extension to the left where it lies beneath the left cupula of the diaphragm and above the cardia of the stomach. The inferior vena cava is embedded in a deep groove on the back of the liver. The visceral peritoneum covering the liver is reflected in certain places from the surface of the liver to join the parietal peritoneum, thus forming several ligaments. On the anterior surface is the falciform ligament, extending to the anterior abdominal wall as far down as the umbilicus; above are the right and left triangular ligaments and the coronary ligament attaching the liver to the diaphragm. The round ligament is a round fibrous cord embedded within the free border of the falciform ligament and extending from the umbilicus to the porta hepatis. This ligament is the remains of the left umbilical vein, a blood vessel which before birth carried blood from the placenta to the liver and inferior vena cava. The under surface of the liver has a deep fissure, the porta hepatis, where the portal vein and hepatic artery pass into the liver and the hepatic ducts leave. The right border of the lesser omentum is

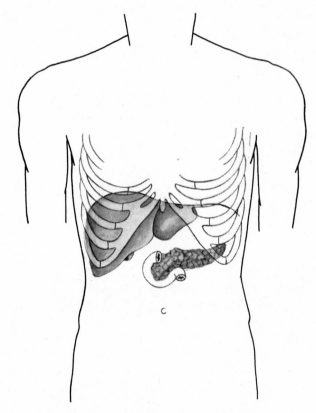

Fig. 272.—The position of liver and pancreas.

attached to the porta hepatis; the portal vein, hepatic artery, and bile ducts lie within the two layers of this omentum. The free border of the lesser omentum forms the epiploic foramen (foramen of Winslow), which opens into the omental bursa, a recess of the general peritoneal cavity.

The liver has four lobes:

1. The right lobe lies beneath the right cupula of the diaphragm.

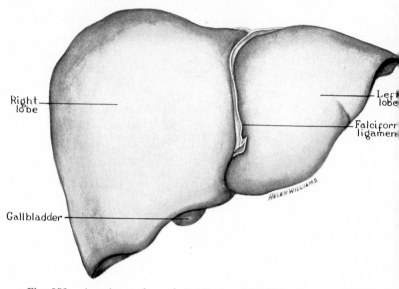

Right
lobe

Left
lobe

Falciform
ligament

Gallbladder

HELEN WILLIAMS

Fig. 273.—Anterior surface of the liver.   (W.R.U. museum specimen.)

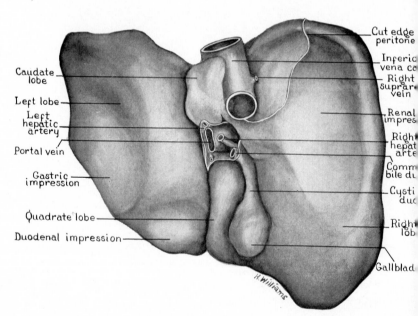

Cut edge
peritone

Inferio
vena ca

Right
suprar
vein

Caudate
lobe

Left lobe

Left
hepatic
artery

Portal vein

Gastric
impression

Quadrate lobe

Duodenal impression

Renal
impres

Right
hepat
arte

Comm
bile du

Cysti
duc

Right
lob

Gallblad

H. Williams

Fig. 274.—Under surface of the liver.   (W.R.U. museum specimen.)

2. The left lobe lies beneath the left cupula and is much smaller than the right.

3. The quadrate lobe is a quadrilateral area on the under surface of the liver lying in front of the porta hepatis and between the gallbladder and the fossa for the round ligament.

4. The caudate lobe is another quadrilateral area on the back of the liver, lying between the inferior vena cava and the fossa for the ductus venosus (a vein in the embryo carrying blood from the portal vein to the inferior vena cava).

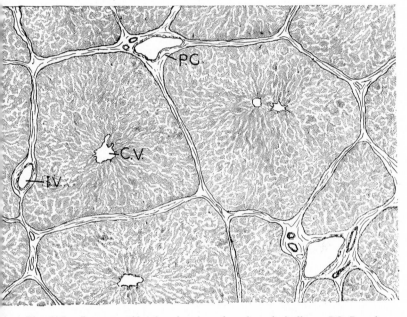

Fig. 275.—Low magnification drawing of section of pig liver. *PC,* Portal canal; *IV,* interlobular vein; *CV,* central or intralobular vein. In the pig each hepatic lobule is surrounded by connective tissue. (From Hoskins and Bevelander: Essentials of Histology, St. Louis, 1956, The C. V. Mosby Co.)

Except for a small area on the back and upper surface of the right lobe the liver is entirely covered by peritoneum.

The liver has a connective tissue sheath from which fibrous bands pass deep into the substance of the gland. This is the capsule of Glisson. These bands, together with the branches of the blood vessels, divide the organ into many small hepatic lobules.

In man the lobules are incompletely separated from each other. In the center of each lobule is a branch of the hepatic vein. Arranged about the periphery of each lobule are several portal canals. Each portal canal consists of connective tissue and branches of the portal vein, the hepatic artery, and the hepatic duct. The secretory cells of the liver are arranged in curved plates radiating outward from the central vein. Bile is secreted into tiny bile capillaries between the secretory cells and is carried to the periphery of

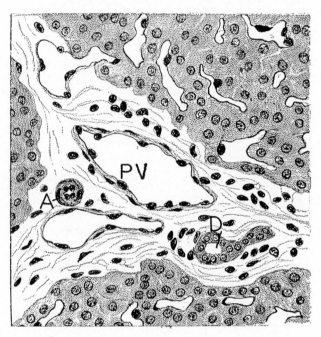

Fig. 276.—Diagram of a portal canal. *PV,* Branch of portal vein; *A,* branch of hepatic artery; *D,* a bile duct. (From Hoskins and Bevelander: Essentials of Histology, St. Louis, 1956, The C. V. Mosby Co.)

the lobules to a branch of the hepatic duct. Between the curved plates of liver cells are capillary blood sinuses which connect the terminal branches of the hepatic artery and portal vein with venules which drain into the hepatic veins. In the lining of these sinuses are macrophages which in the liver are called Kupffer cells. Nerve fibers for the liver are derived from the vagus nerves and the celiac plexus. There is a nerve plexus along the hepatic artery.

The liver has many and varied functions and is essential to life. All liver cells look alike, and so far as is known, no special group of cells has any particular function. Each cell apparently is capable of performing any or all of the hepatic functions. Digested carbohydrates, mainly in the form of glucose, may be stored in the liver as glycogen, and, when required, the glycogen is changed back to glucose. Therefore, the liver plays an important role in maintaining the proper level of blood sugar. Amino acids derived from digested protein are used by the liver to form various body proteins, or they may be consumed as fuel, and the resulting waste products are excreted by the liver. Digested fats may be added to the body stores or burned as fuel. The liver secretes bile and bile salts which are necessary for digestive processes in the intestinal tract. The liver makes substances which are of primary importance in the mechanism of blood clotting, including fibrinogen and prothrombin. Various toxic substances which may be present in the blood stream are detoxified by the liver. Since some of the substances elaborated by the liver are secreted directly into the blood stream, the gland is regarded as an endocrine gland as well as an exocrine gland.

Because of its size the liver is a very important reservoir for storage of blood and body fluid. Also because of its size the liver contains a great deal of reticuloendothelial tissue. The Kupffer cells perform the various functions of macrophages.

Hepatic Ducts and Gallbladder.—Soon after they leave the liver, the right and left hepatic ducts join to form the ductus choledochus or common bile duct, which opens into the second part of the duodenum.

From the common duct a branch is given off, the cystic duct, which passes to the right. Its terminal dilated portion is the gallbladder. In performing a cholecystectomy the surgeon removes the gallbladder and as much of the cystic duct as possible, but must leave the common duct intact. If the common duct is destroyed or blocked, bile cannot be emptied into the duodenum and is then absorbed into the circulation; jaundice results and ultimately death if the obstruction is not relieved. If only the cystic duct is obstructed, as it may be by a gallstone, there is no jaundice for bile flows freely from the liver through the common duct into the duodenum.

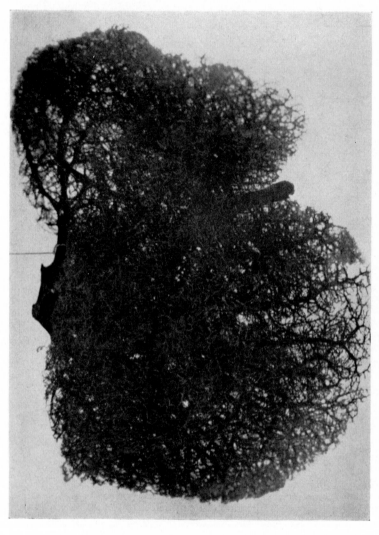

Fig. 277.—Arterial system of the liver.   (Injection by A. Cherney and K.

The gallbladder and the ducts have an inner mucous membrane coat, a middle coat of smooth muscle, and an outer layer of peritoneum. The latter may be partially missing in cases in which the gallbladder is partly buried within the substance of the liver.

PANCREAS

The pancreas is an important gland which secretes pancreatic juice into the duodenum. It also has an endocrine secretion (insulin). It has a head within the curve of the duodenum and a long slender tail extending to the left behind the stomach as far as the spleen. It is a retroperitoneal organ lying in front of the inferior vena cava, aorta, and left kidney.

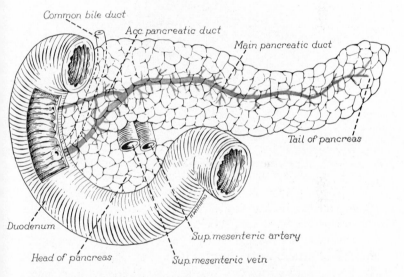

Fig. 278.—Pancreas and duodenum. A window has been cut in the anterior wall of the duodenum to show the openings of the common bile duct and the pancreatic ducts into the lumen of the duodenum.

The pancreas usually has two ducts. The main one (Wirsung's) begins in the tail and passes through the length of the gland to join with the common bile duct in a dilated vestibule, Vater's ampulla, which opens into the duodenum at Vater's papilla. The common bile duct and the main pancreatic duct may have two separate openings or a single common opening into the duodenum. There is also an accessory duct (Santorini's) which, when present, drains a portion of the head and empties into the duodenum by a separate opening about one inch above that of the main duct.

The pancreas is a compound tubuloalveolar gland having an immense number of small lobules. The lining is simple columnar epithelium. The lobules are separated by a delicate connective tissue network. In among the tubules are small islands of granular cells arranged in irregular cords. Each island contains numerous capillaries. These collections of cells are the islands or islets of Langerhans which secrete insulin.

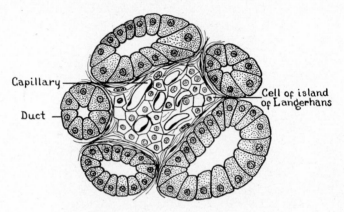

Fig. 279.—Cellular structure of the pancreas showing several ducts in cross section and an island of Langerhans.

The pancreas is richly supplied with blood which comes from branches of the celiac and superior mesenteric arteries. The superior pancreaticoduodenal artery is a branch of the hepatic, the inferior pancreaticoduodenal is a branch of the superior mesenteric, and there are some branches from the splenic artery. The venous drainage is into tributaries of the portal vein. Sympathetic nerves (thoracolumbar outflow) from outlying portions of the celiac ganglion supply the pancreas, and there are also fibers from the vagus nerves (cranial autonomic outflow).

SMALL INTESTINE

The small intestine for purposes of description is divided into three arbitrary divisions—the duodenum, jejunum, and ileum. The duodenum is about nine inches long (twelve fingerbreaths),

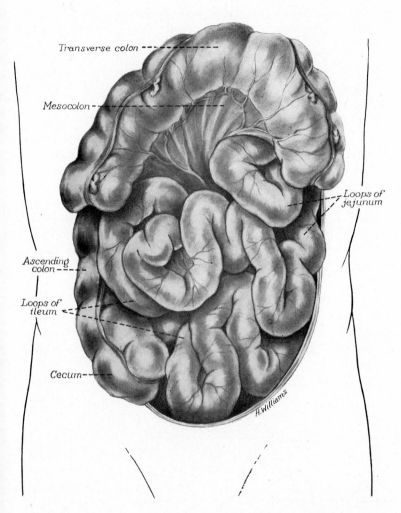

Fig. 280.—Anterior view of intestines. The transverse colon has been turned upward to show the loops of jejunum. (W.R.U. 3750, male, Negro, aged 53 years.)

the jejunum eight feet, and the ileum eleven feet. The whole length is perhaps eighteen feet, but this varies greatly with the degree to which the muscle fibers are contracted.

The wall in the small intestine has the following four layers:

1. The tunica mucosa or mucous membrane consists of a surface layer of simple columnar epithelium lying on a thin sheet of connective tissue, the lamina propria, and having outside this a thin sheet of smooth muscle, the muscularis mucosae. There are many small tubular glands in the mucous membrane.

The mucous membrane has an immense number of small elevations called villi which give the surface a velvety appearance. Each villus is a long, slender, conelike projection having small blood vessels and a large lymphatic in the center. The body of each villus also contains some smooth muscle cells which upon contraction shorten the villus and upon relaxation allow it to elongate. The size and number of villi are greatest in the upper part of the small intestine and gradually decrease toward the ileocecal valve.

The mucous membrane also possesses numerous large, circular folds called plicae circulares. These folds are best developed in the lower duodenum and upper jejunum. They are less numerous in the ileum and disappear near its distal end. The villi and plicae circulares together greatly increase the surface area of the mucous membrane of the small intestine.

Scattered along the mucosal surface of the small intestine are oval, flattened plaques of lymphatic tissue called solitary lymph follicles or nodules. In the lower ileum are groups of these minute lymph nodules forming aggregated lymph nodules or Peyer's patches. A few of these may be found in higher areas of the small bowel.

2. The tela submucosa is composed of a strong layer of connective tissue.

3. The tunica muscularis has an outer longitudinal layer and an inner circular layer of smooth muscle. The longitudinal layer forms a continuous sheet around the entire small intestine.

4. The tunica serosa is composed of visceral peritoneum continuous with that of the mesentery. On the duodenum this coat is incomplete because much of this part of the intestine is retroperitoneal.

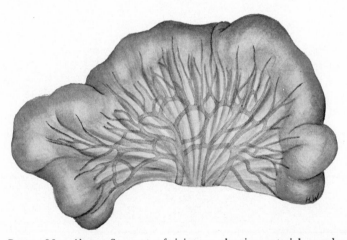

PLATE 26.—*Above,* Segment of jejunum showing arterial arcades in mesentery. *Below,* Segment of ileum showing arterial arcades in mesentery; same subject as above. (W.R.U. 3750, male, Negro, aged 53 years.)

The duodenum receives several arterial branches from the celiac artery, but the remainder of the small intestine is supplied by the branches of the superior mesenteric artery. These branches lie within the mesentery and anastomose freely with each other, forming arterial arcades. Branches from these arcades anastomose,

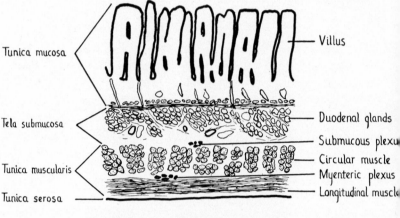

Tunica mucosa — Villus

Tela submucosa — Duodenal glands

— Submucous plexus

Tunica muscularis — Circular muscle

— Myenteric plexus

Tunica serosa — Longitudinal muscle

Fig. 281.—Longitudinal section of duodenum.

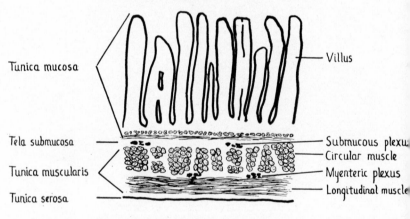

Tunica mucosa — Villus

Tela submucosa — Submucous plexus

— Circular muscle

Tunica muscularis — Myenteric plexus

Tunica serosa — Longitudinal muscle

Fig. 282.—Longitudinal section of jejunum.

forming secondary arcades. The arteries to the jejunum form only one or two arches, but in the lower part of the mesentery the branches are much more complex, and the distal portion of the ileum may have as many as five sets of arches. The final arterial branches pass directly into the gut wall. The veins from the small intestine unite to form the superior mesenteric vein, one of the main tributaries of the portal vein.

The nerve supply to the small intestine comes from the celiac and superior mesenteric ganglia and from the vagus nerves. Within the wall of the gut the nerve fibers intermingle to form two extensive plexuses. Between the longitudinal and circular muscle layers of the tunica muscularis is the myenteric (Auerbach's) plexus, and in the tela submucosa is found the submucous plexus (Meissner's). There are sensory fibers, but the main conscious sensory impressions are those of pain when the wall is pulled, distended, or stretched.

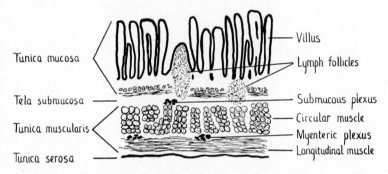

Fig. 283.—Longitudinal section of ileum.

Duodenum.—The duodenum begins at the pylorus. It is a C-shaped tube, with the concavity toward the left and having the head of the pancreas lying within this concavity. It has three parts: a superior portion running to the right, a descending portion running downward along the right side of the vertebral column, and an inferior portion running at first, transversely to the left in front of the inferior vena cava, aorta, and vertebral column and then turning upward and forward to become the jejunum. The ducts of the liver and pancreas open into the descending portion of the duodenum. In the duodenum, only, the intestinal glands extend into the tela submucosa.

Jejunum, Ileum, and Mesentery.—The jejunum and ileum, or main portions of the small intestine, are suspended in the abdomen by the mesentery. This fan-shaped fold of peritoneum is attached

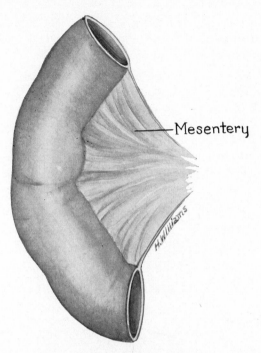

Fig. 284.—Segment of jejunum. In this specimen the mesentery is well filled with fat, thus obscuring the vessels. (W.R.U. museum specimen A1231.)

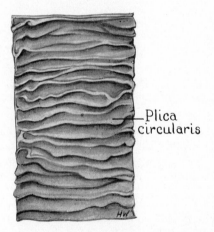

Fig. 285.—Segment of jejunum, showing plicae. (W.R.U. museum specimen A1229.)

to the posterior abdominal wall for about six inches and is obliquely directed from the left side of the second lumbar vertebra over the duodenum, aorta, inferior vena cava, and right ureter to the right lower border of the fifth lumbar vertebra. The free border of the mesentery is about eighteen feet long to correspond with the length of the combined jejunum and ileum. Between the serous or peritoneal layers of the mesentery are the superior mesenteric artery and vein with their branches, many lymphatic vessels and nodes, and nerve fibers.

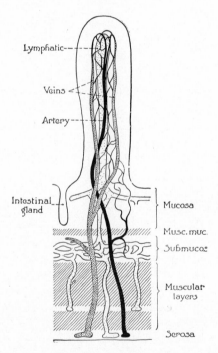

Fig. 286.—Diagram of an intestinal villus. The artery is black; the vein is heavily stippled; the lacteal is lightly stippled. (From McClendon: Physiological Chemistry, St. Louis, 1946, The C. V. Mosby Co.)

The position of the loops of small intestine varies with their distention and the progress of food matter through the bowel. The loops of jejunum occupy the upper left part of the abdominal cavity and the loops of the ileum the lower right portion; some loops of the latter usually extend down into the pelvic cavity.

LARGE INTESTINE

The large intestine begins in the lower right portion of the abdominal cavity. It is continued on the right side of the abdomen as far as the under surface of the liver. It then crosses to the left side by a festoonlike loop, turns downward under the spleen, and continues down the left flank into the pelvic cavity where it ends at the anus. The beginning is called the cecum, on which the vermiform appendix is a pocket. Following the cecum in order are the ascending colon, the hepatic flexure, the transverse colon, the splenic flexure, the descending colon, the iliac colon, the pelvic colon, the rectum, and the anal canal. With the exception of the appendix, rectum, and anal canal the various portions have no delimiting characteristics and are merely names of location given for convenience of description.

The large intestine is distinguished from the small in the following ways:

1. The tunica mucosa is soft and velvety, but has no villi on the mucosal surface and no plicae circulares.

2. The longitudinal muscle layer of the tunica muscularis is not continuous, but is limited to three longitudinal bands which are visible on the surface as taeniae coli.

3. The cecum, transverse colon, and pelvic colon regularly have mesenteries and therefore a complete tunica serosa. The ascending, descending, and iliac colons have a serosa only on the anterior surface unless they possess mesenteries, as sometimes happens.

4. There are many small tags of fat-filled peritoneum along the free border of the large gut called appendices epiploicae.

5. The walls of the transverse colon have definite rounded pouches or sacculations, called haustra, which are separated from each other by semilunar folds. These are less well marked in the ascending and pelvic colons, and poorly developed or absent in the descending and iliac colons. They do not exist in the cecum or rectum.

In summary, a loop of large bowel may be distinguished from a loop of small bowel by the presence of taeniae coli, appendices epiploicae, and haustra.

The appendix, cecum, and proximal portion of the colon receive their arterial supply from the superior mesenteric artery;

the remainder of the colon and the upper portion of the rectum receive arterial branches from the inferior mesenteric artery; and the distal end of the anal canal has arterial branches from the internal iliac artery. The superior hemorrhoidal (rectal) artery is a branch of the inferior mesenteric; the middle hemorrhoidal (rectal) is a branch of the anterior division of the internal iliac artery; and the inferior hemorrhoidal (rectal) is a branch of the internal pudendal artery.

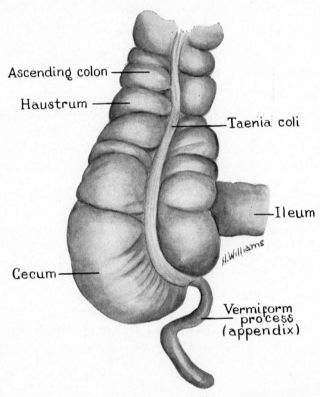

Fig. 287.—The cecum and appendix. (W.R.U. museum specimen A561.)

The superior mesenteric vein has important tributaries from the veins of the proximal portion of the colon, and the inferior mesenteric vein drains blood into the portal system from the remainder of the colon and upper rectum. The two mesenteric veins anastomose with each other, and in the wall of the rectum the inferior mesenteric vein communicates with the veins of the distal end of the gut which drain into the inferior vena cava. There is likewise an anastomosis between systemic and portal veins at the lower end of the esophagus, along the round ligament of the liver, and at the root of the mesentery.

The cecum, ascending colon, and proximal portion of the transverse colon receive nerve fibers from the superior mesenteric plexus and from the vagus nerves. The smooth muscle of the rest of the large gut receives fibers from the inferior mesenteric plexus and from pelvic ganglia. Sensory fibers from the intestine pass along the splanchnic nerves to the thoracic segments of the cord. Sensory fibers from the body wall go to the same segments. For this reason the pain of appendicitis may seem to be in the pit of the stomach.

Cecum.—The cecum is a multilocular pouch which lies below the level of the ileocecal opening. It is about two inches long and during childhood is surrounded by peritoneum. In the adult the cecum often becomes adherent secondarily to the posterior wall of the peritoneal cavity, and then it possesses a serous covering on its anterior wall only. On its anterior surface the taenia coli is well marked, terminates below on the appendix, and therefore serves as a guide in finding the appendix. The vermiform process or appendix is a slender tube attached to the base of the cecum. It varies greatly in length and position and usually has a small mesentery of its own. The cavity of the appendix opens into that of the cecum.

The opening of the ileum into the cecum is guarded by liplike folds. These folds are composed of mucous membrane and circular muscle bundles, forming a valvelike orifice which allows the contents to flow into the cecum but not back into the ileum.

Ascending Colon.—The ascending colon extends from the level of the ileocecal valve upward to the hepatic flexure. It is variable in length but is usually about six inches long and as a rule has a larger caliber than the descending colon. It usually has no peritoneum on its posterior surface and therefore no mesentery. The lower portion is close to the anterior abdominal wall, but the upper portion lies deeper behind the right lobe of the liver and in front of the anterior surface of the right kidney.

Transverse Colon.—The transverse colon passes in a long loop below the stomach and is about twenty inches long. It begins at the hepatic flexure, passes transversely across the abdominal cavity, and ends at the splenic flexure near the spleen. This portion has a mesentery, the transverse mesocolon. In the adult the meso-

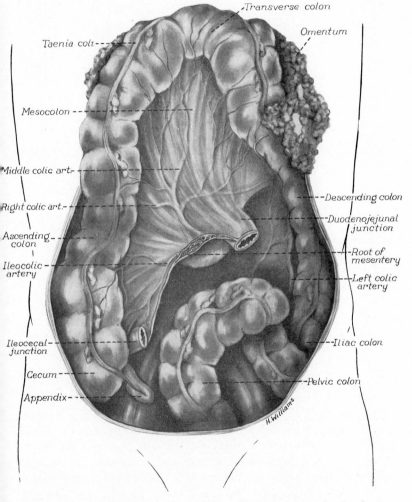

Fig. 288.—Colon and root of mesentery. The transverse colon has been turned upward to show the duodenojejunal junction. (W.R.U. 3750, male, Negro, aged 53 years.)

colon is usually blended with the great omentum. The peritoneum forming the mesocolon is reflected from that which covers the pancreas. The midportion of the transverse colon is freely movable and varies greatly in its position and in the length of its mesentery. At either end the mesocolon becomes much shorter and disappears at either flexure. Both the hepatic and splenic flexures are well anchored to the posterior abdominal wall and vary little in position. The splenic flexure usually lies at a somewhat higher level than the hepatic.

Descending Colon.—The descending colon is about six inches long, ordinarily has no mesentery, but is firmly attached to the left posterior wall of the abdominal cavity. In diameter it is usually much smaller than the ascending colon.

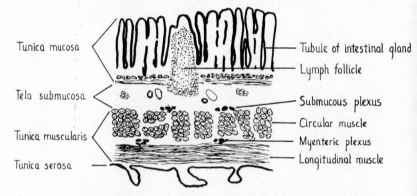

Fig. 289.—Longitudinal section of transverse colon.

Iliac Colon.—The iliac colon is that portion lying on the inner surface of the left iliacus muscle; it is about six inches long and usually has no mesentery. It is quite often considered as a portion of the descending colon and is not described separately.

Pelvic Colon.—The pelvic colon begins where the bowel passes over the pelvic brim into the pelvic cavity. This portion is about sixteen inches long and has a well-developed mesentery, the pelvic mesocolon. This loop of bowel varies greatly in length and therefore in position, but usually remains within the pelvic cavity. It makes a curve within the pelvis which is somewhat S shaped and is therefore often called the sigmoid colon and its mesentery the mesosigmoid. The longitudinal muscle bundles of the tunica muscularis spread out so that in the distal portion of the pelvic colon the longitudinal muscle layer becomes continuous, and taeniae coli and haustra disappear.

Rectum.—The rectum has no mesentery, no appendices epiploicae, and no haustra. At its beginning it is covered by peritoneum on the anterior surface, but lower down has no peritoneal covering at all. It lies on the anterior surface of the sacrum and coccyx, surrounded by pelvic fascia. It is curved somewhat from side to side and from front to back but none of the curves is acute. In the male it lies behind the prostate gland and bladder and in the female behind the uterus and vagina. There are several crescentic folds in the lateral walls of the rectum which project into its cavity. The terminal portion narrows rapidly, and the mucous

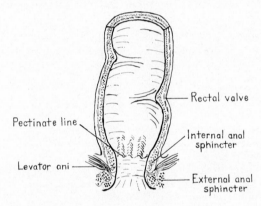

Fig. 290.—Diagram of vertical section of rectum and anal canal.

membrane has a number of vertical folds called rectal columns, with spaces between called rectal sinuses. The veins present in the mucosa covering the rectal columns frequently become dilated, thus forming internal hemorrhoids. A line drawn around the rectum at the base of the rectal columns is undulating or wavy and is called the pectinate or dentate line. This line is frequently used by anatomists and surgeons to mark the junction of the rectum and anal canal. The name rectum would imply that this portion of the bowel is straight. In many animals this is true, but in man it is not. For convenience the name has been retained in human anatomy.

Anal Canal.—The anal canal, a narrow passage between two levator ani muscles, is about one inch long. These two muscles form a muscular diaphragm in the floor of the pelvic cavity. They are attached to the side walls of the pelvic girdle and meet in the midline in a raphe extending from the coccyx behind to the midpoint of the perineum in front of the anus. The anal canal is directed downward and backward, and in the recumbent position often forms an angle with the horizontal of as much as 45 degrees. The lining of the anal canal is stratified squamous epithelium.

Some descriptions of this area include the terminal part of the rectum containing the rectal columns and sinuses as the first part of the anal canal and, therefore, refer to these structures as anal columns and anal sinuses.

The levator ani muscles act as a sphincter of the gut, but there are in addition two other sphincters: (1) an internal sphincter which is a thickened portion of the circular muscle layer of the tunica muscularis and therefore smooth or involuntary muscle, and (2) an external sphincter composed of small bundles of striate or voluntary muscle lying beneath the skin about the anus.

Review Questions

1. What structures bound the mouth?
2. Describe the soft palate.
3. Describe the hard palate.
4. Describe the tongue.
5. Name the extrinsic muscles of the tongue. Give one function of each.
6. Name the salivary glands. Where is each located? What is the source of the secretory nerve fibers to each?
7. How many teeth are in the deciduous dentition? How many in the permanent dentition?
8. Name the muscles of mastication. Give one function of each.
9. Describe the pharynx.
10. Name the muscles of the pharynx. How do they function in the act of swallowing?
11. Give the location of the various tonsils.
12. What structures form the wall of the abdominal cavity?
13. What is meant by a retroperitoneal organ?
14. Describe the wall of the stomach.
15. What are the three subdivisions of the small intestine?
16. Give two functions of the pancreas.
17. Describe the liver.
18. Describe the gallbladder.
19. How may the large intestine be distinguished from the small intestine?
20. What are the subdivisions of the large intestine?
21. Describe the cecum.
22. Describe the rectum.

CHAPTER 14

THE URINARY SYSTEM

The urinary system consists of a pair of kidneys which secrete urine, a pair of ureters which convey the urine from the kidneys to the bladder, a bladder which holds the urine, and a urethra which carries the urine to the exterior. The urethra is much longer in the male than in the female, but otherwise there are no sexual differences in the urinary system.

KIDNEY

In life the kidney is a dark reddish-brown color which shows through the glistening, translucent capsule. The shape of the kidney is so characteristic that it needs little description. The convex border of the kidney is on the lateral side, and the concave border is turned toward the vertebral column. On the concave border is a deep excavation in the substance of the organ called the renal sinus, the opening of which is the hilus of the kidney. The renal vessels enter and leave the kidney through the hilus, and the pelvis of the ureter is attached there. The adrenal gland, which is further discussed in Chapter 9, The Endocrine System, fits like a cap on the upper end of the kidney. The right kidney is ordinarily a little lower than the left. The lower border of the kidney is about one and one-half inches above the level of the iliac crest when the body is erect; the organ ascends somewhat in the horizontal position.

The thin, smooth capsule closely enveloping the kidney is called the tunica fibrosa or proper renal capsule. Outside this is a considerable mass of mixed connective and fatty tissue within which the kidney is embedded. The fatty tissue is sometimes called the adipose capsule or perirenal fat, and the fibrous tissue is called the fascia renalis or capsule of Gerota. This fibrous and fatty tissue helps to keep the kidneys in their normal position. In front of the kidney is the parietal peritoneum and behind it are the deep muscles of the back.

Underneath the tunica fibrosa is the cortex of the kidney, forming a complete layer, and within that again is the medullary substance arranged in conical masses called renal pyramids. Each pyramid has its base placed against the cortical layer and its apex projecting into the sinus as a renal papilla. The medulla has a

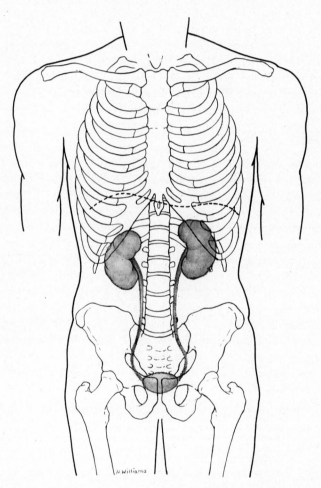

Fig. 291.—The position of the urinary system.

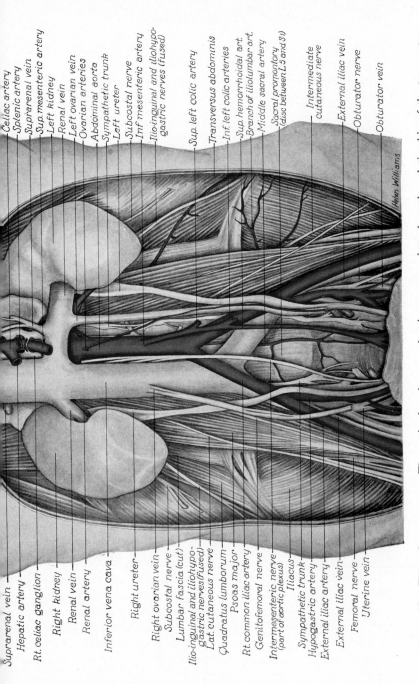

Celiac artery
Splenic artery
Suprarenal vein
Sup. mesenteric artery
Left kidney
Renal vein
Left ovarian vein
Ovarian arteries
Abdominal aorta
Sympathetic trunk
Left ureter
Subcostal nerve
Inf. mesenteric artery
Ilio-inguinal and iliohypo-
gastric nerves (fused)

Sup. left colic artery
Transversus abdominis
Inf. left colic arteries
Sup. hemorrhoidal art.
Branch of iliolumbar art.
Middle sacral artery
Sacral promontory
(disc between L5 and S1)

Intermediate
cutaneous nerve

External iliac vein
Obturator nerve

Obturator vein

Suprarenal vein
Hepatic artery
Rt. celiac ganglion
Right kidney
Renal vein
Renal artery
Inferior vena cava

Right ureter

Right ovarian vein
Subcostal nerve
Lumbar fascia (cut)
Ilio-inguinal and iliohypo-
gastric nerves (fused)
Lat. cutaneous nerve
Quadratus lumborum
Psoas major
Rt. common iliac artery
Genitofemoral nerve
Intermesenteric nerve
(part of aortic plexus)
Iliacus
Sympathetic trunk
Hypogastric artery
External iliac artery
External iliac vein
Femoral nerve
Uterine vein

Helen Williams

PLATE 27.—The urinary system. The parietal peritoneum has been removed to show the relationship of the two ureters. The intermediate cutaneous nerve is in an unusual position in this dissection. (W.R.U. 2975, female, white, aged 31 years.)

more striated appearance than the cortex and is deeper red in color. The cortex is granular and has a pale red color. This granular appearance is due to an immense number of kidney corpuscles. Each corpuscle is composed of a glomerulus or loop of capillaries surrounded by a thin-walled sac or capsule of epithelial tissue (Bowman's capsule). The capsule opens into a tubule which, after a tortuous course through cortex and medulla, opens into the renal sinus (Fig. 295). Blood laden with waste material

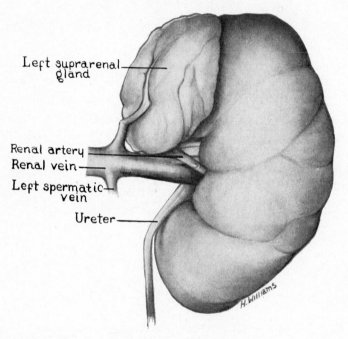

Fig. 292.—Left kidney and suprarenal gland, anterior view. (W.R.U. museum specimen C275.)

enters the hilus through the renal artery, which breaks up into many small radiating branches terminating in the capillaries of the renal corpuscles. From the renal corpuscles waste material is passed into the capsule of the glomerulus. The blood passes into veins which radiate toward the hilus to form the tributaries of the renal veins. The substance of the kidney is therefore formed of blood vessels and tubules within a small amount of framework composed of connective tissue.

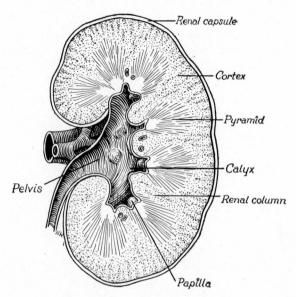

Fig. 293.—Longitudinal section of kidney. (From Anthony: Textbook of Anatomy and Physiology, St. Louis, 1946, The C. V. Mosby Co.)

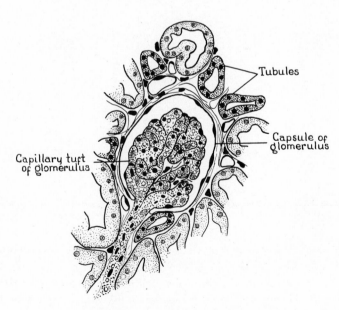

Fig. 294.—Glomerulus of kidney.

A renal or uriniferous tubule has a very characteristic design. Soon after its beginning at the capsule of the glomerulus it becomes coiled, forming the proximal convoluted tubule which in turn connects with Henle's loop. The ascending and descending limbs of the loop pass in a straight line through the medulla of a pyra-

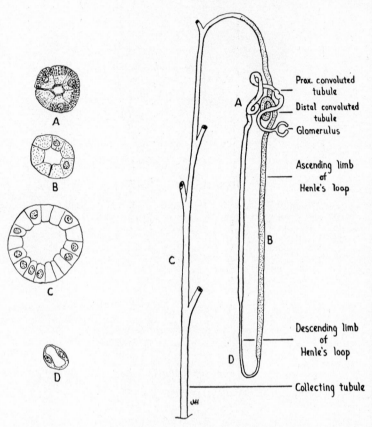

Fig. 295.—A single glomerulus and tubule. On the left are diagrams of the cross section of the tubule at four levels, indicated by the letters, A, B, C, and D.

mid toward the hilus and are connected by a short curved piece. The ascending limb is followed by a distal convoluted portion which in turn empties into the collecting tubule which passes through the pyramid and carries the urine into the pelvis of the ureter.

Within the substance of the kidney the renal artery gives off
interlobar arteries which lie between the pyramids, and these in
turn form a series of incomplete arches, the arciform arteries, crossing the base of the pyramids. Radiating outward toward the
surface of the kidney from the arciform arteries are the interlobular arteries. These give off the afferent vessels to the glomeruli.

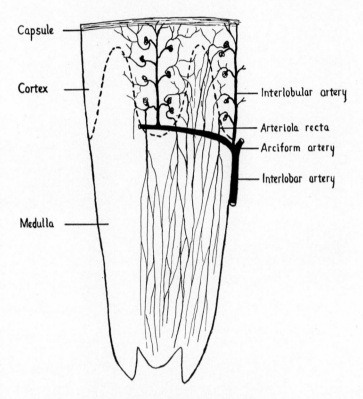

Fig. 296.—The arterial supply of glomeruli and tubules. The kidney section has been drawn wider and shorter than it actually is.

The efferent vessels from the glomeruli break up into a second set
of capillaries about the convoluted tubules. From these blood
passes into the venous system of the kidney. Other vessels, the
arteriolae rectae or straight arterioles, radiate inward from the
efferent glomerular arteries.

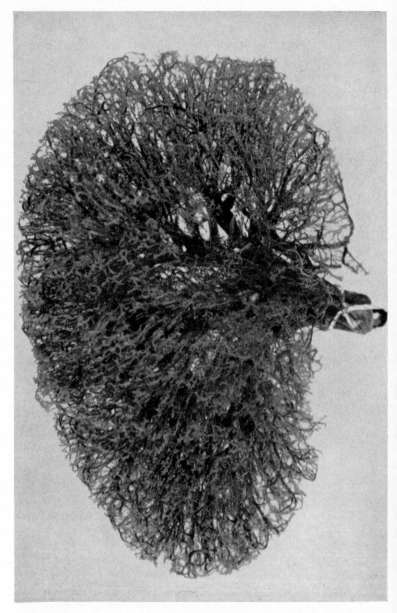

Fig. 297.—The arteries of a kidney. (Injection by A. Cherney and K. Wolfe. Photograph by Dr. D. R. L. Duncan.) (W.R.U. adult female *Rhesus macacus* monkey.)

Fig. 298.—The veins of a kidney. (Injection by A. Cherney and K. Wolfe. Photograph by Dr. D. R. L. Duncan.) (W.R.U. adult female *Rhesus macacus* monkey.)

The renal arteries are branches of the abdominal aorta, and the renal veins drain into the inferior vena cava. Frequently there are accessory renal blood vessels. The nerves to the kidney are small branches which come from a plexus of fibers about the renal artery and accompany arterial branches into the renal substance. Sensory fibers from the kidney are probably carried by the tenth, eleventh, and twelfth thoracic nerves; autonomic fibers come from the splanchnic and vagus nerves.

In the fetus each renal pyramid forms a distinct lobe. Occasionally these lobes persist more or less distinctly into adult life.

URETER

The ureter is about ten inches long. It begins as a funnel-shaped tube, the renal pelvis, attached to the renal sinus. At the junction of the renal sinus and renal pelvis the wall of the ureter breaks up into a number of thin-walled tubes called major and minor renal calyces. There are usually about eight minor renal calyces, and each calyx fits over two or three renal papillae. The minor calyces unite to form two or occasionally three major calyces which in turn unite to form the renal pelvis proper. The mucosa of these structures has an epithelium continuous with the epithelium lining the renal tubules. At the level of the lower border of the kidney the pelvis of the ureter narrows and is converted into a thick-walled tube intimately united to the parietal peritoneum. It passes downward parallel to the vertebral column on the muscles behind the abdominal cavity and usually just over the tips of the transverse processes of the lumbar vertebrae. Within the pelvic cavity the ureter turns forward and medially and enters the bladder from below. Where they open into the bladder, the ureters are about two inches apart. In the female the uterine artery crosses over the ureter just before its termination and in ligating the artery during removal of the uterus a surgeon must take care to avoid injury to the ureter. In the male the ductus deferens crosses over the lower end of the ureter in place of the uterine artery.

The lumen of the ureter is variable in size and there is a definite constriction at its outlet. Small kidney stones usually pass down the ureter and become lodged at this constriction, giving rise to extreme pain, or renal colic.

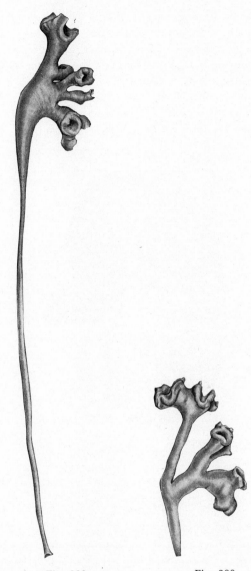

Fig. 299.   Fig. 300.

Fig. 299.—The left renal pelvis and ureter, viewed from the front.
(Cast by Dr. H. P. Trattner.)   (W.R.U. museum specimen.)

Fig. 300.—A bifid renal pelvis. This is a common variation.   (Cast
by Dr. H. P. Trattner.)   (W.R.U. museum specimen.)

The upper end of the ureter receives its arterial blood from branches of the renal artery, the lower end receives blood from arteries which supply the urinary bladder, and the midportion receives small arterial branches from the spermatic artery, aorta, or common iliac artery. There is a free anastomosis of these various small arteries within the wall of the ureter itself. The nerve fibers supplying the ureter follow along the arteries and come from the thoracolumbar and sacral autonomic outflows.

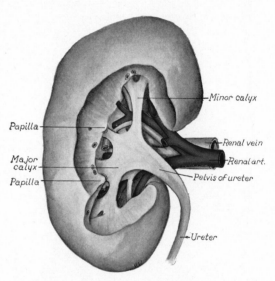

PLATE 28.—The left renal pelvis and calyces, posterior view. (W.R.U. museum specimen C266.)

The wall of the ureter has three coats:

1. The tunica mucosa has a number of layers of epithelial cells, continuous downward with the mucous membrane of the bladder and upward with that lining the renal pelvis into which open the renal tubules.

2. The tunica muscularis is composed of smooth muscle bundles, some arranged in circular fashion and some longitudinal, with bands of connective tissue between them.

3. The tunica adventitia is an outer layer of connective tissue.

URINARY BLADDER

The urinary bladder is a hollow, muscular viscus lying in the midline in front of the parietal peritoneum and behind the symphysis pubis. In the male it lies in front of the rectum above the prostate gland, and in the female it lies in front of the uterus and vagina. A fibrous cord passes up beneath the peritoneum from the apex of the bladder to the umbilicus. This is the median umbilical ligament and is the remains of an embryonic passage, the urachus. The floor of the bladder is triangular in outline, with a ureter opening at each corner of the base behind and the urethra opening at the apex in front. The base of the bladder has a relatively smooth surface which changes but little in size no matter whether the viscus is full or empty, but the remainder of the wall is thrown into folds when the bladder is empty. When the viscus is distended with urine, its wall is smooth. The bladder is capable of considerable distention, but is usually emptied when it contains some twelve ounces of urine, though it can contain twenty ounces without too great discomfort. As the bladder distends, it pushes its way upward between the abdominal wall and the parietal coat of peritoneum. In great distention the apex may almost reach the level of the umbilicus.

Since the anterior surface of the bladder is not covered with peritoneum, it is possible, if the organ is distended, for the surgeon to cut through the anterior abdominal wall just above the symphysis and enter the cavity of the bladder without opening the peritoneal cavity.

The wall of the bladder has four coats:

1. The mucous coat has transitional stratified epithelium.

2. The submucous coat has fibrous connective tissue with some elastic fibers.

3. The muscular coat is composed of smooth muscle bundles arranged in three incomplete layers. At the outlet of the bladder the bundles are arranged to form the involuntary sphincter of the bladder.

4. The serous coat, present only where the bladder is covered by peritoneum, is elsewhere replaced by an outer layer of fibrous connective tissue.

Branches derived from the internal iliac artery pass into the bladder from either side and are accompanied by nerve fibers from the upper lumbar nerves (thoracolumbar autonomic outflow) and from the third and fourth sacral nerves (sacral autonomic outflow).

URETHRA

In the female the urethra is a simple tube about one and one-half inches long passing down behind the symphysis, through the urogenital diaphragm, and emptying between the labia minora, in front of the vagina, and below the clitoris. As it passes through the urogenital diaphragm, it is surrounded by a sphincter of striate muscle, the sphincter of the membranous urethra or the voluntary sphincter.

The wall of the urethra has an inner mucous membrane layer, a thin submucous coat, and a thick muscular layer.

In the male the urethra is much longer. It has three portions: a prostatic portion about one inch long, a membranous portion about one-quarter of an inch long passing through the urogenital diaphragm, and a cavernous portion within the corpus cavernosum urethrae. The membranous portion has a voluntary sphincter, as in the female.

The coats of the urethra of the male are the same as those of the female, but there are certain male sex glands which empty their secretions into the urethra. These are discussed in Chapter 17, The Male Reproductive System.

Because of illness or injury it is occasionally impossible to relax the sphincters and thus to empty the bladder. Catheterization is then necessary. This is easy in the female because the urethra is short and straight. It is more difficult in the male because the urethra has an S-shaped course. The first curve is the downward passage through the prostate; the second curve is produced by the pendulous penis; there is no second curve in the erect organ.

It is possible for a surgeon to pass a hollow tube (a cystoscope) through the urethra into the bladder and by means of a complicated system of mirrors and lights to examine the mucosa of the bladder, to perform operations within the organ, and to catheterize each ureter separately.

Review Questions

1. What structures form the urinary system?
2. Describe the structure of a ureter.
3. Describe the urinary bladder.
4. What are the various portions of a renal tubule?
5. The renal arteries are branches of what artery?   To what vein do the renal veins drain?
6. What are the three portions of the male urethra?
7. What is catheterization of the urinary bladder?

CHAPTER 15

THE SKIN AND SUBCUTANEOUS TISSUES

SKIN

The skin is the outer covering of the body. At the margins of the eyelids it is continuous with the conjunctiva. At other openings on the body surface, such as the mouth, nose, and anus, it is continuous with mucous membrane linings. The skin contains blood vessels, sebaceous (oil) and sudoriferous (sweat) glands, and the endings of sensory nerves. In certain areas of the body modified skin cells form nails and hair.

Skin is composed of two main layers or strata: (1) a superficial layer of stratified squamous epithelium called the epidermis or cuticle, and (2) a deeper layer of connective tissue called the derma, corium, or true skin. The epidermis is subdivided into a deep stratum called the Malpighian layer or germinative stratum, an intermediate stratum granulosum, the cells of which contain many granules, and an outer stratum composed of many layers of closely packed squamous cells which have lost their nuclei. The surface layers of squamous cells are being shed constantly and replaced by deeper cells. The derma is composed of interlacing bundles of fibrous and elastic tissue which gradually blend with the areolar subcutaneous tissue. Over most of the body the outer surface of the derma is folded into irregular ridges forming papillae, with the deeper cell layers of the epidermis filling in the spaces between the papillae. Embedded within the derma are sweat glands, sebaceous glands, and hair shafts. Very small blood vessels, lymphatics, and nerve fibers have their endings in the derma. In the subcutaneous tissue small arteries form an arterial plexus from which small vessels pass into the derma and form another plexus under the papillae. The epidermis contains no blood vessels.

The color of the skin varies with the amount of pigment in the cells of the epidermis and with the blood supply. According to the amount of pigmentation of the skin, mankind is divided into various groups: white, yellow, brown, and black. The skin is more deeply pigmented in certain parts of the body, such as the perineum, armpits, areolae of the nipples, and the exposed surfaces

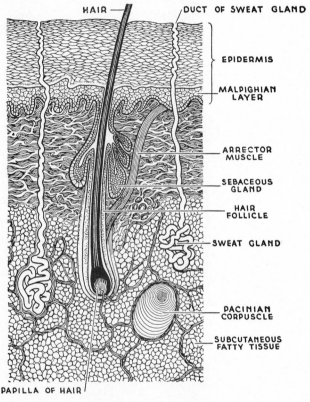

Fig. 301.—Vertical section of skin (schematic). (Modified from Cunningham; from Zoethout: Introduction to Human Physiology, St. Louis, 1948, The C. V. Mosby Co.)

of the body. It may also become more deeply pigmented in any part of the body subjected to direct rays of the sun. In old age the skin becomes more deeply pigmented with yellow and frequently contains irregular brown areas. In obstruction of the common bile duct the skin may become a dark brown.

The deeper layers of the skin contain many small blood vessels which, in health, give a pink tint to the skin. If the blood is poorly oxygenated, the resulting blue tint is known as cyanosis. After death, the body surface becomes whitened in areas where the blood has drained away and a bluish purple in areas which contain stagnant blood.

The skin varies in thickness, that covering the exposed areas of face and hands being thicker than that on the areas protected by clothing. The soles of the feet are calloused, and the hands of a laborer are really horny in character. The protected skin surface of the inner side of the arms and legs is more delicate than that on the outer surface. The skin of a person in poor health is usually

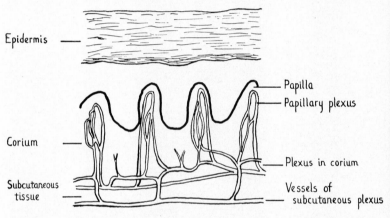

Fig. 302.—Arterioles of skin. The deeper layers of the cuticle have been left blank.

dryer and more sensitive than that of a person in robust health. An invalid or an unconscious person may suffer a *severe* burn from a hot water bottle at a temperature which would not harm a well person. The skin of a person with a hypothyroid disorder (one having an underactive thyroid) is thick, dry, and leathery. The skin of a person with a hyperthyroid disorder (one having an overactive thyroid) is warm, moist, and flushed. The skin is a delicate indicator of health and of encroachments on functional efficiency.

The skin is quite elastic and in most areas, particularly over the extensor side of joints, is freely movable. In certain areas, such as palms and soles and on the flexor side of joints, the skin is bound to the underlying structures, thus producing the flexor folds. On the palms and soles the epidermis forms ridges which produce the characteristic and distinctive patterns seen in the skin over the terminal phalanges. These patterns remain constant throughout life and form the basis for identification by fingerprints.

The segmental sensory distribution to the skin has been delineated in Chapter 7 in the discussion on the Peripheral Nervous System, and the cutaneous sensory nerve endings have been described in Chapter 8, The Special Sense Organs. The fibers of the thoracolumbar outflow to sweat glands and to pilomotor muscles attached to hair shafts have been described in the discussion of the Autonomic Nervous System, in Chapter 7.

HAIR

Hair grows from certain specialized cells of the skin. The color and character of the hair vary with race. The Negro has kinky black hair; the American Indian has straight black hair; the northern European has wavy flaxen hair. The color of the hair changes with age, the white hair of the aged being due to loss of pigment.

In both sexes there are well-marked areas of hair on the scalp, the eyebrows, the eyelids, and at the anterior openings of the nose. At puberty hair appears in the armpits, around the genitalia of both sexes and on the face of the male. In the female the genital hair is confined to the labia majora and to a small triangular area over the symphysis. In the male the area covered by hair extends upward to the umbilicus, and there is usually a hairy area on the chest as well. The palms and soles have no hair, but the parts of the body not already mentioned are sparsely provided with scattered hairs, larger and more numerous in the male.

A small bundle of smooth muscle, the arrector pili, is attached to certain hair shafts. When their muscles contract, the hairs stand more nearly erect, and the consequent small wrinkles of skin give the appearance known as "goose flesh."

SEBACEOUS GLANDS

Wherever there are hairs, there are small glands which secrete sebum, an oily substance. In certain areas, particularly on the nose where the hairs are quite small, the sebaceous glands are large. If the outlet of a gland becomes blocked, a sebaceous cyst results.

The tarsal glands lying within the tarsus of each eyelid are modified sebaceous glands. These are also known as Meibomian glands and occasionally a Meibomian cyst occurs when the oulet of a gland is blocked. An infection of one of these glands produces a stye.

SUDORIFEROUS GLANDS

There are sweat or sudoriferous glands distributed over the entire body; they are more abundant in the palm of the hand, the sole of the foot, and in the armpit than on the rest of the body surface. The sweat glands are an important part of the heat-regulating mechanism of the body.

The ceruminous glands of the external ear canal which secrete wax are modified sudoriferous glands. The ciliary glands located in the eyelids behind the eyelashes are also modified sweat glands (glands of Moll).

NAILS

Nails are produced by specialized skin cells on the dorsal aspect of the terminal phalanges of fingers and toes. The hoofs and claws of other animals are similar structures. Nails protect the ends of the fingers and form a stiff backing to the soft sensitive pulp of the finger tips. The stubby finger ends seen in persons who continually bite their nails result from the loss of this stiffening.

The appearance of the nails changes with age and with fluctuations in health. In healthy young adults they should be smooth and free from ridges or grooves and should be neither too brittle nor too soft. In illness the nails become ridged and grooved and are easily broken and torn. In old age they are likely to be brittle, rather opaque, thickened, and roughened.

SUPERFICIAL FASCIA

Beneath the skin is a layer of loose connective tissue filled with fat. The thickness of this layer varies in different parts of the body and also varies with age, health, and sex. This tissue is also called the subcutaneous tissue, or the panniculus adiposus.

Healthy infants of both sexes have a thick subcutaneous tissue well filled with fat which is rather evenly distributed over the entire body, thus giving the baby its round, chubby appearance.

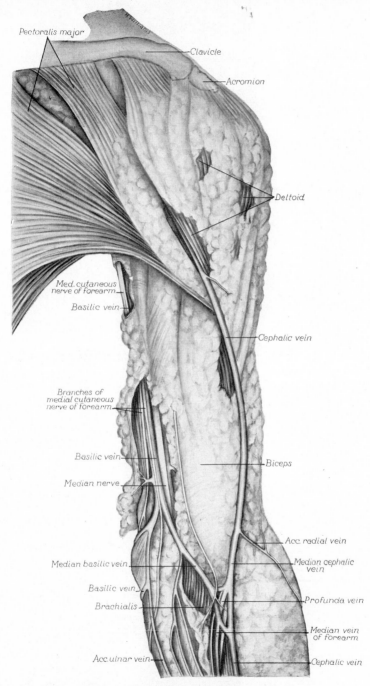

Fig. 303.—Superficial fascia, nerves, and blood vessels of anterior aspect of the left arm. (W.R.U. 3320, male, white, aged 87 years.)

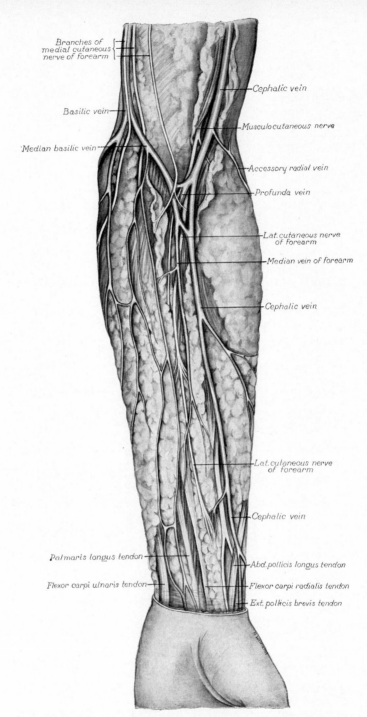

Branches of
medial cutaneous
nerve of forearm

Basilic vein

Median basilic vein

Palmaris longus tendon

Flexor carpi ulnaris tendon

Cephalic vein

Musculocutaneous nerve

Accessory radial vein

Profunda vein

Lat. cutaneous nerve
of forearm

Median vein of forearm

Cephalic vein

Lat. cutaneous nerve
of forearm

Cephalic vein

Abd. pollicis longus tendon

Flexor carpi radialis tendon

Ext. pollicis brevis tendon

Fig. 304.—Superficial fascia, nerves, and blood vessels of volar aspect of
the left forearm. (W.R.U. 3320, male, white, aged 87 years.)

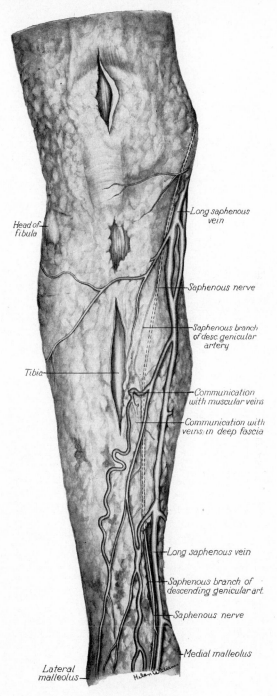

Head of fibula

Tibia

Lateral malleolus

Long saphenous vein

Saphenous nerve

Saphenous branch of desc. genicular artery

Communication with muscular veins

Communication with veins in deep fascia

Long saphenous vein

Saphenous branch of descending genicular art.

Saphenous nerve

Medial malleolus

Fig. 305.—Superficial fascia, nerves, and blood vessels of front of left leg. (W.R.U. 3333, male, white, aged 62 years.)

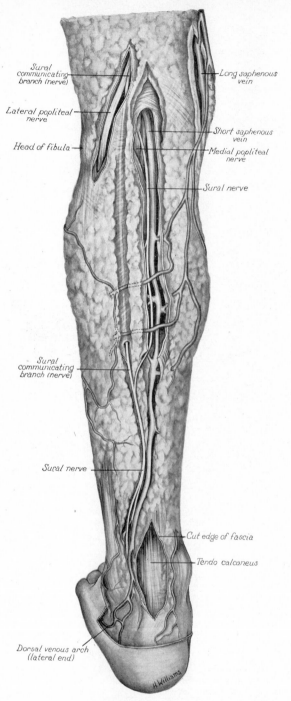

Sural communicating branch (nerve)

Lateral popliteal nerve

Head of fibula

Sural communicating branch (nerve)

Sural nerve

Long saphenous vein

Short saphenous vein

Medial popliteal nerve

Sural nerve

Cut edge of fascia

Tendo calcaneus

Dorsal venous arch (lateral end)

H. Williams

Fig. 306.—Superficial fascia, nerves, and blood vessels of back of left leg. (W.R.U. 3333, male, white, aged 62 years.)

When the fat is particularly abundant, the skin lies in folds. After the child begins to walk, there are changes in the distribution of fat which is nowhere very abundant, both boys and girls tending to lose the chubby appearance of infancy.

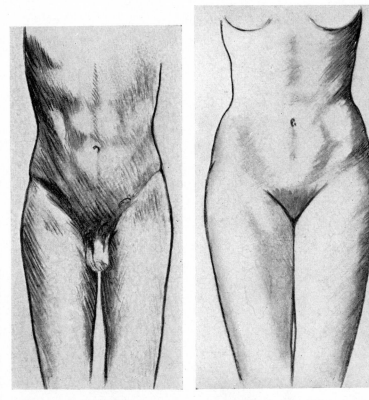

Fig. 307.   Fig. 308.

Fig. 307.—Male figure, front view. Note absence of fat pads. (After John Millard.)

Fig. 308.—Female figure, front view, showing contours produced by fat pads. (After John Millard.)

In adolescence a sex difference is apparent in the distribution of fat; the female develops fat pads over the shoulders, buttocks, outer side of the thighs, the symphysis pubis, and the breasts. The fat pads in the male are thinner and more evenly distributed over the body.

In middle life both sexes tend to accumulate reserves of fat in their subcutaneous tissues. In old age the fat is lost and, owing to loss of elastic tissue from its deeper layers, the skin becomes wrinkled, folded, and flabby.

Subcutaneous tissues of the eyelids, the areolae of the breasts, the penis, the scrotum, and the clitoris contain no fat.

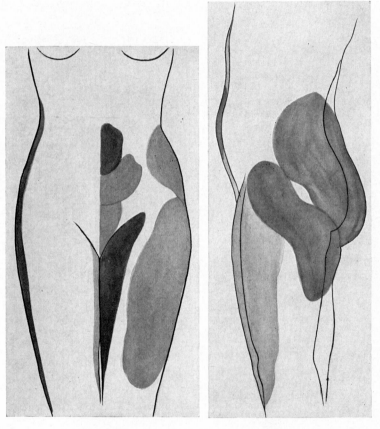

Fig. 309.   Fig. 310.

Fig. 309.—Fat pads of female. On the left side of the figure pads are shown in frontal view and on the right side the thickness in cross section. (After John Millard.)

Fig. 310.—Fat pads of female, lateral view. The outline of the male is superposed. (After John Millard.)

The subcutaneous tissues act as a storehouse for reserves of fat, as a protective layer for the deeper structures, as a loose tissue in which blood vessels and nerves may freely ramify, and as a temporary reservoir for excess body fluid.

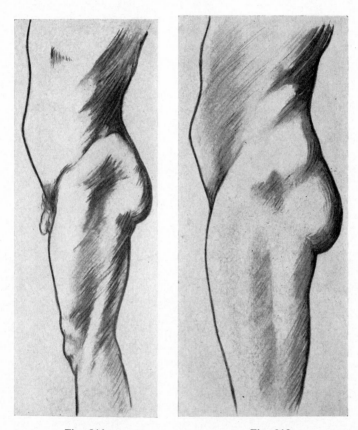

Fig. 311.   Fig. 312.

Fig. 311.—Male figure, lateral view. Note absence of fat pads. (After John Millard.)

Fig. 312.—Female figure, lateral view, showing contours produced by fat pads. (After John Millard.)

DEEP FASCIA

Beneath the superficial fascia is a thin layer of rather dense white connective tissue which contains no fat and is called the deep fascia. It forms an investment for muscles, and from its deep surface sheets of fascia pass inward to form intermuscular septa. This layer has certain thickenings which have been described elsewhere as ligaments and retinacula. It should be clearly kept in mind that no fascia is a discrete structure, but that fasciae are everywhere continuous and that certain areas or thickenings are

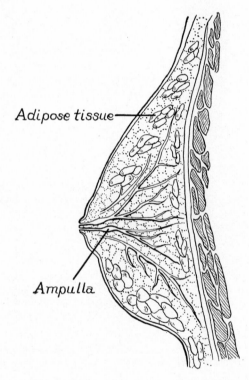

Fig. 313.—Vertical section of breast. (From Anthony: Textbook of Anatomy and Physiology, St. Louis, 1946, The C. V. Mosby Co.)

given names for convenience in anatomical descriptions. Certain of these bands of deep fascia, such as the iliotibial tract, lumbodorsal fascia, and plantar aponeurosis, are among the most important supporting structures of the body. They have been described in Chapter 6, Muscles.

BURSAE

In various places in the subcutaneous tissue there develop small closed sacs, called bursae, filled with a clear serum and lined with synovial membrane. These bursae are usually found over bony prominences and beneath tendons. There is always one such bursa over the olecranon of the ulna, one over the ischial tuberosity, and several about the knee joint. If the skin over a bursa is chronically irritated, the amount of fluid in the sac is increased, rendering the bursa large and tense. The fluid may even become infected, transforming the bursa into an abscess.

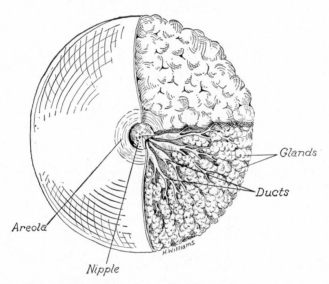

Fig. 314.—Anterior view of breast. The skin of the right upper quadrant has been removed to show the subcutaneous tissue filled with fat. In the right lower quadrant the fat has been removed to show four of the glands radiating from the nipple. (From Anthony: Textbook of Anatomy and Physiology, St. Louis, 1946, The C. V. Mosby Co.)

TENDON SHEATHS

In areas where muscle tendons pass beneath specialized thickenings of the deep fascia, such as the retinacula at the wrist and ankle, sheaths are found surrounding the tendons. These sheaths are closed tubular sacs similar to bursae having an inner layer closely applied to the tendon and an outer layer attached to the walls of the channel through which the tendon runs. These sheaths enable the tendons to glide back and forth more easily.

MAMMARY GLAND

Since the mammary gland is very intimately connected with the subcutaneous tissue of the thorax, it will be discussed here, although functionally it is associated with the reproductive system.

Each breast is a diffuse glandular organ located in the subcutaneous tissue of the anterior chest wall. Its lobes are not separated from the connective tissue by any capsule, and there are from fifteen to twenty lobes in each breast. Each lobe is a compound alveolar gland, and the saccules are lined with cuboidal or low columnar epithelium. The lobes are interspersed with fat so that the size of the breast depends partly on glandular tissue but much more on the interspersed fat. The left breast is usually larger than the right.

Each breast is hemispheric in shape, but on the upper, outer quadrant there is a projecting portion extending up toward the armpit. In large breasts this projection or axillary tongue is correspondingly large.

The nipple projecting from each breast contains minute openings for the milk ducts, one from each lobe. The distal portion of each duct has a dilated portion, the ampulla. Surrounding the nipple is a circular band of skin called the areola, which is more heavily pigmented than the surrounding skin. In women who have had no children it is a brownish-pink color. This color changes to a deep brown during the early months of the first pregnancy, and the brown pigment is never thereafter entirely lost.

During childhood the breasts are small and show little sex difference. At puberty the breast in the female develops rapidly. In the male the nipple is distinct though small, but the glandular portion of the breast is rudimentary.

Review Questions

1. What are the two layers of the skin?
2. Give four factors which influence the color of the skin.
3. Name two types of glands associated with the skin, and name the substance secreted by each.
4. What are four functions of subcutaneous tissue?
5. How does deep fascia differ from superficial fascia?
6. Describe the mammary gland.

unit 5   **REPRODUCTION**

CHAPTER 16

THE FEMALE REPRODUCTIVE SYSTEM

The female reproductive organs include a pair of ovaries, two uterine tubes, a uterus, a vagina, and the external genitalia composed of the labia majora, labia minora, clitoris, bulb of the vestibule and the vestibular glands. The orifice is called the vulva. The vestibule is a capacious pocket about two inches deep connecting the vulva with the vagina and delimited from the latter by an incomplete septum called the hymen.

OVARY

The ovary is a solid gland about one and one-half inches long lying on the side wall of the pelvic cavity and attached by a fold of peritoneum, the mesovarium, to the broad ligament of the uterus. A round cord called the ligament of the ovary passes from the ovary to the uterus near the attachment of the uterine tube. The margin of the broad ligament between the ovary and the fimbriated end of the uterine tube on the one hand and the lateral pelvic wall on the other is called the infundibulopelvic ligament.

The ovary has an outer layer of low columnar epithelium continuous with the mesothelium of the peritoneum. The substance of the gland, subdivided by strands of connective tissue through which run blood vessels and nerves, is composed of columns and nests of germinal epithelial cells. The ova are formed from the germinal epithelium. A nest of cells increases in size and number, and the cells assume a definite arrangement. The outer cells form a stratified columnar wall about a clear central cavity filled with fluid. The remaining cells collect into a mass, forming a thickening of one area of the wall. Such a structure is known as an ovarian (Graafian) follicle. One of the cells of the inner mass is destined to become the ovum. When the ovum is ripe, the

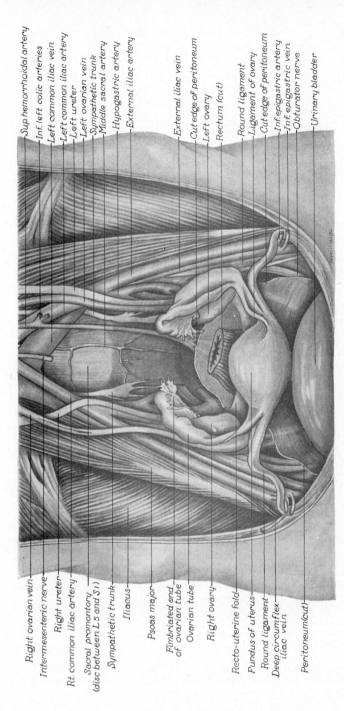

Sup. hemorrhoidal artery
Inf. left colic arteries
Left common iliac vein
Left common iliac artery
Left ureter
Left ovarian vein
Sympathetic trunk
Middle sacral artery
Hypogastric artery
External iliac artery

External iliac vein
Cut edge of peritoneum
Left ovary
Rectum (cut)
Round ligament
Ligament of ovary
Cut edge of peritoneum
Inf. epigastric artery
Inf. epigastric vein
Obturator nerve
Urinary bladder

Right ovarian vein
Intermesenteric nerve
Right ureter
Rt. common iliac artery
Sacral promontory (disc between L5 and S1)
Sympathetic trunk
Iliacus
Psoas major
Fimbriated end of ovarian tube
Ovarian tube
Right ovary
Recto-uterine fold
Fundus of uterus
Round ligament
Deep circumflex iliac vein
Peritoneum (cut)

Fig. 315.—Internal female genitalia. This is an anterior view, and the uterus is anteflexed. (W.R.U. 2975, Negro, female, aged 31 years.)

follicle ruptures and the ovum escapes from the ovary into the peritoneal cavity, from which it is picked up by the trumpet-shaped termination of the uterine tube.

The ruptured follicle collapses, and the cavity becomes filled with a yellow-colored material and is known as a corpus luteum (yellow body). If a pregnancy occurs, the corpus luteum becomes larger during the pregnancy. Ultimately a corpus luteum becomes smaller, loses its color and becomes a corpus albicans (white body),

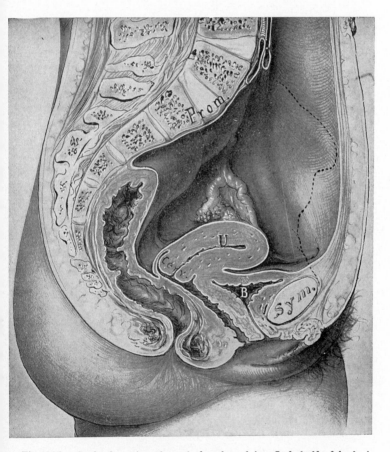

Fig. 316.—Sagittal section through female pelvis. Left half of body is shown with intestines removed. *Prom.,* Sacral promontory; *Cerv.,* cervix of uterus; *U,* uterus; *B,* bladder. (From Crossen and Crossen: Diseases of Women, St. Louis, 1948, The C. V. Mosby Co.)

and finally disappears. In a young woman the ovary is smooth, but in old age it becomes shrunken and wrinkled.

The ovarian arteries are a pair of long, slender vessels arising from the front of the aorta just below the level of origin of the renal arteries. They pass down behind the peritoneum, through the infundibulopelvic ligament, and into the ovary between the folds of the mesovarium where they anastomose with branches of the uterine artery. Each ovarian artery is accompanied by a plexus of veins which on the left side empties into the left renal

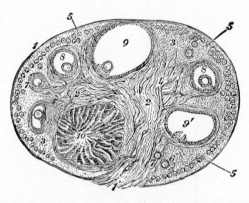

Fig. 317.—Section of the ovary of a cat. *1*, The free border; *1'*, the attached border; *2*, connective tissue stroma; *3*, epithelial cells; *4*, blood vessels; *5*, dormant ovarian follicles; *6, 7, 8, 9,* and *9'*, ovarian follicles at various stages of development; *10*, corpus luteum. An ovum is seen in *8* and *9*. (From Zoethout and Tuttle: Textbook of Physiology, St. Louis, 1955, The C. V. Mosby Co.)

vein and on the right into the inferior vena cava. The ovarian nerves contain sensory fibers and filaments of the thoracolumbar outflow which accompany the arteries and pass through the aortic and renal plexuses. These vasomotor nerve fibers go to the blood vessels of the ovary. There is no known parasympathetic supply to the ovary.

The ovary is also classed as an endocrine gland.

UTERINE TUBE

The uterine tube, Fallopian tube, or oviduct is the passage by which the ovum travels from the ovary to the cavity of the uterus. It is about four inches long and is attached to the broad ligament of the uterus by a fold of peritoneum, the mesosalpinx. The end of the tube near the ovary has a trumpet-shaped opening with a fringelike border. This opening with its fringe of fingerlike processes or fimbriae overhangs the ovary but is not usually directly connected with it.

The tube has the following coats:

1. An inner mucous coat continuous with the inner coat of the uterus, but having many complex longitudinal folds or plicae, the epithelium being columnar, and in some areas ciliated.

2. A submucous layer of connective tissue.

3. A muscular coat of two strata of smooth muscle, one longitudinal and one circular in arrangement, the longitudinal fibers being outside the circular.

4. An outer tunic of connective tissue covered by serous membrane (peritoneum).

The uterine tube is supplied by arterial branches from the uterine and ovarian arteries, and nerve fibers come from the branches which supply the ovary. The venous drainage is into uterine and ovarian veins.

The uterine tube becomes narrower as it nears the uterus; it is about 1 millimeter in diameter where it passes through the uterine wall. The ovum is fertilized in the uterine tube and passes into the uterus where it is implanted in the uterine wall. If the fertilized ovum is unusually large or if the inner end of the tube is constricted, the ovum may become implanted in the tube and a tubal pregnancy results.

UTERUS

The uterus is a thick-walled, muscular organ in the anterior part of the pelvic cavity, lying between the bladder in front and the rectum behind. It is a pear-shaped organ, about three inches long, two inches wide, and one inch thick in a nonpregnant adult woman. The upper end or fundus is dome-shaped. The cervix, about one inch long, projects into the vagina. Between the fundus and cervix is the corpus which is about two inches long. The cavity of the uterus is quite small; its outline is triangular with the base above. The uterine tubes open into each angle of the base. The lower end or apex of the uterine cavity opens through the cervix into the vagina.

Usually the long axis of the uterus points forward and upward in the anteverted position, and the body of the uterus is slightly bent on the cervix to produce anteflexion. Often the fundus lies a little to one side of the midline, usually toward the right.

The cervix of the uterus is surrounded by the visceral fascia of the pelvis, but the corpus and fundus are clothed in front and behind by visceral peritoneum, continuous on each side with the broad ligament which attaches the uterus to the sides of the pelvic cavity. The uterine artery, a branch of the internal iliac artery, passes through the base of the broad ligament to be distributed

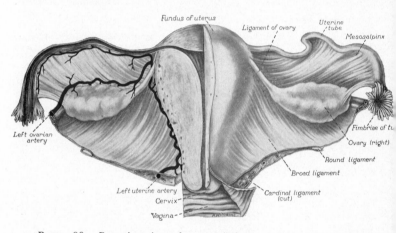

PLATE 29.—Posterior view of uterus and associated structures. On the left side of the drawing the posterior portion of the uterus has been removed to show the cavity, and the left uterine tube has been opened longitudinally.

throughout the uterine wall. Within a fold of the broad ligament is a flattened band of fibromuscular tissue, the round ligament of the uterus, which passes from the uterus through the anterior abdominal wall by way of the inguinal canal to terminate in the labium majus. Occasionally an outpouching of parietal peritoneum accompanies the round ligament through the inguinal canal as the canal of Nuck and may be the site of an inguinal hernia.

The upper portion of the broad ligament has a covering of visceral peritoneum on either side, with some areolar connective tissue between. In the lower portion of the ligament surrounding the uterine artery and veins the connective tissue gradually increases in amount. At the base of the broad ligament is a strong dense mass of connective tissue, called the cardinal or lateral uterosacral ligament, which runs on either side from the cervix of the uterus to the wall of the pelvic cavity. There is also a heavy band of connective tissue running backward on either side of the midline from the cervix to the sacrum, called the (posterior) uterosacral ligament. The cardinal and uterosacral ligaments have some smooth muscle fibers in addition to the connective tissue and are very important supports for the uterus and adjacent structures.

The uterine wall has three layers:

1. An inner mucous coat having columnar epithelium (some ciliated) and tubular glands, becoming at the cervix continuous with the stratified squamous epithelium of the vagina.

2. A muscular coat, a thick layer of interlacing bands of smooth muscle with fibers running longitudinally, circularly, and diagonally.

3. An outer serous layer of visceral peritoneum.

During pregnancy the uterus greatly increases in size. Not only does the cavity enlarge, but the muscular walls also become much thicker. After delivery the uterus shrinks rapidly, and under normal conditions should reach its nonpregnant size in six weeks. The mucous membrane of the uterus becomes thicker and more vascular during pregnancy, and it is into this layer that the placenta is implanted.

The mucous membrane also thickens and becomes more vascular before menstruation. During menstruation the outer layers are shed, but these are quickly regenerated at the end of menstruation.

The uterus receives fibers from the hypogastric plexus (thoracolumbar autonomic outflow) and from the sacral nerves (sacral autonomic outflow). Sensory fibers go mainly to the ninth and tenth thoracic segments of the spinal cord.

VAGINA

The vagina is a passage connecting the cervix of the uterus with the vestibule of the vagina. It lies in front of the rectum and behind the urethra and bladder and is about three inches long. Because the anterior and posterior walls lie in contact with each other, the cavity is reduced to a narrow cleft capable of great distention in childbirth.

Since the cervix projects into the vagina from above, the posterior wall of the vagina is longer than the anterior, and on either side of the cervix is a recess called the lateral fornix. The upper part of the posterior wall of the vagina is in contact with the parietal peritoneum which forms a pouch behind the uterus and in front of the rectum, the rectouterine pouch (pouch of Douglas). Infections of this region may be drained by the surgeon by making an incision upward from the vagina.

In the perineum between the vestibule and rectum is a fibromuscular mass called the perineal body or gynecologic perineum. Numerous perineal muscles find attachment at this point; these form a sphincter for the vestibule. In childbirth this mass may be weakened or even extensively torn. The scar tissue resulting from the healing of this wound is not elastic, and thus the circumference of the vulva may be increased. Using the operation called perineorrhaphy a surgeon seeks to reconstruct the perineal body.

The wall of the vagina has an inner lining of stratified squamous epithelium, a muscular layer of interlacing longitudinal and circular smooth muscle bundles, and an outer connective tissue layer which blends with that of surrounding structures. The wall of the vagina usually possesses many folds. Near the outlet there is a striate sphincter (the bulbocavernosus muscle).

EXTERNAL GENITALIA

The labia majora are a pair of rounded folds of skin lying on each side of the vestibule and continuous with each other in front through the mons pubis. The mons is an elevation of the lower portion of the abdomen over the symphysis pubis caused by an accumulation of adipose tissue in the subcutaneous fascia. This fatty tissue is prolonged as a fingerlike projection into each labium majus. The skin of the labia majora and mons is covered by hair after adolescence.

The labia minora are a pair of smaller folds of skin lying on each side within the labia majora. In front the lesser labia are continuous with the prepuce or fold of skin covering the glans of the

clitoris. The skin of the labia minora is smooth and hairless; it is
continuous with the mucous membrane lining of the vagina. The
labia minora have a central core of connective tissue but contain
no fat.

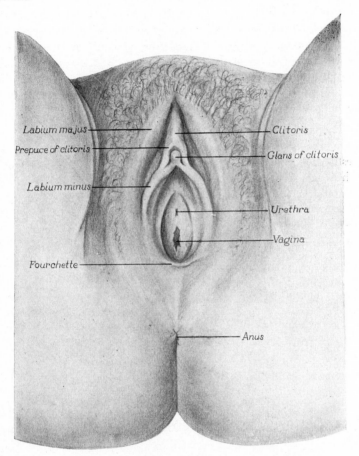

Fig. 318.—External female genitalia. The labia majora have been parted
to show deeper structures.

The vestibule of the vagina is the space between the labia
minora and below the clitoris. It contains the openings of the
urethra, vagina, and ducts of the vestibular glands. The labia
minora are connected behind by a thin shelf of tissue called the
fourchette, a structure which is destroyed by the first parturition.

The clitoris is a C-shaped cylindrical mass composed of two small cylinders of erectile tissue placed side by side, the corpora cavernosa clitoridis. At the back the two corpora diverge, forming the crura of the clitoris and each is attached to the pubic arch. The clitoris is attached by means of a suspensory ligament to the front of the symphysis pubis. The glans is a small mass of erectile tissue capping the free ends of the corpora cavernosa. The erectile tissue of the glans is continuous on the under aspect of the corpora cavernosa with a bilateral mass of erectile tissue, the bulb, in the walls of the vestibule. The clitoris, unlike the penis of the male, is not traversed by the urethra.

The greater vestibular glands, or glands of Bartholin, lie one on each side of the vestibule behind the bulb. They open into the vestibule between the fold of the labium minus and the hymen. The lesser vestibular glands are microscopic mucous glands emptying into the anterior part of the vestibule.

Review Questions

1. What structures are included in the female reproductive system?
2. Where do the ovarian arteries arise?
3. Where do the ovarian veins drain?
4. Describe the uterine tube.
5. Describe the layers of the wall of the uterus.
6. In the base of the broad ligament what is the relation of the ureter to the uterine artery?
7. Where does the fertilization of the ovum occur normally?
8. Where are the cardinal ligaments located?
9. Describe the clitoris.
10. How do the labia majora and labia minora differ?

CHAPTER 17

THE MALE REPRODUCTIVE SYSTEM

The male reproductive system includes the testes with their ducts, the epididymis and ductus deferens, the prostate gland, the bulbourethral glands, the penis, the scrotum, and the urethra.

TESTIS

The testis, or testicle, the male reproductive gland, is an oval organ about two inches long. The epididymis, which is the first part of the duct to the testis, is a convoluted tube massed into a comma-shaped structure which is attached to the back of the testis. The duct emerges from the epididymis as the ductus deferens.

The testis has an outer coat, the tunica albuginea, composed of dense, white, fibrous tissue from the inner surface of which fibrous septa pass deep into the substance of the gland, separating it into wedge-shaped lobules. The septa end behind in a mass of fibrous tissue, called the mediastinum testis. The arteries, veins, nerves, and lymph vessels pass through this mass to supply the testis.

The fibrous structures just described form the framework of the testis; interspersed among them is the parenchyma of the testis. The parenchyma is composed of very numerous small coiled seminiferous tubules which look like fine threads. The germinal epithelium lining these seminiferous tubules produces the spermatozoa or male reproductive cells.

The seminiferous tubules empty their reproductive cells into other tubules in the mediastinum testis which form the rete testis. The epididymis is composed of closely coiled tubules which receive the reproductive cells from the rete testis and after a very tortuous passage empty them into the ductus deferens of the spermatic cord.

The testis is developed during fetal life within the abdominal cavity. Shortly before birth the testes descend through the inguinal canals into the scrotum. The arteries supplying the testis arise from the abdominal aorta. The vein of the right testis drains into the inferior vena cava and that of the left testis into the left renal vein. The lymphatics of the testes drain into lymph nodes around the aorta. These vessels accompany the ductus deferens in

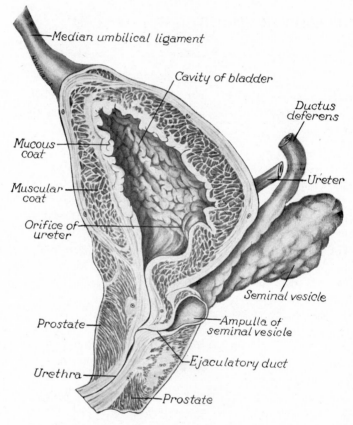

Median umbilical ligament

Cavity of bladder

Ductus deferens

Mucous coat

Muscular coat

Orifice of ureter

Ureter

Seminal vesicle

Prostate

Ampulla of seminal vesicle

Ejaculatory duct

Urethra

Prostate

Fig. 319.—Sagittal section through male bladder and prostatic urethra. The left half has been removed. (W.R.U. museum specimen C293.)

the spermatic cord. The vascular and nerve supplies of the testes are entirely independent of that of the scrotum. The blood vessels of the testis receive vasomotor fibers from the thoracolumbar outflow. There is no known parasympathetic nerve supply to the testis. Visceral sensory fibers accompany the thoracolumbar fibers.

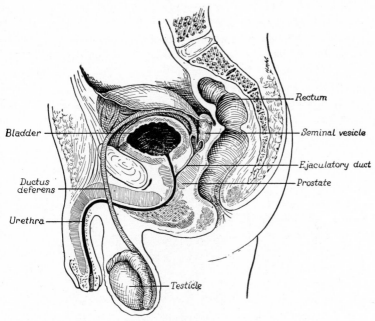

Rectum

Bladder

Seminal vesicle

Ejaculatory duct

Prostate

Ductus deferens

Urethra

Testicle

Fig. 320.—Diagram of male reproductive system. (From Anthony: Text-book of Anatomy and Physiology, St. Louis, 1946, The C. V. Mosby Co.)

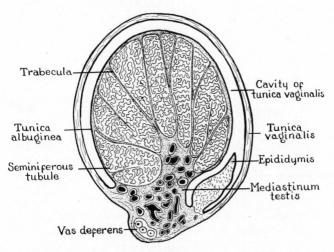

Trabecula

Cavity of tunica vaginalis

Tunica albuginea

Tunica vaginalis

Seminiferous tubule

Epididymis

Mediastinum testis

Vas deferens

Fig. 321.—Transverse section of testis and epididymis.

Early in fetal life there is an evagination of a tube of peritoneum through each inguinal canal into the scrotum, called the vaginal process of the peritoneum. Each testis and associated epididymis originally lie behind the posterior parietal peritoneal coat of the abdominal cavity. Late in fetal life the testes descend behind the peritoneum and pass into the scrotum. Then the vaginal process disappears except for the portion adjacent to the testis. This

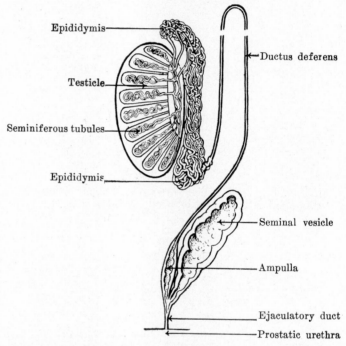

Fig. 322.—Vertical section of testis and its ducts, diagrammatic. (From Pitzman: Fundamentals of Human Anatomy, St. Louis, 1920, The C. V. Mosby Co.)

portion is called the tunica vaginalis of the testis; it is lined with serous membrane and has a parietal and a visceral layer. If this closed sac is distended with fluid, it is called a hydrocele. Occasionally the vaginal process persists, and may be the site of an inguinal hernia. The vaginal process is also present in the female, but it usually disappears entirely.

The three coverings received by the testis as it passes into the scrotum from the inguinal canal are discussed in the section on The Inguinal Canal, Chapter 6, Muscles.

DUCTUS DEFERENS AND SEMINAL VESICLE

The ductus deferens (vas deferens) is about eighteen inches long. It passes from the lower end of the epididymis upward

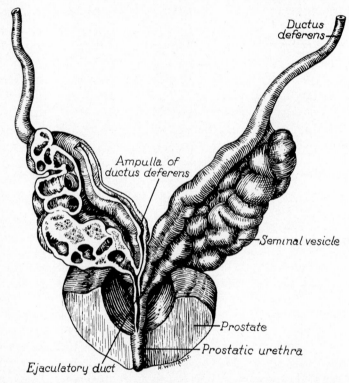

Fig. 323.—Seminal vesicle and ductus deferens. The upper portion of the right seminal vesicle has been removed to show internal structure and relationship to ejaculatory duct. The upper portion of the prostate has been dissected away from the prostatic urethra. (W.R.U. museum specimen C298.)

within the spermatic cord through the inguinal canal into the abdominal cavity. It lies just beneath the parietal peritoneum, passes over the pelvic brim into the pelvic cavity, and continues its course behind the bladder. Here the end of the duct dilates to form the ampulla and joins the duct of the seminal vesicle to form the ejaculatory duct. The ductus deferens has an inner mucous coat, a middle muscular coat, and an outer fibrous coat. It can be palpated within the spermatic cord as a firm, slender cord about as thick as the lead of a pencil.

The seminal vesicles are a pair of convoluted tubes partly covered by peritoneum and lying behind the bladder. One end empties into the ejaculatory duct and the other terminates as a blind pouch. The seminal vesicles secrete a fluid which bathes the spermatozoa passing through the ductus deferens. To this is also added the secretion of the prostate, and thus the seminal fluid is formed.

The ejaculatory duct is a slender tube about one inch long passing through the substance of the prostate to open into the urethra close to the orifices of the prostatic ducts.

The spermatic cord is composed of the ductus deferens and the testicular vessels and nerves surrounded by connective tissue. The veins from the testes are numerous and form the pampiniform plexus. If these veins become dilated, a condition known as varicocele results. The veins of each plexus ultimately unite to form a single testicular vein.

SCROTUM

The scrotum is a sac composed of skin and subcutaneous tissue. The skin is more heavily pigmented than that covering the general body surface and after adolescence is covered with hair. The subcutaneous tissue contains no fat but does contain scattered fibers of smooth muscle, the dartos muscle. When its fibers are contracted, the walls of the scrotum are wrinkled, and the testes are held close up to the perineum. When the fibers are relaxed, the scrotum is pendulous and the wrinkles disappear. The left testis usually hangs lower than the right.

There is a ridge on the surface of the midline of the scrotum called the raphe, which is continued forward on the under surface of the penis and backward toward the anus. The scrotum is incompletely divided by a median septum into two cavities, one for each testis.

The scrotal arteries are branches of the pudendal vessels which supply the perineum, and the sensory nerves come from the pudendal nerves. The lymphatics drain into the inguinal nodes and the veins into vessels accompanying the pudendal arteries. The scrotum may be injured or infected without involvement of the testis.

PENIS

The penis is composed of three columns of erectile tissue surrounded by skin and a thin layer of subcutaneous tissue. The skin, like that of the scrotum, is more pigmented than the skin of the body but is free of hair except near the root. The subcu-

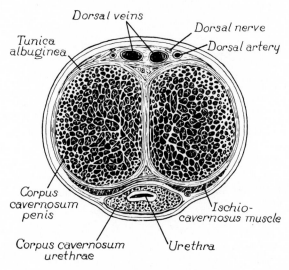

Fig. 324.—Cross section of shaft of penis. This specimen has a double dorsal vein. A single vein is more common. (W.R.U. museum specimen C338.)

taneous tissue contains no fat and attaches the skin loosely to the underlying structures. At the distal end the skin forms a free fold, the preputium, prepuce, or foreskin, which contains a sphincter similar to the dartos muscle of the scrotum. The lining of the prepuce is continued over the glans in intimate union with the substance of the glans.

The corpora cavernosa penis are two fused cylinders of erectile tissue forming the bulk of the shaft of the penis. The line of fusion is marked by a median septum and on the dorsal surface

by a groove.   The suspensory ligament of the penis extends from
the loose fibrous tissue of the penis to the symphysis of the pubis.
Posteriorly the corpora cavernosa penis diverge as the crura of the
penis, and each crus is attached to the pubic arch.

The corpus cavernosum urethrae is a cylinder of erectile tissue
softer in consistency than the corpus cavernosum penis.   At the
distal end it is enlarged to form the glans which caps the ends of
the corpora cavernosa penis.   Behind, it is also enlarged to form
the bulb of the urethra which lies in the midline between the two
diverging corpora cavernosa penis.   The urethra enters the bulb
and traverses the entire length of the corpus cavernosum urethrae
ending in the glans.

Each corpus cavernosum penis has an outer covering, the tunica
albuginea, formed of dense fibrous connective tissue.   The erectile
tissue is a spongelike mass of venous sinuses lined with endothelium.   The corpus cavernosum urethrae has no strong outer coat
and is therefore usually known as the corpus spongiosum.

The arteries of the penis which are branches of the internal
pudendal artery are: (1) the deep artery of the penis to the
corpora cavernosa penis, (2) the artery of the bulb to the corpus
cavernosum urethrae, and (3) the dorsal artery of the penis to the
tunica albuginea and to the glans.   The veins drain into the
venous plexus on either side of the prostate gland and the lymphatics into the superficial inguinal nodes.

The nerves come from the second, third, and fourth sacral nerves
(sacral autonomic outflow) and from the lower part of the hypogastric plexus (thoracolumbar autonomic outflow).   Sensory impulses go to the sacral segments of the cord.

PROSTATE GLAND

The prostate gland lies between the bladder and the rectum,
surrounding the first part of the urethra.   Above, it is covered by
the wall of the bladder, on each side is a rich plexus of veins
coming from the penis, and below, it is supported by the pelvic
fascia.   The capsule of the prostate is poorly defined, but there is
an interlacing structure of connective tissue and smooth muscles
on the outer portion of the gland which sends septa deep into the
substance.   Glandular epithelium is found in the lobules between

the septa. The secretion of the prostate is emptied by a number of small ducts into the prostatic urethra.

Frequently in old men the prostate enlarges. That portion which lies between the ejaculatory ducts may form a projecting tongue more or less completely blocking the urethra like a ball valve.

A sheath of fibrous tissue formed from the visceral pelvic fascia surrounds the prostate. From this sheath the prostate can be shelled out in the operation of prostatectomy.

BULBOURETHRAL GLANDS

The bulbourethral or Cowper's glands are a pair of small glands about the size of a pea, placed one on each side of the membranous portion of the urethra, just behind the bulb. Each empties by a single duct into the third part of the urethra just beyond the bulb.

Review Questions

1. What structures are included in the male reproductive system?
2. Where do the testicular arteries arise?
3. Where do the testicular veins drain?
4. What is the function of the seminiferous tubules?
5. What is the function of the seminal vesicles?
6. Describe the penis.
7. What is the function of the prostate gland?

GLOSSARY

Abdomen, portion of the body between thorax and pelvis; *abdominis,* "of the abdomen."

Abducent, drawing away from. The sixth cranial nerve supplies the lateral rectus muscle which draws the eye from the midline.

Abduct, to draw away from the midline; opposite of adduct.

Abduction, the act of drawing away from the midline; opposite of adduction.

Abductor, a muscle performing the function of abduction.

Abscess, localized collection of pus.

Acetabulum, "little vinegar cup"; the cavity in the os coxae into which the head of the femur fits.

Achilles tendon, tendon of the calcaneus; in Greek mythology Achilles' mother held him by the heel when she dipped him as an infant in the river Styx in order to make him invulnerable.

Acoustic, pertaining to the sense of hearing.

Acromegaly, literally "great extremity"; a chronic disease due to over-function of the pituitary gland characterized by overgrowth of the extremities and face; also spelled *acromegalia.*

Acromion, bony process of the scapula which forms the point of the shoulder.

Acute, severe and of short duration; opposite of chronic; used in speaking of duration and severity of disease.

Adamant, extremely hard, as enamel of tooth.

Adduct, to draw toward the midline; opposite of abduct.

Adduction, the act of drawing toward the midline; opposite of abduction.

Adenoid, resembling a gland.

Adipose, fatty; the Latin adjective is *adiposus.*

Adolescence, youth; period between puberty and maturity.

Adrenal, near the kidney; same as suprarenal.

Adventitia, outer coat of a vessel or tube; also called *externa.*

Afferent, carrying or bringing to the center from the periphery; opposite of efferent.

Ala, wing; plural, *alae.*

Alar, pertaining to a wing, or winglike.

Alba, white.

Albicans, white.

Albuginea, a white fibrous tissue (layer).

Alveolus, small cavity; *alveoli* is the plural, and *alveolar* the adjective.

Amphiarthrosis, a joint with little movement and no joint cavity.

Ampulla, a flasklike dilatation; dilated end of a tube or duct.

Anastomosis, a communication. Plural, *anastomoses.*

Anconeus, pertaining to the elbow.

Angina, any disease or symptom having sudden suffocative attacks. In angina pectoris there are sudden attacks of severe pain, shortness of breath, and collapse.

Ankylosis, the abnormal fixation of a joint.

Ansa, literally a handle; any looplike structure.

Anteflexion, a forward curvature; a condition in which the upper part of an organ is bent forward; opposite of retroflexion.

Anterior, placed in the front or forward part; same as ventral; opposite of posterior or dorsal.

Anteversion, a forward turning; a condition in which an entire organ is abnormally tipped forward; opposite to retroversion.

Antrum, a cavity, or chamber; plural, *antra.*

Anus, lower end of large intestine; *ani,* "of the anus."

Aorta, the great artery carrying blood from the left ventricle.

Apex, top or summit.

Aponeurosis, a flat sheet of white fibrous tissue, usually serving as an attachment for a muscle. Plural, *aponeuroses; aponeurotica,* Latin adjective.

Appendectomy, removal of the appendix; also termed *appendicectomy.*

Appendiceal, pertaining to the appendix.

Appendicular, having the nature of an appendix; attached; opposite of axial.

Appendix, an appendage; a part attached to a larger portion; plural, *appendices.*

Aqueduct, a canal for the conduction of fluid; Latin noun, *aqueductus.*

Aqueous, watery.

Arachnoid, resembling a spider web.

Arbor vitae, "tree of life."

Arciform, bow-shaped.

Areola, (1) any very small space; adjective *areolar.* (2) The ring about the nipple.

Arrector pili, "raiser of a hair"; plural, *arrectores pilorum.*

Arteriole, a very small arterial branch.

Arteriosus, pertaining to an artery.

Artery, a vessel carrying blood from the heart.

Arthritis, inflammation of a joint.

Arthrosis, a joint; from the Greek.

Articular, pertaining to a joint.

Articulation, (1) a joint; from the Latin. (2) The mechanics of speaking.

Arytenoid, shaped like a jug or pitcher; a cartilage of the larynx.

Aspect, position, surface, or face.

Aspera, rough.

Aspirate, to remove by means of suction.

Atlantic, pertaining to the atlas; *atlanto,* combining form.

Atlas, the first cervical vertebra; in Greek mythology Atlas held the earth on his back.

Atrium, the first chamber of an organ; Latin word for hall.

Atrophy, a wasting away of tissue.

Auditory, pertaining to the sense of hearing; see acoustic.

Auerbach, German anatomist (1828-1897).

Auricle, (1) portion of external ear attached to the side of the head. (2) An ear-shaped appendage of each atrium of the heart.

Auricular, pertaining to the ear or earlike; pertaining to an auricle.

Autonomic, being self-controlled; independent.

Axial, pertaining to the axis or line about which a body turns, therefore pertaining to the trunk; opposite of appendicular.

Axilla, the armpit.

Axon, process of a nerve cell carrying impulses from the cell body; also spelled *axone.*

Azygos, unpaired.

Barium, a chemical element; barium sulphate is used in visualizing the gastrointestinal tract in x-rays.

Bartholin, Danish anatomist (1616-1680).

Basal, pertaining to the base or lower part; basilar; *basalis,* Latin adjective.

Basilic, important or prominent.

Basophil, staining with basic dyes; also spelled *basophile.*

Biaxial, turning about two axes.

Biceps, having two heads.

Biconcave, having two concave surfaces.

Bicuspid, having two cusps or points.

Bifid, divided into two parts.

Bifurcate, forked; divided into two branches.

Bigelow, American surgeon (1816-1890).

Bipennate, double feathered; sometimes spelled *bipinnate.*

Bipolar, having two poles or processes.

Blood, a fluid tissue circulating through heart, arteries, veins, and capillaries.

B.N.A., Basle Nomina Anatomica; an anatomic terminology accepted at Basle in 1895 by the Anatomical Society.

Boss, a rounded eminence.

Bowman, English physician (1816-1892).

Brachial, pertaining to the arm.

Brachium, (1) the arm; strictly that portion between shoulder and elbow; plural, *brachia.* (2) An armlike process; *brachii,* "of the arm."

Brevis, short; opposite of longus.

Bronchiole, small subdivision of a bronchus.

Bronchus, one of the two divisions of the trachea; plural, *bronchi.*

Buccal, pertaining to the cheek.

Buccinator, muscle of the cheek, from the Latin word for trumpeter.

Bursa, sac or pouch, usually lined with a synovial membrane.

Buttock, the breech; the prominence over the gluteal muscles.

Calcaneus, the heel bone; also termed *calcaneum.* Adjective may be either *calcanean* or *calcaneal.*

Calcarine, spur-shaped.

Callosum, thick.

Calyx, cup-shaped cavity; plural, *calyces.*

Canaliculus, little canal; plural, *canaliculi.*

Canine, pertaining to a dog; a fanglike or pointed tooth.

Capillary, (1) the smallest blood vessels connecting arterioles and venules. (2) The smallest lymphatic vessels.

Capitate, bone of the wrist having a head-shaped process.

Capitulum, little head.

Capsule, fibrous or membranous envelope.

Caput, head; *capitis,* "of the head."

Cardia, the esophageal opening of the stomach.

Cardiac, pertaining to the heart.

Carneae, "fleshy."

Carotid, chief artery of the neck, from the Greek meaning "deep sleep." Pressure on the artery may produce unconsciousness.

Carpal, pertaining to the wrist.

Carpus, the wrist; *carpi,* "of the wrist."

Cartilago, Latin word for cartilage.

Catheter, a slender tubular instrument for drawing off fluid from a body cavity or for distending a passage.

Catheterize, to use a catheter; to remove fluid from a body cavity by means of a hollow tube; particularly to remove urine from the bladder.

Cauda, tail.

Caudal, pertaining to the tail; opposite of cephalic.

Caudate, having a tail, or taillike.

Cava, a cavity; plural, *cavae.*

Cavernous, containing hollow spaces.

Cecum, (1) pouch at the beginning of the large bowel. (2) Any blind pouch. Also spelled *caecum.*

Cele, suffix meaning a swelling or distention; see hydrocele and varicocele.

Celiac, pertaining to the abdomen; also spelled *coeliac.*

Cementum, a layer of bony tissue covering the root of a tooth; also known as *cement.*

Central, situated in the midportion as opposed to peripheral.

Cephalic, pertaining to the head; opposite of caudal.

Cerebellum, literally "the little brain"; a division of the brain behind the cerebrum and above the pons and medulla; *cerebelli,* "of the cerebellum."

Cerebrum, the two great hemispheres forming the upper and larger portion of the brain; adjective, *cerebral; cerebri,* "of the cerebrum."

Ceruminous, pertaining to a waxlike secretion.

Cervix, a neck; adjective, *cervical; cervicis,* "of the neck."

Chiasm, an X-shaped crossing; also spelled *chiasma.*

Choana, a funnel-shaped cavity or opening; plural, *choanae.*

Cholecystectomy, removal of gallbladder.

Choledochus, the common bile (duct).

Chopart, French surgeon (1743-1795).

Chorda, a cord; plural, *chordae.*

Chorda tympani, nerve running across the middle ear.

Choroid, resembling skin; also spelled *chorioid.*

Chromaffin, having an affinity for chrome salts.

Chromatin, that portion of the nucleus of a cell which is more easily stainable.

Chronic, of long duration; opposite of acute.

Chyle, a milky fluid; lymph containing fat in the lacteals of the intestine; *chyli,* "of chyle."

Cilia, hairlike processes; plural of *cilium.*

Ciliary, pertaining to cilia.

Cinguli, "of the girdle"; so named because the gyrus encircles the corpus callosum.

Circumduction, the act of moving along the surface of a cone, the joint being at the apex.

Circumflex, bent or turned about.

Cisterna, Latin word for cistern.

Clavicle, the collar bone.

Cleido, pertaining to the clavicle; from the Greek.

Clinoid, "resembling a bed"; the four processes bear a resemblance to four bedposts.

Clitoris, erectile genital organ of the female, homologous with the penis; *clitoridis,* "of the clitoris."

Coccyx, last portion of vertebral column; named from the Greek word for cuckoo, whose bill the bone somewhat resembles; *coccygeum* and *coccygeus,* Latin adjective forms.

Cochlea, a snail shell; therefore a structure having a similar form.

Collagen, the main organic constituent of connective tissue.

Collateral, secondary or accessory.

Colliculus, a small elevation; plural *colliculi.*

Colon, portion of large intestine between cecum and rectum; *coli,* "of the colon."

Columnae carneae, "fleshy columns," bundles of muscle in the ventricles of the heart.

Commissure, a joining together.

Communis, common.

Concave, having a depressed surface; center is at a lower level than edge; opposite of convex.

Concha, a shell; a shell-like structure.

Condyle, a rounded knob on the end of a bone; a knuckle.

Condyloid, resembling a knuckle.

Congestion, an excessive amount of blood.

Conjunctiva, a delicate membrane lining the eyelids and covering the front of the eyeball.

Conjunctivum, connecting.

Convex, having a rounded elevated surface; opposite of concave.

Convoluted, rolled together or coiled.

Coracoid, like a crow's beak; variant of coronoid.

Corium, the true skin; see cutis.

Cornea, transparent portion of eyeball in front of pupil and iris.

Corniculate, cornlike; a cartilage of the larynx.

Cornu, a horn; plural, *cornua.*

Coronal, pertaining to the crown of the head.

Coronary, encircling like a crown; as the arteries of the heart.

Coronoid, see coracoid.

Corpus, body; plural, *corpora.*

Corpus callosum, body of fibers joining the two cerebral hemispheres.

Corpuscle, a small body.

Corrugator, a "wrinkler," a muscle that wrinkles the forehead.

Cortex, the bark, rind, or outer layer; *cortical,* pertaining to the cortex; *cortico,* combining form.

Corti, Italian anatomist (1822-1876).

Costal, pertaining to a rib or ribs.

Costarum, "of the ribs."

Cowper, English surgeon (1666-1709).

Coxa, the hip; *coxae,* "of the hip."

Cranial, pertaining to the cranium.

Cranium, the skull or brain pan.

Cremaster, from the Greek to suspend.

Cretin, a person who is a dwarf due to underactivity of the thyroid gland.

Cribriform, sievelike; *cribrosa,* Latin form of adjective.

Cricoid, ring-shaped.

Crista galli, "cock's comb."

Cruciate, shaped like a cross.

Crus, a leg or a part resembling a leg; plural, *crura.*

Cubital, pertaining to the space in front of the elbow joint.

Cuboid, resembling a cube.

Cuneatus, wedge-shaped.

Cuneiform, wedge-shaped.

Cupula, a small cup.

Cusp, (1) a pointed projection of a tooth. (2) A valve with a pointed segment.

Cutaneous, pertaining to the skin.

Cuticle, the outer layer of skin.

Cutis, the skin; see corium.

Cyanosis, a condition in which skin appears blue due to poor oxygenation of the blood.

Cyst, a closed sac containing a fluid or semisolid.

Cytoplasm, protoplasm of a cell exclusive of the nucleus.

Dartos, smooth muscle of scrotum.

Deciduous, that which is shed; temporary; same as first or milk teeth; opposite of permanent; *decidua,* Latin noun.

Decussation, a crossing in the form of an X.

Deferens, carrying away.

Deltoid, triangular; resembling the Greek letter, *delta.*

Dendrite, a branched or treelike process of cytoplasm of a nerve cell; the process carrying impulses to the cell body; also called *dendron.*

Dens, a tooth.

Dentate, toothlike.

Dentine, main substance of the tooth, surrounds the pulp and is covered by enamel; also spelled *dentin;* formerly called ivory or substantia eburnea.

Dentition, the teeth as a group; the milk dentition; the permanent dentition.

Descendens, descending.

Diaphragm, a cross wall; a septum.

Diarthrosis, a freely movable joint; plural *diarthroses.*

Diencephalon, the "between" brain.

Digestion, the process of changing food into materials which may be absorbed and assimilated by the body.

Digiti, "of a digit."

Digitorum, "of the digits."

Diploë, from the Greek, a fold.

Distal, remote; opposite of proximal.

Diverticulum, a small pouch leading from a larger cavity.

Dorsal, toward the back; opposite of ventral.

Dorsiflex, to turn toward the back; opposite of plantar flex.

Douglas, Scottish anatomist (1675-1742).

Duct, a passage or tube; *ductus,* Latin for tube.

Duodenum, the first part of the small intestine; literally twelve (fingerbreadths).

Dura mater, "strong" or "hard mother"; the outer covering of brain and spinal cord.

Eburnea, like ivory; substantia eburnea, an old name for dentine.

Efferent, to carry from; opposite of afferent.

Effusion, escape of fluid into a part or tissue.

Ejaculatory, pertaining to a sudden act of expulsion.

Elastin, the essential organic constituent of elastic connective tissue.

Embolism, blocking of a blood vessel by material in the blood stream.

Embryo, the early stages of the fetus; particularly before the end of the third month.

Embryology, the science which deals with the development of the embryo.

Emesis, vomiting.

Emissary, affording an outlet.

check

Empyema, pus in a cavity; particularly within the chest.

Enamel, the very hard, white substance covering the dentine of the teeth.

Endocrine, secreting into the blood or lymph; opposite of exocrine.

Endolymph, fluid within the membranous labyrinth of the inner ear; see perilymph.

Endosteum, tissue surrounding the medullary cavity of bone.

Endothelium, simple squamous epithelium lining blood vessels and lymphatics.

Eosinophil, a white blood cell readily stained by eosin; also spelled *eosinophile.*

Eparterial, above an artery.

Epi, a prefix meaning "on" or "above"; opposite of hypo.

Epicolic, "on the colon."

Epicondyle, a prominence on a bone above or upon a condyle.

Epicranius, "above the cranium."

Epidermis, outermost layer of skin.

Epididymis, on the testis, a structure attached to the back of the testis; plural, *epididymides.*

Epiglottis, cartilage of the larynx; the cartilage "above the glottis."

Epinephrine, adrenaline.

Epiphysis, a part or process of a bone which ossifies separately before making osseous union with the main portion of the bone.

Epiploic, pertaining to the omentum.

Epistropheus, a pivot.

Epithelium, the covering tissue of the body; plural, *epithelia.*

Epitrochlear, above the trochlea (of the humerus).

Equina, pertaining to a horse.

Erythrocyte, a red blood corpuscle.

Esophagus, the gullet; portion of digestive tract between pharynx and stomach; also spelled *oesophagus.*

Ethmoid, sievelike.

Eustachian, named after Eustachio, Italian anatomist (1520-1574).

Eversion, the act of turning outward; opposite of inversion.

Evert, to turn out; to turn the sole of the foot outward; opposite of invert.

Exhalation, the act of breathing out; opposite of inhalation.

Exocrine, secreting into a duct; opposite of endocrine.

Extension, a movement at a joint bringing the two parts into or toward a straight line from a flexed position; opposite of flexion.

External, on the surface or outer side; opposite of internal. Latin adjective, *externus,* or *externa.*

Extra, prefix meaning "outside of"; opposite of intra.

Extrinsic, external, not pertaining exclusively to a part.

Exudate, material found in tissue spaces or on surfaces in inflammation.

Facet, a small, plane surface.

Falciform, sickle-shaped.

Fallopian, named after Fallopius, Italian anatomist (1523-1562).

Falx, a structure shaped like a sickle.

Fascia, a sheet of connective tissue; plural, *fasciae.*

Fasciculus, a small bundle; plural, *fasciculi.*

Fauces, a passageway.

Femur, thigh; bone of the thigh; *femoral* is the adjective; *femoris,* "of the thigh."

Fetal, pertaining to a fetus.

Fetus, the child, from the end of the third fetal month until full term; also spelled *foetus.*

Fiber, a long, threadlike structure; also spelled *fibre;* adjective *fibrous;* Latin adjective, *fibrosa* or *fibrosus.*

Fibril, a minute fiber; Latin form *fibrilla.*

Fibula, smaller bone of leg; the splint bone.

Filament, a delicate thread or fiber.

Filiform, thread-shaped.

Filum, a threadlike structure.

Fimbria, a fringe or fringelike structure; plural *fimbriae.*

Fissure, a cleft or groove.

Flack, English physician (1889-1931).

Flavum, yellow.

Flexion, sagittal plane movement in which the anterior surfaces of two segments are brought closer to each other; opposite of extension. In knee and toe flexion the posterior surfaces are approximated.

Flexure, the curved or bent part of a structure.

Fluoroscope, an instrument for holding a luminous screen during a roentgenoscopic examination.

Follicle, (1) a very small sac or gland. (2) A lymphatic nodule.

Fontanelle, unossified area of cranium of an infant; word literally means "little fountain"; also spelled *fontanel.*

Fonticulus, same as fontanelle.

Foramen, a hole; plural, *foramina* or *foramens.*

Foreskin, the prepuce.

Fornix, vaultlike space.

Fossa, a pit or hollow; plural, *fossae.*

Fourchette, a fold of mucous membrane joining the posterior ends of the labia majora.

Frontal, pertaining to the forehead.

Fundus, the portion of a hollow organ farthest from the outlet.

Fungiform, shaped like a fungus or mushroom.

Funiculus, (1) a bundle of nerve fibers. (2) A cord; the spermatic cord.

Fusiform, spindle-shaped.

Galea, a helmet.

Galen, Greek physician (130-200).

Ganglion, a group of nerve cells, usually placed outside the central nervous system; plural, *ganglia* or *ganglions.*

Gasserian, named after Gasser, Austrian surgeon (1505-1577).

Gastric, pertaining to the stomach.

Gastrocnemius, "belly of the leg"; a muscle in the calf of the leg.

Gemellus, twin; plural, *gemelli.*

Genial, pertaining to the chin.

Geniculate, bent like a knee.

Genioglossus, pertaining to chin and tongue.

Genitalia, the reproductive organs.

Genu, Latin word for knee.

Gerota, Roumanian anatomist (1867-1939).

Gland, a secretory organ.

Glans, Latin word for gland or acorn.

Glenoid, resembling a pit or pocket.   The glenoid fossa of the scapula is very shallow.

Glisson, English physician and anatomist (1597-1677).

Globule, a small spherical mass.

Glomerulus, a little tuft or cluster.

Glomus, a tuft or ball; plural, *glomera.*

Glossal, pertaining to the tongue.

Glossopharyngeal, pertaining to the tongue and pharynx.

Glottis, space between the vocal cords.

Gluteal, pertaining to the buttocks; *gluteus,* Latin adjective.

Goiter, enlargement of the thyroid gland; also spelled *goitre.*

Gonad, essential sex gland, either testis or ovary.

Graafian, named after Graaf, Dutch physician and anatomist (1641-1673); a follicle of the ovary.

Gracilis, slender.

Granule, a small particle; a little grain.

Groin, the lowest portion of the lateral anterior abdominal wall, near the thigh.

Gustatory, pertaining to the sense of taste.

Gyrus, a convolution of the brain; plural, *gyri.*

Hallux, the great toe; *hallucis,* "of the great toe."

Hamate, the "hooked" bone; this carpal bone has a hooklike process.

Hamstring, a tendon of the back of the knee; the muscles sending tendons to this area.

Hamulus, a little hook.

Haustra, sacculations of the colon; plural of *haustrum.*

Haversian, named after Havers, English anatomist (1650-1702).

Hemoglobin, coloring matter of red blood corpuscles containing iron; also spelled *haemoglobin.*

Hemopoiesis, the formation of blood; also called *hematopoiesis.*

Hemopoietic, pertaining to the formation of blood; also called *hematopoietic.*

Hemorrhoidal, pertaining to dilated veins.

Henle, German anatomist (1809-1885).

Hepar, the liver, *hepatic* is the adjective; *hepatis,* "of the liver."

Hernia, abnormal protrusion of an organ or tissue through an opening.

Herniorrhaphy, operation to repair a hernia.

Highmore, English surgeon (1613-1684).

Hilus, a depression or pit at the place of entrance or exit of vessels supplying an organ; also termed *hilum;* adjective *hilar.*

Hippocampus, literally a "sea horse"; a curved structure in the floor of the middle horn of the lateral ventricle of the brain; not the hippocampal gyrus.

His, German anatomist (1831-1904); and Wilhelm His, Jr., German physician (1863-1934).

Histology, science of the minute structure of tissues.

Hormone, the product of a gland of internal secretion.

Humerus, the arm bone.

Humor, any fluid or semifluid of the body.

Hunter, English anatomist and surgeon (1728-1793).

Hyaline, glasslike.

Hydrocele, a circumscribed collection of fluid, particularly in the scrotum; also spelled *hydrocoele.*

Hymen, a membrane; specifically a fold which may practically occlude the external opening of the vagina.

Hyoid, U-shaped.

Hyper, prefix meaning above; opposite of hypo.

Hyperplasia, increase in the size of a tissue or organ due to an increase in the number of cells.

Hypertrophy, increase in the size of a tissue or organ due to an increase in the size of its constituent cells.

Hypo, a prefix meaning below or under; opposite of *epi* or *hyper.*

Hypoglossal, placed below the tongue; *hypoglossi,* Latin adjective.

Hypophysis, from the Greek, meaning "growing under"; an endocrine gland growing from the under surface of the brain.

Hypothenar, the mound of the palm over the bones of the medial (ulnar) metacarpal bones.

Ileum, the distal part of the small intestine; from a Latin word meaning "twisted"; adjective is *ileac; ileo* is the combining form.

Ilium, the bone of the flank; adjective is *iliac; ilio* is the combining form.

Incisive, pertaining to the incisor teeth.

Incisor, a tooth used for cutting; from the Latin verb "to cut."

Incus, an anvil; an anvil-shaped bone of the middle ear.

Index, referring to the forefinger or "pointing" finger.

Inferior, situated or placed below; opposite of superior; *inferioris,* a Latin form of the adjective.

Infra, a prefix meaning "beneath"; opposite of supra.

Infraclavicular, below the clavicle.

Infrahyoid, beneath the hyoid.

Infraspinous, below the spine (of the scapula).

Inguinal, pertaining to the groin.

Inhalation, the act of breathing in; opposite of exhalation.

Innominate, literally "nameless"; *innominatum,* Latin adjective.

Inscriptiones, literally "writings"; the *inscriptiones tendineae* have a certain resemblance to a line of script.

Inter, a prefix meaning "between."

Intercellular, situated between cells.

Intercostal, situated between ribs.

Interdigital, situated between digits.

Interosseous, situated between bones; *interosseus,* Latin adjective.

Intima, innermost.

Intra, a prefix meaning "within"; opposite of extra.

Intravenous, within a vein.

Intrinsic, situated entirely within or pertaining exclusively to a part; opposite of extrinsic.

Intubation, the insertion of a tube, particularly into the larynx.

Inversion, the act of turning inward; opposite of eversion.

Invert, to turn in; to turn the sole of the foot inward; opposite of evert.

Involuntary, performed without the will; opposite of voluntary.

Iris, from the Greek word meaning "rainbow" or "halo"; the colored disc of the eye.

Ischium, bone of the hip; adjective is *ischiatic, ischial,* or *sciatic.*

Ivory, a bonelike covering of the teeth, now called dentine.

Jejunum, portion of small intestine between duodenum and ileum; literally the "empty" (gut).

Jugular, pertaining to the neck.

Keith, English physician (1862-1955).

Krause, German anatomist (1833-1910).

Kupffer, German anatomist (1829-1902).

Labium, a lip; plural, *labia.*

Labyrinth, a system of complicated passages or channels.

Lacertus, literally "torn."

Lacerum, torn.

Laciniate, fringelike.

Lacrimal, pertaining to tears; also spelled *lachrymal.*

Lactation, secretion of milk.

Lacteal, (1) pertaining to milk. (2) An intestinal lymphatic containing chyle.

Lacuna, a small hollow or space; plural, *lacunae.*

Lambdoid, shaped like the Greek letter, *lambda.*

Lamella, a small leaf or sheet; plural, *lamellae.*

Lamina, a leaf or sheet; plural, *laminae.*

Langerhans, German pathologist (1847-1888).

Larynx, the voice box; adjective, *laryngeal.*

Lata, wide.

Lateral, pertaining to the side; opposite of medial.

Latissimus dorsi, the widest (muscle) of the back.

Leukemia, a fatal disease characterized by a great increase in the white blood cells; also spelled *leucemia.*

Leukocyte, a white blood cell, also spelled *leucocyte.*

Levator, a lifting or raising muscle.

Ligament, a band.

Linea, a line; plural, *lineae.*

Lingual, pertaining to the tongue.

Lipoid, fatlike.

Lobe, a portion of an organ separated from the rest by fissures or septa.

Lobule, a little lobe.

Loin, part of back between thorax and pelvis.

Longissimus, longest.

Longus, long; opposite of brevis.

Lumbar, pertaining to the loin; *lumborum,* "of the loins."

Lumbrical, wormlike.

Lumen, space within a tube or organ.

Lunate, a bone of the carpus shaped like a crescent moon.

Lutein, a yellow pigment found in corpus luteum, fat cells, and egg yolk.

Luteum, yellow.

Lymph, a transparent, slightly yellow fluid filling lymphatic vessels.

Lymphocyte, a variety of white blood cells. Such cells are also found in large numbers in lymph nodes and lymphatic tissue.

Lymphoid, (1) resembling lymph. (2) Tissue containing many lymphatic cells enmeshed in reticular tissue.

Magnus, large; *magnum* is neuter adjective.

Major, larger, opposite of minor, *majus* is neuter adjective.

Malar, pertaining to the cheek.

Malleolus, a little hammer; a hammer-shaped process.

Malleus, a hammer; a hammer-shaped bone of the middle ear.

Malpighian, named after Malpighi, Italian anatomist (1628-1694). (1) Any lymphatic nodule of the spleen. (2) Any glomerulus of the kidney. (3) Layer of epidermis.

Mammary, pertaining to the breast.

Mammillary, like a nipple; also spelled *mamillary.*

Mandible, bone of lower jaw.

Manubrium, a "handle"; uppermost portion of the sternum.

Marrow, soft central part of a bone.

Masseter, a "chewer"; a muscle of mastication.

Mastication, chewing.

Mastoid, nipple-shaped.

Mastoiditis, inflammation of mastoid air cells.

Matrix, the groundwork or substance in which anything is cast or placed.

Maturation, the process of ripening or becoming adult.

Maxilla, a jawbone; particularly the bone of the upper jaw.

Maximus, largest; opposite of minimus.

Meatus, a passageway.

Media, middle.

Medial, pertaining to the center; opposite of lateral.

Median, pertaining to the middle, that is, between two other structures; see mesial.

Mediastinum, a median septum or partition.

Medulla, (1) marrow. (2) The central portion of an organ as opposed to the periphery or cortex. (3) *M. oblongata,* the portion of the brain between the pons and the spinal cord.

Meibomian, named after Meibom, German anatomist (1638-1700).

Meissner, German physiologist (1829-1905).

Membranacea, membranous.

Membrane, a thin layer or sheet; *membrana,* Latin noun.

Meninx, Greek word for membrane; plural, *meninges.*

Meniscus, a crescent; plural, *menisci.*

Menstruation, the monthly flow of blood from the uterus beginning at puberty and ceasing at the menopause or "change of life."

Mental, (1) pertaining to the chin. (2) Pertaining to the mind.

Mesencephalon, the midbrain.

Mesentery, specifically the fold of peritoneum attaching the small intestine to the posterior abdominal wall.

Mesial, situated in the middle; see median.

Mesothelium, epithelium lining certain serous cavities.

Metacarpus, "after or beyond the wrist"; the five bones of the hand.

Metatarsus, "beyond the instep"; the five bones of the foot between the toes and tarsal bones.

Metopic, pertaining to the forehead.

Micturition, urination.

Minimus, least; opposite of maximus.

Minor, smaller or lesser; opposite of major; *minus* is neuter adjective.

Mitral, similar in shape to a miter; valve of heart between left atrium and left ventricle.

Modiolus, a small central pillar or hub.

Molar, pertaining to the grinding teeth.

Moll, Dutch physiologist (1849-1914).

Moniliform, shaped like a string of beads.

Monro, English surgeon (1697-1767).

Mons, a mound or prominence; the mons pubis is also called the mons veneris; "the mound of Venus."

Mucosa, mucous.

Mucus, a viscid watery secretion; adjective, mucous.

Multangular, having many angles.

Multifidus, split into many parts.

Multilocular, having many small cavities or cells.

Multipolar, having more than two poles or processes.

Myelin, a fatlike substance forming a sheath around myelinated (medullated) nerve fibers.

Myeloid, resembling bone marrow.

Naris, a nostril; plural, *nares; naris* "of the nostril."
Nasi, "of the nose."
Navicular, boat-shaped.
Neurilemma, nerve sheath.
Neuroglia, supporting structure of the nervous system.
Neuron, a complete nerve cell including its processes; also spelled *neurone*
Neutrophil, staining with neutral dyes; also spelled *neutrophile.*
Node, a swelling, protuberance, or knob.
Nodule, a little swelling or mass.
Nucha, nape of the neck.
Nuchal, pertaining to the nape of the neck.
Nuck, Dutch anatomist (1650-1692).
Nucleolus, a little nucleus.
Nucleus, (1) a spherical body within a cell, forming the vital part. (2) A group of cell bodies in the central nervous system.

Obese, fat.
Oblique, slanting; between horizontal and vertical in direction; Latin adjective, *obliquus.*
Oblongata, oblong.
Obturator, Latin word for a plate covering an opening.
Occiput, the back of the head.
Oculi, "of the eye."
Olecranon, from the Greek word for elbow.
Olfactory, pertaining to the sense of smell.
Omentum, from a Latin word for cover, a fold of peritoneum attached to the stomach; plural, *omenta.*
Ophthalmic, pertaining to the eye.
Opponens, opposing.
Opposition, the act of opposing one part to another.
Optic, pertaining to vision.
Orbicular, circular.
Orbital, pertaining to the orbit.
Organ, a portion of the body having a special function.
Os, Latin for mouth; plural *ora; oris,* "of the mouth."
Os, Latin for bone; plural, *ossa.*
Osmosis, passage of fluid across a membrane from a lesser to a more highly concentrated solution.
Ossicle, a little bone.
Ossification, formation of bone.
Otic, pertaining to the ear.
Ovale, oval.
Ovalis, oval.
Oviduct, passageway for ovum.
Ovum, egg; plural, *ova.*

Pacchionian, named from Pacchioni, Italian anatomist (1665-1726).

Pacinian, named for Pacini, Italian anatomist (1812-1883).

Palate, roof of the mouth; adjective, *palatine; palatini,* "of the palate."

Palm, the hollow of the hand.

Palpebra, eyelid; plural, *palpebrae.*

Pampiniform, shaped like a tendril.

Pancreas, "all flesh"; a digestive gland.

Panniculus, a layer or membrane.

Papilla, a small nipple-shaped elevation; plural, *papillae.*

Papillary, pertaining to a nipple, or nipplelike.

Para, prefix meaning "beside," "accessory to," or "near."

Paracolic, lying along or near the colon.

Paralysis, loss of motion or sensation in a living part.

Parathyroid, near the thyroid.

Parenchyma, the functional elements of an organ as distinguished from its framework.

Parietal, pertaining to the walls of a cavity; see visceral.

Parotid, situated near the ear.

Parturition, the act of giving birth to a child.

Patella, "little pan"; the kneecap.

Pectinate, shaped like a comb.

Pectineal, pertaining to the pubic bone; Latin adjective, *pectineus.*

Pectoral, pertaining to the breast or chest; Latin adjective, *pectoris.*

Pedal, pertaining to the foot.

Pedicle, a process connecting the lamina of a vertebra with the centrum.

Peduncle, a stem or supporting structure.

Pelvis, a basin or basinlike structure.

Pendulous, pendent; hanging.

Penis, erectile genital organ of the male.

Pennate, shaped like a feather; same as penniform.

Peri, prefix meaning "around."

Pericardium, sac around the heart.

Perichondrium, membrane covering the surface of cartilage.

Perilymph, fluid within bony labyrinth of the inner ear, but outside the membranous labyrinth; see endolymph.

Perimysium, sheath of connective tissue surrounding a muscle bundle.

Perineorrhaphy, operation on perineum to repair lacerations or relaxation.

Perineum, space bounded by anus, pubic arch, and the rami of the ischium.

Periodontal, around a tooth, formerly peridental.

Periosteum, a tough fibrous membrane surrounding a bone.

Peripheral, pertaining to the periphery, the surface, or outer margin; opposite of central.

Peristalsis, a wave of contraction passing along a muscular tube.

Peritoneum, serous membrane lining the abdominal cavity and covering the viscera in that cavity.

Peroneus, "of the fibula"; variant, peroneal.

Pes, the foot; pedis, "of the foot."

Petrous, resembling a rock; the dense portion of the temporal bone.

Peyer, Swiss anatomist (1653-1712).

Phagocytosis, the engulfing of particles by a cell.

Phalanges, plural of *phalanx,* which refers to any bone of finger or toe.

Pharynx, the Greek name for space behind the nose and mouth; adjective, *pharyngeal.*

Phrenic, pertaining to the diaphragm.

Pia mater, "tender mother"; innermost lining of brain and cord, which is thin and delicate.

Pilomotor, mover of a hair.

Pineal, shaped like a pine cone.

Piriformis, pear-shaped.

Pisiform, pea-shaped.

Pituitary, the hypophysis.

Placenta, a round, flat organ by which the fetus is attached to the inner wall of the uterus.

Plantar, pertaining to the sole of the foot; *plantaris,* Latin adjective; *plantae,* "of the sole of the foot."

Plaque, a flat area or plate.

Plasma, fluid portion of the blood.

Platysma, a platelike muscle.

Pleura, serous membrane lining the thoracic cavity and covering each lung.

Plexus, a braid or network; plural, *plexus* or *plexuses.*

Plica, a fold; plural, *plicae.*

Pollex, the thumb; *pollicis,* "of the thumb."

Polymorphonuclear, having nuclei of many shapes.

Pons, a bridge; *pontis,* "of the bridge."

Popliteal, pertaining to the ham or back of the knee; *popliteus,* Latin adjective.

Porta, gateway; *portal,* pertaining to a gateway.

Posterior, situated behind or toward the back; opposite of anterior.

Postganglionic, beyond the ganglion; see preganglionic.

Poupart, French anatomist (1661-1709).

Preganglionic, before the ganglion; see postganglionic.

Premolar, in front of a molar tooth.

Prepuce, the foreskin; a fold of skin covering the glans of the penis (or the clitoris).

Preputium, same as prepuce.

Procerus, stretched out or long.

Process, a slender projecting point; Latin, *processus.*

Profundus, deep; opposite of sublimis or superficialis.

Prolapse, a falling down or sinking of an organ.

Pronate, to turn palm downward.

Prone, lying with face downward.

Propria, proper.

Proprius, belonging to one only.

Prostate, a gland in the male surrounding the neck of the bladder and first part of the urethra.

Prostatectomy, surgical removal of prostate gland.

Protoplasm, living matter; the essential material of all plant and animal cells.

Protract, to pull forward; opposite of retract.

Protraction, the act of pulling forward; opposite of retraction.

Proximal, nearest; opposite of distal.

Pseudo, a prefix signifying "false."

Psoas, pertaining to the loin.

Pterygoid, shaped like a wing.

Puberty, the age at which the reproductive organs become functional.

Pubic, pertaining to the region of the pubic bone.

Pubis, the pubic bone; plural, *pubes.*

Pudendal, pertaining to the pudendum.

Pudendum, the external genitalia, especially of the female.

Pulmonary, pertaining to the lung.

Punctum, a point; plural, *puncta.*

Purkinje, Hungarian physiologist (1787-1869).

Pylorus, opening from stomach into duodenum.

Pyramidalis, shaped like a pyramid.

Quadrate, four-sided; having a square or rectangular shape.

Quadratus, four-sided.

Quadriceps, four-headed.

Quinsy, an acute inflammation outside the capsule of the tonsil with formation of pus.

Quinti, pertaining to the fifth.

Racemose, resembling a bunch of grapes.

Radius, a spoke; a bone of the forearm.

Ramus, a branch; plural, *rami.*

Ranvier, French pathologist (1835-1922).

Raphe, a seam or ridge.

Rectum, straight; the portion of the large intestine between the colon and the anus. It is not straight in man but is in many animals.

Rectus, straight.

Renal, pertaining to the kidney.

Restiform, shaped like a rope.

Rete, a net.

Reticular, netlike.

Retina, innermost coat of eye.

Retinaculum, a halter; a structure which retains an organ or tissue in its place; plural, *retinacula.*

Retract, to pull back; opposite of protract.

Retraction, the act of pulling back; opposite of protraction.

Retro, prefix meaning behind.

Retroflexion, a backward bending of one part of an organ on another portion; opposite of anteflexion.

Retroperitoneal, behind the peritoneum.

Retropharyngeal, behind the pharynx.

Retroversion, a backward turning; the entire organ is turned backward; opposite of anteversion.

Rhinencephalon, the olfactory portion of the brain.

Rhomboid, shaped like a kite; *rhomboideus,* Latin adjective.

Risorius, pertaining to laughing or grinning.

Roentgen, German physicist (1845-1923).

Roentgenogram, a photograph made by means of roentgen rays or x-rays. The rays are named in honor of their discoverer.

Roentgenoscopy, examination by means of a fluoroscope.

Rotation, the act of turning about a centrally located length axis.

Rotundum, round.

Ruga, a ridge or fold; plural, *rugae.*

Sac, any baglike organ.

Saccule, a little sac.

Sacrum, "sacred"; five fused vertebrae below the last lumbar vertebra.

Sagittal, pertaining to the median vertical plane of the body.

Salpinx, a tube, particularly the oviduct; *salpingo,* combining form.

Santorini, Italian anatomist (1681-1737).

Saphenous, from a Greek word meaning "manifest"; the name of two prominent superficial veins of the leg.

Sappey, French anatomist (1810-1896).

Sartorius, "tailor's"; name of a muscle of the thigh which is used when one sits cross-legged like a tailor.

Scala, literally a "staircase."

Scalene, a triangle which has three unequal sides; *scalenus,* Latin adjective.

Scaphoid, boat-shaped.

Scapula, the shoulder blade.

Sciatic, pertaining to the ischium; contraction of ischiatic.

Sclera, hard or dense.

Scrotum, a bag.

Sebaceous, pertaining to sebum.

Sebum, suet; an oily secretion of the skin.

Secretion, (1) the product made by a gland.   (2) Also the function of elaborating such a product.

Sella turcica, "Turkish saddle"; fossa of sphenoid bone so named from its shape.

Semen, fluid secreted by the male reproductive glands containing the male reproductive cells.

Semilunar, shaped like a half moon.

Semimembranosus, partly made of membrane or fascia.

Seminal, pertaining to semen.

Seminiferous, producing semen.

Semitendinosus, partly tendinous.

Serosa, any serous membrane.

Serous, pertaining to or resembling serum.

Serratus, having a saw-tooth edge.

Serum, clear portion of any animal fluid.

Sesamoid, seedlike.

Sibson, English physician (1814-1876).

Sigmoid, shaped like the Greek letter *sigma*.

Sinus, a cavity.

Sinusitis, inflammation of a sinus.

Skeleton, the hard framework of the body. In man the bones of the body collectively.

Soleus, "pertaining to the sole"; muscle is shaped like the sole of a shoe.

Somatic, pertaining to the body or body wall.

Sperm, a mature male reproductive cell; a spermatozoon.

Sphenoid, wedge-shaped.

Sphenopalatine, pertaining to the sphenoid and palatine bones.

Sphincter, a binder; a ringlike band.

Spinous, a spinelike process; Latin adjective, *spinatus*.

Splanchnic, visceral.

Splenic, pertaining to the spleen.

Splenius, shaped like a bandage.

Squamous, scalelike.

Stapedius, pertaining to the stapes.

Stapes, a stirrup; a stirrup-shaped bone of the middle ear.

Stensen, Danish anatomist (1638-1686).

Sternum, the breast bone.

Stratified, having layers.

Stratum, a layer; plural, *strata*.

Striate, having transverse lines; Latin adjective, *striatum*.

Stye, inflammation of sebaceous gland of eyelid; also spelled *sty*.

Styloid, resembling a stylus; long and pointed.

Sub, prefix meaning "below" or "beneath."

Subclavian, beneath the clavicle.

Subcutaneous, beneath the skin.

Sublimis, high or superficial; opposite of profundus.

Sublingual, beneath the tongue.

Submandibular, below the mandible.

Submaxillary, beneath the mandible (formerly mandible was called sub-maxilla).

Submental, beneath the chin.

Subpubic, beneath the pubis.

Subscapular, beneath the scapula.

Substantia, Latin word for substance.

Sudoriferous, secreting sweat.

Sulcus, a groove or furrow; plural, *sulci*.

Supercilium, the eyebrow; plural, *supercilia; supercilii,* "of the eyebrow."

Superior, higher; opposite of inferior; *superioris,* a Latin form of the adjective.

Supinate, to turn the palm of the hand upward.

Supine, lying flat on the back.

Supra, prefix meaning "above"; super has same meaning; opposite of sub.

Supraclavicular, above the clavicle.

Supracondylar, above a condyle.

Suprarenal, above the kidney; see adrenal.

Suprascapular, above the scapula.

Supraspinatus, above the spine (of the scapula); variant, *supraspinous.*

Suture, a joint between bones of the cranium.

Sylvius, French anatomist (1614-1672).

Symphysis, a growing together.

Synarthrosis, an immovable joint.   See synchondrosis and syndesmosis.

Synchondrosis, a union of bones by means of cartilage.

Syndesmosis, a union of bones by means of a ligament or membrane.

Synovia, literally "with egg"; the fluid resembles egg white.

Tactile, pertaining to touch.

Taenia, a flat band; plural, *taeniae.*

Talus, the ankle; a bone of the ankle.

Tarsus, (1) the instep; the seven bones forming the back portion of the foot.   (2) Connective tissue framework of the eyelids.

Tawara, Japanese physiologist (1873-   ).

Tela, a web; a weblike tissue.

Temporal, pertaining to the region of the temple.

Tendinea, tendinous or fibrous.

Tendo, Latin for tendon.

Tendon, a fibrous band of dense connective tissue by means of which a muscle is attached to a bone or other structure.

Tenon, French surgeon (1724-1816).

Tentorium, a tent.

Teres, long and round; cylindrical.

Tertius, third.

Testis, a testicle or male reproductive gland; plural, *testes.*

Thalamus, a mass of gray matter at the base of each cerebral hemisphere along the side of the third ventricle.

Thenar, mound on the palm at the base of the thumb.

Thoracic, pertaining to the chest; *thoracico* or *thoraco,* combining forms.

Thorax, the chest.

Thrombosis, formation or development of a blood clot within a vessel.

Thyroid, like a shield; also spelled *thyreoid.*

Tibia, Latin name for shin bone.

Tibial, pertaining to the tibia; Latin adjective, *tibialis.*

Tissue, a collection of similar cells specialized to perform a particular function.

Tonsil, small mass of lymphatic tissue in the pharynx.

Tonsillectomy, surgical removal of tonsil.

Torus, a swelling or projection.

Trabecula, a septum passing into the substance of a structure from the margin or surface; plural, *trabeculae.*

Trachea, the windpipe; from the Greek.

Tracheotomy, the formation of an artificial opening into the trachea.

Transfusion, the transfer of blood from the vessels of one person to those of another.

Transversus, turning across; variant, *transversalis.* The muscle is so named because its fibers pass directly across the abdomen.

Trapezius, having the shape of a trapezium, or a four-sided figure.

Trapezoid, table-shaped.

Triceps, three-headed.

Tricuspid, having three cusps or points; valve between right atrium and right ventricle.

Trigeminal, triple.

Triquetrum, three-cornered.

Triticeous, resembling a grain of wheat.

Trochanter, either of two processes of the upper femoral shaft; from a Greek word meaning a "runner."

Trochlea, a pulley.

Trochlear, pertaining to a pulley; the nerve supplying the superior oblique eye muscle whose tendon passes through a "pulley" of fibrous tissue.

Tubarius, pertaining to a tube.

Tubercle, a small nodule or eminence.

Tuberosity, a broad eminence on a bone.

Tubular, shaped like a tube.

Tubule, a small tube.

Tunica, a covering.

Turbinate, shaped like a top.

Tympanic, pertaining to the eardrum.

Tympanum, a "drum"; the middle ear; *tympani,* "of the drum."

Ulcer, an open sore.

Ulna, Latin name for the bone.

Umbilicus, the navel.

Unipolar, having one pole or process.

Unmyelinated, without myelin.

Urachus, from the Greek, "to hold urine."

Ureter, tube from the pelvis of the kidney to the bladder.

Urethra, tube from the bladder to the exterior of the body; *urethrae,* "of the urethra."

Urinary, pertaining to urine.

Urine, secretion of the kidney.

Uriniferous, transporting urine.

Uterus, the womb.

Utricle, a little sac.

Uvula, a small fleshy mass hanging from the soft palate; literally "a little grape."

Vagina, a sheath.

Vaginal, pertaining to a vagina; *vaginalis,* Latin adjective.

Vagus, wandering.

Vallate, having a rim or wall.

Vallecula, little valley.

Valsalva, Italian anatomist (1666-1723).

Valve, a fold in a tube or passage preventing backflow of contents.

Varicocele, distention of veins of spermatic cord; also spelled *varicocoele.*

Vas, (1) a vessel. (2) A duct; plural, *vasa.*

Vascular, pertaining to or full of blood vessels.

Vasomotor, presiding over the muscular movements of walls of blood vessels; that is, of relaxation or contraction.

Vastus, wide or great.

Vater, German anatomist (1684-1751).

Vein, a vessel carrying blood to the heart.

Veli, "of a veil."

Venepuncture, to make a small opening into a vein for the purpose of drawing off blood or injecting some substance into the blood stream; also spelled *venipuncture.*

Venous, pertaining to a vein or veins; Latin adjective, *venosus.*

Ventral, pertaining to the front or to the abdomen; opposite of dorsal.

Ventricle, any small cavity.

Venule, a small vein.

Vera, true.

Vermiform, shaped like a worm.

Vertex, the summit or apex.

Vesicle, a small sac containing fluid.

Villus, a minute projection; plural, *villi.*

Visceral, pertaining to the viscera; see parietal.

Viscous, sticky or gummy.

Viscus, an organ within a body cavity; especially the abdomen; plural, *viscera.*

Vitreous, glassy.

Volar, pertaining to the palm; opposite of dorsal.

Voluntary, performed in accordance with the will; opposite of involuntary.

Vomer, a plowshare; the bone is shaped like a plowshare.

Vulva, external genitalia of the female.

Waldeyer, German anatomist (1836-1921).

Wharton, English physician and anatomist (1614-1673).

Willis, English anatomist and physician (1621-1675).

Winslow, French anatomist (1669-1760).
Wirsung, German physician (-1643).
Wormian, named from Worm, Danish anatomist (1588-1654).
Wright, American pathologist (1869-1928).

Xiphoid, shaped like a sword.

Zygoma, a yoke.
Zygomatic, pertaining to the zygoma.

INDEX

A

Abdomen, areas of, 34
  arteries of, 328
  cavity of, 410
  lymphatics of, 357
  muscles of, 202
  quadrants of, 34
  regions of, 34
  surface anatomy of, 30
  wall of, 207
Abdominal inguinal ring, 211
Abducent nerve, 243
Abduction, definition of, 131, 144
  of eye, 280
  of fingers, 184
  of vocal cords, 380
Abductor digiti quinti muscle of
    foot, 202
  of hand, 179
  hallucis muscle, 202
  pollicis brevis muscle, 179
    longus muscle, 30, 173
Abscess peritonsillar, 409
  retropharyngeal, 347
Accessory hemiazygous vein, 339
  nerve, 166, 212, 245
Acetabulum, 103
Acoustic nerve, 244, 290
Acromegaly, 296
Acromioclavicular joint, 26, 135
Acromion, 26, 92
Action, demonstration of muscle,
    169
Activities, body, 19
Adam's apple, 26, 80
Addison's disease, 300
Adduction, definition of, 131, 144
  of fingers, 184
Adductor brevis muscle, 188
  hallucis muscle, 202
  longus muscle, 188
  magnus muscle, 36, 188, 192
  pollicis muscle, 179
  tubercle of femur, 36, 106
Adenohypophysis, 295
Adenoid, 409
Adipose renal capsule, 437
  tissue, 47
Adolescence, superficial fascia in,
    461

Adrenal gland, 306
  plexus, 250
  vessels, 328
Adrenocorticotropic hormones, 296
Afferent lymphatics, 344
  nerves, 222
Afterbirth, 302, 316
Age changes in bones of face, 121
  in brain case, 118
  in fiber tracts of nerves, 274
  in long bones, 124
  in lymph nodes, 345
  in muscles, 162
  in pattern of bones, 128
  in proportions of skeleton, 125
  in skeletal maturation, 123
    mineralization, 128
  in skin, 453
  in superficial tissues, 456
  in thymus, 365
  in tonsils, 407
Aggregate lymph follicles, 343, 424
Air cells of ethmoid, 76, 370
  of mastoid, 72, 371
  sinuses, 72, 122, 369
Ala of nose, 366
Alar ligament, 133
Alimentary tract, 394
Alveolar ducts, 389
  glands, 42
  process, 64, 77, 78
Alveoli of lungs, 389
Amino acids, 419
Amphiarthrosis, 130
Ampulla of milk ducts, 466
  of semicircular canals, 289
  seminal vesicles, 484
  of Vater, 421
Anal canal, 435
  columns, 436
  sinuses, 436
  sphincter muscles, 213
  triangle, 213
Anastomosis of arteries, 329
  of intestinal veins, 431
Anatomical snuff box, 30
Anatomy, definition of, 19
  surface, 23
Anconeus muscle, 173
Angina pectoris, 316